MICROPROCESSOR FUNDAMENTALS

Second edition

MICROPROCESSOR FUNDAMENTALS

Second edition

Fred Halsall
School of Engineering and Applied Sciences
University of Sussex
Brighton, Sussex, England

Paul Lister
School of Engineering and Applied Sciences
University of Sussex
Brighton, Sussex, England

revised by
Richard A. Schmitt
ENTRON Systems Company
Anaheim Hills, California

Louis L. Covert
Naval Weapons Center
China Lake, California

PITMAN PUBLISHING

PITMAN PUBLISHING
128 Long Acre, London WC2E 9AN

© F Halsall, P F Lister
R A Schmitt, L L Covert 1987

First published in Great Britain 1980
Reprinted 1981, 1982, 1983, 1985, 1986
Second edition published in Great Britain 1987
Reprinted 1988

Printed and bound by The Bath Press, Avon

ISBN 0 273 02820 0

The Pitman Publishing printing
of this second edition is NOT
for sale in the United States
of America and Canada.

The second edition is published
in the USA and Canada by
John Wiley & Sons Inc.
605 Third Avenue
New York NY 10158

To Rhiannon, Lisa, Richard, Muriel, Jenny and Ben

PREFACE

The purpose of this text is to provide the student with an understanding of microprocessor technology. It is an update of a text in use by both electronics majors and students from other fields.

Today, we are using microprocessors in ways that were not even considered when the technology first appeared. From toys and telephones to ships and spacecraft, these chips are beginning to permeate our society. The original edition of this text anticipated the growth of this field. The authors designed it for students from a variety of backgrounds. They planned it with a wide range of applications in mind. We have revised the text to bring the material up to date. We have also extended the material into areas germane to today's applications.

Using this text, the student will be able to design microprocessor applications for a standard 8-bit machine. The 8-bit machine is a basic component of many microprocessor systems. Based on this technology, industry has developed very complex microprocessor devices. These components include 16- and 32-bit machines and high-speed digital signal processing (DSP) devices. This text is an excellent stepping-stone to studies of these sophisticated devices.

Virtually all microprocessors use the same general techniques. Each family, however, has its own unique software and hardware. Our goal has been to present the technology common to all these devices. At the same time we wanted to avoid becoming lost in a sea of different software and hardware implementations. We also wanted to provide real-world examples and problems that the student can use in laboratory work. To do this, we selected a standard microprocessor family—the 8085—for both software and hardware discussions.

Although straightforward in design, the 8085 has all the major microprocessor features. It has both memory and input/output (I/O) address spaces. Its instruction set provides a variety of addressing modes, conditional branches, arithmetic and logic operations, among other features. It supports nested, prioritized interrupts. The 8085 trainer from Intel—the SDK-85—is inexpensive but provides a full hardware environment.

With little or no modification, the student can run the examples and problems used in the text on the SDK-85. We have used 8085 assembly language for all examples and exercises. We have also employed 8080 and 8085 family devices for all hardware discussions.

In writing this text, we were primarily concerned with the microprocessor and its associated components. The text uses assembly language exclusively. We have left higher-level languages to other courses. The emphasis is on the world from the microprocessor's standpoint. For this reason most of the examples deal with embedded systems rather than general-purpose computers. Again, other courses can cover general-purpose machines and all the complexities involved.

We wrote this text for use in a first course in microprocessor technology. The student need not have a background in electronics, although such a background is helpful. Microprocessor system design uses both the binary and the hexadecimal number systems. For students unfamiliar with these systems, we have included an appendix introducing them. This appendix contains both examples and problems. It also introduces binary logic and arithmetic.

We have added detailed, concrete hardware examples to the text for students familiar with basic electronics. Those unfamiliar with the electronics involved can bypass them. The examples extend the text, however, so that it covers complete hardware and software systems.

A microprocessor is the central component in a microcomputer system. Each element of such a system interacts with each of the others. This text begins with a discussion of these systematic features. The first three chapters discuss, first, the history of this technology. Second, they introduce the basics of computer operation and the structure of a typical microprocessor system. These first three chapters conclude with a discussion of memory techniques for microprocessors. By the end of this first section, the student can begin the important study of microprocessor software.

Chapters Four through Six address primarily microprocessor programming. We have divided the study into data transfer, data manipulation, and machine control sections. The chapters also introduce the mechanics of assembly language programming. Chapter Four gives a simple version of 8085 assembly language. Chapter Six concludes with guidelines for good programming practice.

A third section of the text discusses the machine's interface with the outside world. We first address digital input and output (I/O) in Chapter Seven. Chapter Eight extends this discussion into analog I/O. Finally, Chapter Nine develops interrupt processing. These three chapters present an integrated development of both the hardware and the software involved. Such a discussion requires a much greater emphasis on hardware implementation than the earlier chapters.

The final chapter develops application examples, with each a little more complex than the preceding. Each example sketches a different approach to microprocessor system design. Some of the examples primarily address software issues, whereas others contain extensive hardware details.

The text closes with back matter intended to be an aid to the student. Together with the body of the text, it provides a considerable amount of reference material. An extensive glossary defines the important terms introduced. In some entries this glossary goes beyond the current text by defining many related terms.

Appendix One is the introduction to number systems and binary math mentioned earlier. The next two appendices provide a reference guide for the Intel 8085. Appendix Two is an outline of the 8085 assembly language. Appendix Three sketches the operation of the SDK-85. Finally, we have given a brief overview of development aids in general in Appendix Four.

Each chapter, except Chapter One, contains detailed examples and exercises to put into practice the subjects covered. Most of the exercises reinforce the material covered in the chapter. Some provide a look at the material from a different point of view. Some help to reinforce or to introduce material from other chapters.

CONTENTS

CHAPTER ONE
COMPUTER PRINCIPLES   1

1.1 Introduction   1
1.2 Computer History   1
1.3 IC History   3
1.4 Computer Structure and Operation   6
1.5 Microprocessor Families   13

CHAPTER TWO
MICROCOMPUTER ARCHITECTURE   17

2.1 Introduction   17
2.2 The Microprocessor   17
     Registers   18
     The Arithmetic Logic Unit   19
     Timing and Control   20
2.3 Bus Structure   21
2.4 Memory and I/O   23
     Memory Map   24
     Input/Output   26
     Address Decoding   26
     Timing   27
2.5 The 8085 Microprocessor   28
     The ALU and Associated Registers   29
     Register Section   31
     Timing and Control   31
     Exercises   32

CHAPTER THREE
MEMORY 35

3.1 Introduction 35
3.2 Read Only Memory 35

Diode-Matrix ROM 36
Mask-Programmed ROM 37
PROM 38
EPROM 39
Example 3.1 EPROM Programming (8755) 41

3.3 Read/Write Memory 44

Static RAM 44
Dynamic RAM 44
Example 3.2 RAM Read/Write Cycle (8156) 47

3.4 Memory Organization and Addressing 50

Example 3.3 Address Decode 51
The 8085 51

3.5 Mass Storage 52

Punched Paper Tape 53
Magnetic Tape 54
Floppy Disks 57

Exercises 59

CHAPTER FOUR
INTRODUCTION TO PROGRAMMING AND DATA TRANSFER 61

4.1 Introduction 61
4.2 Microprocessor Registers 61
4.3 Assembly Language 62
4.4 Types of Instructions 65
4.5 Operand Addressing Modes 66
4.6 Data Transfer Instructions 67

Register Addressing 68
Immediate Addressing 69
Example 4.1 Register and Immediate Addressing 70
Direct Addressing 71
Example 4.2 Immediate and Direct Addressing 72
Indirect Addressing 73
Example 4.3 Data Transfer Operations 74

4.7 Other Addressing Modes 75
4.8 The Intel 8085 Instruction Set 75
4.9 The Assembly Process 76

Hand Coding 77
Example 4.4 Manual Assembly 78

4.10 Single-Board Systems   78
      Hardware Tests   80
      Exercises   80

CHAPTER FIVE
DATA MANIPULATION   83

5.1   Introduction   83
5.2   Data Representation   83
      Unsigned Binary   84
      Signed Binary   84
      Binary-Coded Decimal   87
      Other Forms of Data Representation   87
5.3   Arithmetic Instructions   88
      Add Instructions   89
      Subtract Instructions   91
      Increment Instructions   91
      Decrement Instructions   92
      Example 5.1 Unsigned Arithmetic   93
      Example 5.2 Signed Arithmetic   93
5.4   Multiprecision Arithmetic Instructions   94
      Sixteen-Bit Arithmetic   94
      Multiprecision Arithmetic—The Carry Flag   95
      Example 5.3 Multiprecision Addition   96
5.5   BCD Arithmetic   97
      Example 5.4 BCD Addition   100
5.6   Logical Operations   100
      Logical AND   101
      Logical OR   102
      Exclusive-OR Operation   102
      Rotate/Shift   104
      Compare Instructions   105
      Other Operations   105
      Example 5.5 Transfers, Arithmetic, and Logic   106
      Exercises   107

CHAPTER SIX
TRANSFER OF CONTROL AND PROGRAMMING TECHNIQUES   109

6.1   Introduction   109
6.2   Jump Operations/Labels   109
      Unconditional Jump   109

Labels   110
Conditional Jump   111
Example 6.1 Short Delay   112

6.3 Subroutines   113

Example 6.2 Long Delay   117
Parameter Passing   117
Nested Subroutines   118

6.4 Other Operations   118

Stack Operations   118
Input/Output   120
Miscellaneous   120

6.5 Programming Techniques   121

Documentation   122
Modular Design   124
Flowcharts   125
Example 6.3 Data Conversion   126

Exercises   130

CHAPTER SEVEN
DIGITAL INPUT AND OUTPUT

                                                133

7.1 Introduction   133
7.2 CPU I/O Interface   133

Example 7.1 I/O-Mapped I/O   135

7.3 Parallel Ports   139

Example 7.2 Simple Output Port (8212)   139
Example 7.3 Simple Input Port (8212)   142
Handshake Techniques   142
Example 7.4 Handshake   144
Programmed Devices   145
Example 7.5 Programmed I/O (8755)   145
Example 7.6 Printer Interface Program   148

7.4 Serial Ports   151

Serial Communication Formats   151
Programmed Devices   154
Example 7.7 Programmed Serial I/O (8251)   155
8085 Serial Port   159

Exercises   160

CHAPTER EIGHT
ANALOG INPUT/OUTPUT

                                                163

8.1	Introduction	163
8.2	Bit-Mapped I/O	163
	Example 8.1 Auto Light Monitor, Bit-Mapped Input	164
	Example 8.2 Monitor with Bit-Mapped Output	167
8.3	Digital-to-Analog Conversion	167
	Example 8.3 DAC Program/Schematic	169
8.4	Analog-to-Digital Conversion	173
	Counter-Based ADC	173
	Successive Approximation ADC	176
	Example 8.4 Software-Based ADC	177
	Other Techniques	179
	Shannon's Sampling Theorem	180
	Exercises	182

CHAPTER NINE
INTERRUPTS

	INTERRUPTS	185
9.1	Introduction	185
9.2	Basics	185
	Example 9.1 Aircraft VOR	187
9.3	Vector Techniques	188
	Smart Interrupts	189
	Hardware Vectoring	191
	Example 9.2 Printer Control	192
9.4	Multiple Interrupts	194
	Interrupt Mask	194
	Interrupt Priority Levels	197
	Example 9.3 Building Monitor	199
9.5	Other Exceptions to Normal Processing	202
	Exercises	202

CHAPTER TEN
APPLICATION EXAMPLES

	APPLICATION EXAMPLES	205
10.1	Introduction	205
10.2	Sequencing	205
	Example 10.1 Traffic Light Sequencer	206
10.3	Conditional Sequencing	212
	Example 10.2 Washing Machine Sequencer	213
10.4	Additional Applications	216

Example 10.3 Digital Clock   217
Example 10.4 Waveform Generation   228

Exercises   231

GLOSSARY   233

APPENDIX ONE
REVIEW   247
Exercises   256

APPENDIX TWO
THE INTEL 8085 INSTRUCTION SET   259

APPENDIX THREE
THE INTEL SDK-85 COMMANDS AND OPERATION   265

APPENDIX FOUR
DEVELOPMENT AIDS   269

INDEX   275

CHAPTER ONE

COMPUTER PRINCIPLES

1.1 INTRODUCTION

Microprocessor technology is the product of a successful marriage between digital computers and integrated circuits. This chapter reviews the history of computer and integrated circuit technology. Many of the terms and techniques used in modern systems are deeply related to this historical context. The chapter also outlines the general structure and operation of most modern computers and, in particular, microprocessor-based systems.

1.2 COMPUTER HISTORY

The history of practical digital computers is a short one. It only spans about 40 years. However, the first theoretical work was done over 150 years ago. In the 1830s, mathematician Charles Babbage proposed the basic structure and operation of a digital computer. Numerous advances in technology were required before his dream of an intelligent machine was to be realized. Although Babbage's Analytical Engine contained all the elements of a digital computer, it could not be constructed because of the mechanical intricacy of his design and the tight machining tolerances required; it is doubtful that it could be constructed even today.

Babbage's machine processed data using instructions stored separately from the data. If a problem required few instructions, the unused instruction storage area could not be filled with data. The machine was thus inefficient. A mathematician named John Von Neumann, among others, later proposed a computer in which both data and machine instructions are stored in the same memory. Virtually all modern digital computers use this technique and are hence known as **Von Neumann** machines.

It was not until 1943 that the first practical digital computer was constructed. This machine, designed and built at Harvard University and dubbed the Mark I, was electromechanical. It used relays as its active elements. It was thus very slow by present standards. This speed problem was alleviated in the ENIAC, developed at the University of Pennsylvania, by using vacuum tubes instead of relays. The first commercial digital computer, the UNIVAC I, was a direct descendant of ENIAC and was introduced in 1951. The same group that developed ENIAC designed UNIVAC I.

These machines suffered from excessive heat, large size—they were often housed in their own separate buildings—and a high rate of failure. It was not until the transistor became available that these problems were overcome.

The invention of the transistor was a major breakthrough for computer technology, as well as for the entire electronics industry. Moreover, its introduction became the beginning of a revolution. The early solid-state computers, which used discrete transistors and magnetic core memory, were a great improvement over the vacuum-tube machines. They still required considerable space—a single active memory circuit took about one cubic inch—and were very expensive.

Another breakthrough came in 1959 when the first integrated circuit (IC) was introduced by Fairchild Corporation. With the use of ICs, the physical size of computers began to shrink rapidly, reliability improved further, and power consumption went down. Throughout the 1960s, the trend was toward more and more integration, with the number of devices on a chip approximately doubling every year. By 1970 single-chip calculators were being manufactured, and we had moved into the era of large-scale integration.

The first **microprocessor** was a logical consequence of this growth in semiconductor technology. Introduced in 1971 by Intel Corporation, the Intel 4004 was a complete central processor on a single chip of silicon. With the addition of one or more memory devices, the 4004 could be transformed into a powerful small computer. Intel soon introduced an improved version, the 8008.

By 1975 speed had been increased by an order of magnitude with the introduction of more new microprocessors: the MOS Technology 6502, the Intel 8080, and the Motorola M6800. By this time several other semiconductor manufacturers, including Rockwell, National Semiconductor, and Fairchild, had introduced their own microprocessors. The Intel 8085 will be used extensively in this book to illustrate various points in detail. It is an improved version of the 8080, which has become one of the industry standards.

These microprocessor devices were first developed to perform system control functions. The problem was to process digital numbers to control such devices as numerically controlled machine tools. It was found that computer techniques could be used to produce a flexible, single-chip processor. The microprocessor is thus not a computer in itself. It forms the core—called the **central processing unit (CPU)**—of a computer system.

In the late 1970s the first devices to include all these functions on a single chip (in effect, single-chip computers) were introduced. Although they generally do not provide the full capability of the larger microprocessor systems, these "computers on a chip" can often be used to produce a very powerful computer for many applications. Their capabilities can generally be extended with external devices. Examples of such devices would be the Zilog Z8 system, the Intel 8048 through 8096 series, and various extensions of the Motorola 6800.

The sea of terms used in this growing field can be very confusing. Part of the problem is that these devices are used for such a broad range of applications. In a personal computer, one microprocessor might be the center of the system, running software that solves very complex mathematical problems; another identical chip might have the lowly job of controlling the hammers on the printer. Generally, the microprocessor, with its support chips, forms what is termed a **microcomputer.** If the CPU and the support devices reside on the same chip, the device is intended, generally, for control applications. Therefore, these devices are usually called **microcontrollers.**

The cost of a simple microprocessor-based system is becoming low enough that today a powerful computer can be regarded, in effect, as a simple component in a system. The future will likely bring more and more products that use microprocessor technology to add "intelligent" functions to an array of devices.

1.3 IC HISTORY

Today's integrated circuits represent the culmination of developments that have taken place in semiconductor technology since the first transistors were produced in the late 1940s.

A transistor is fabricated by adding a pattern of impurities, metal, and insulation to a semiconductor crystal, usually silicon. The base semiconductor material is a very thin and nearly perfect crystal called a wafer. It is normally about 3 inches in diameter. The impurities are elements such as boron, which are introduced by a process called diffusion. The wafer is heated in an oven filled with the impurity atoms, some of which are thus forced into the wafer. The pattern of impurities is formed using photographically produced masks called diffusion masks. Using impurity patterns in different areas of the same silicon wafer allows a number of independent transistors to be produced simultaneously. The individual transistors are then cut (diced) from the wafer.

Other similar processes create patterns of insulation (such as silicon dioxide), patterns of metal, or etching patterns on the silicon. Different sequences of these processes produce various types of transistors, each type having useful characteristics.

Groups of transistors can be interconnected with a deposited pattern of metal (or other conductor) to form a usable circuit. Such a device is known as an **integrated circuit (IC)**. The ICs are generally about a quarter inch on a side and are called **chips.** Several chips are made from each wafer.

A photomicrograph of a typical microprocessor chip is shown in Figure 1. After fabrication, the IC chip is mounted onto a flat base containing a number of connecting pins, and the terminal areas on the chip are connected to the corresponding pins on the base by means of very small wires. The entire assembly is then sealed to form an IC package.

In the early 1960s digital ICs involved **small-scale integration (SSI)**, a typical circuit being a few logic gates. Later came **medium-scale integration (MSI)** with a complete functional component such as a counter or register possible on a single IC. Further refinements and changes in technology have resulted in **large-scale integration (LSI)** devices being commercially available at low cost. LSI devices contain up to 1000 individual gates on a single silicon chip. Large functional components or groups of smaller ones are possible using LSI technology.

Further improvements in IC fabrication have led to chips that contain a number of large functional components. Such devices are known as **very large-scale integrated (VLSI)** circuits. In order for such a device to be widely applicable, it must be very flexible. Manufacturers have introduced VLSI devices that are parts of a digital computer. A microprocessor is one such device. It forms the central part of a computer, the processor. VLSI technology continues to grow rapidly. The Motorola 68020 microprocessor, which has about 200,000 transistors on a single chip, is an example of a very dense modern chip. Hewlett-Packard has developed a microprocessor that uses nearly 400,000 transistors on an IC. The Intel 80386—which is the outgrowth of a series of extensions of the 8080 microprocessor—is of similar complexity.

The future holds great promise for further advances. Extensions of current ICs can be expected, including very capable computers on a single chip, significant increases in the size and capability of IC functional blocks, multiple processors on a single chip, and other such improvements. Another direction in which technology is moving is increasing speed. A major military VLSI technology program has produced a family of devices referred to as **very high-speed integrated circuits (VHSICs)**. These chips have great capability, owing both to their speed and to their complexity.

Obviously, there are constraints on the capabilities of VLSI devices. Such constraints involve very complex relations between size, performance, complexity, and production yield. As the size of the smallest fea-

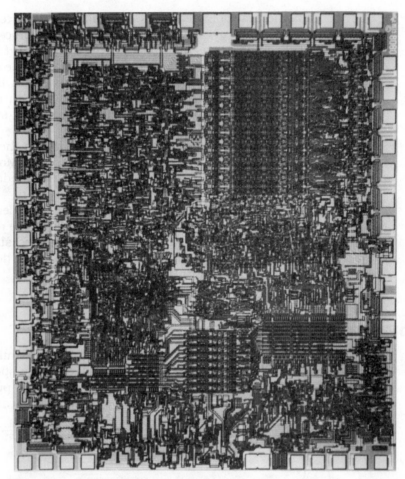

Figure 1.1
Photomicrograph of a Microprocessor IC. (Reprinted by permission of Intel
Corporation, copyright © 1980.)

tures (called the feature size) in an IC become smaller, the number of
transistors in a given area can be increased. However, the smaller size
makes the job of getting repeatable performance much more difficult.
Small feature size in an IC also means that small imperfections have a
great effect. Imperfections might include problems with the silicon material, with the various layers of diffusion, deposition, and etching used
to build the IC, or with the fine mechanical alignment required for the
various layers.

The net result is that as feature size is reduced, the number of usable
chips from a processed wafer is reduced dramatically. Eventually, the
yield of usable chips becomes zero for very small feature sizes.

Another way of increasing IC capability is simply to make a larger IC. Because there are always some imperfections on a processed wafer, building larger chips means that there is a greater chance of encountering an imperfection. Again, device yield suffers greatly if the chip size is made too large. The thrust of modern IC development is thus to refine the wafer-processing methods so that defects can be reduced in number and size. This refinement then allows the use of a very small feature size, chips very large in area, or both.

Current feature-size capability is approaching the submicron level. The largest chips are a few tenths of an inch square. Most of the dramatic growth in IC capability in the past has come from reductions in feature size. This is the likely area for future improvements.

Figure 1.2 shows a plot of the complexity of IC devices over the last several years. Although the dramatic advances of the recent past can be seen, the most exciting part of the plot is its forecast for the future. If these trends continue, we can forecast very capable devices in the near future. A revolution is in the offing.

1.4   COMPUTER STRUCTURE AND OPERATION

Almost all common digital computers work in a similar fashion. To a great extent, their operation is independent of the specific application. The computer—large or small—is a flexible, general-purpose system intended to be tailored by a user for a particular application.

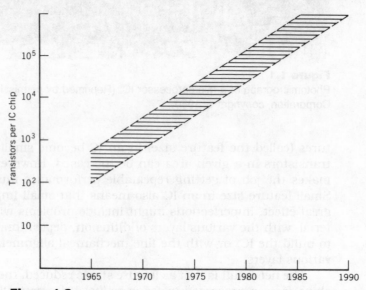

Figure 1.2
Trends in IC Complexity.

A computer is tailored to an application by devising the sequence of operations needed to perform the task at hand. Consider a basic electronic calculator that offers the user a variety of operations—add, subtract, and so forth. It is up to the user to select the particular sequence of these operations necessary to solve a specific problem. Similarly, a digital computer can perform a number of basic operations called **machine instructions.** The user selects the sequence of instructions in a way that solves a particular problem. The computer's memory stores this sequential list of operations.

An electronic calculator typically executes each of its basic operations in a few milliseconds. However, the user requires much more time to enter instructions. Consequently, the time taken to solve a problem with a calculator is determined primarily by the rate at which the user keys in the individual operations. The intrinsically high speed of execution of each operation is lost, to a great extent.

A digital computer, however, utilizes the very high-speed execution of each machine instruction by automatically executing each instruction in a sequence called a **program.** This stored-program capability is not the only difference between a computer and a calculator. Although the distinctions are not always clear, a computer is generally designed to be much more flexible in the range of operations possible, as well as in interfaces with the outside world. The calculator is generally dedicated to specific tasks, whereas the computer has a design open to many tasks.

In performing a program, a computer goes through a methodical process. The computer **fetches** an instruction from **memory** and then **executes** this instruction. The next instruction is fetched and then executed. This process is continued. Each fetch/execute cycle takes a few microseconds for a typical microprocessor-based machine.

The details of this fetch/execute cycle vary greatly from computer to computer. We will be using the Intel 8085 extensively for the study of microprocessor operation in this book. The process for the 8085 begins with a **memory read** operation which brings a binary number, or **word,** into the processor. This first word defines the machine operation for the rest of the cycle. The 8085 takes a short period of time to **decode** this instruction word. Other memory read operations may be required to obtain additional data for execution of the instruction. Finally, some data may be written to memory as a result of the instruction. Thus, the fetch/execute operation time for the 8085 may vary greatly from instruction to instruction.

For most instructions, the time required to complete a fetch/execute cycle is taken up mainly with data transfers out of and into memory. Figure 1.3 shows an outline of a sample 8085 operation. This particular instruction adds two numbers, with the result being left in the CPU. First, the instruction is read. This instruction is called ADD and causes data from the memory (any valid address in it) to be added to data

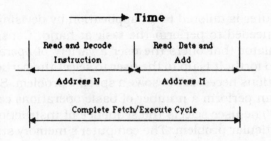

Figure 1.3
Outline of 8085 ADD Instruction.

already present in the CPU. One additional read is thus required to get the number from memory. The actual addition is made very rapidly in dedicated logic; the whole operation amounts to an instruction read, a decode at the end of this read operation, and a data read with the addition performed with this read.

The computer's instructions are normally located in its memory in sequence. Knowing the location of the last-fetched instruction allows the processor to find the next one. To start a program, we must simply indicate the location of the first instruction to the processor. Data can be stored in any location where there are no instructions stored. Such a design thus becomes a Von Neumann machine since instructions and data share the same memory.

Some very fast digital processors have moved away from the Von Neumann structure. By using separate memory for instructions and data, these machines read instructions and data at the same time. One form of this is called a **Harvard machine.** To the programmer, these machines operate in a fashion very similar to the Von Neumann machine. One of many examples of Harvard, or Harvard-like, machines is the Texas Instruments TMS-320 family. This family has what are called modified Harvard machines because they can be commanded to swap information between instruction and data memory spaces; a pure Harvard machine would not allow this.

Computer memory is composed of a large collection of individual data storage locations. Each location has a number assigned to it, called an

address. These addresses are unique. No two locations have the same address. As far as the processor is concerned, the address numbers and hence the address locations normally occur in sequence. Sometimes the addresses occur in blocks; within the blocks, however, the addresses occur in sequence.

The complete set of instructions that a given microprocessor can perform is called the processor's **instruction set.** Commonly, the microprocessors from the same manufacturer will have similar instruction sets. A specific manufacturer will generally maintain a similar instruction set for newer and improved devices. It is also common for the manufacturer of a new microprocessor family to base its instruction set on that of another manufacturer's successful device. For example, the Zilog Z80 uses and extends the Intel 8080 instruction set. Intel's 8088, 8086, 80186, 80286, and 80386 all use—sometimes major—extensions of the 8080 instruction set. The Motorola 68008, 68010, 68012, and 68020 all use the 68000 instruction set with extensions.

A computer does three kinds of operations internally. It stores program instructions and data, manipulates data, and changes its operation based on data. The latter is referred to as **decision making.** Processor decision-making instructions allow the computer to alter its path through a program based on available data. This deviation from the sequence of executing instructions is known as **branching;** the process of using a branch to repeat a sequence of instructions is called **looping.**

Branching is often done based on logical decision-making instructions, such as an instruction that forces a branch when a specific number exceeds some limit. To perform a branch, the processor simply alters the location for fetching the next instruction.

The use of a microprocessor in the emission control system of an automobile provides an example of looping. The processor would be required to go through a sequence of operations that read data from various sensors and send data to adjust fuel injection and ignition timing. Because this is a continuous operation, as soon as the sequence is completed, the computer must loop back to the beginning of the sequence to start over.

Whether to retard or advance the ignition timing based on the output of a particular transducer might be a decision confronting the computer within the loop. The computer might compare the output of the transducer with a number permanently stored in its memory. It would then select as the next instruction address either a sequence that advances the timing or a sequence that retards the timing, depending on whether the transducer output is greater than or less than the reference number. This operation is known as **conditional branching.**

Altering the normal sequence of operations, regardless of the outcome of any previous operation, is another form of branching, called **unconditional branching.** An unconditional branch would occur when either the advance or retard sequence ends and the computer returns to the main emission control program loop.

Modern electronics has made available a large array of digital devices that can very reliably and accurately achieve two electrical states when active. The reliability of this **binary** (two-state) system is a principal reason for the digital revolution. The computer that was used to write this book displays, formats, and stores millions of bits of information, making almost no errors. Other processing schemes, such as analog circuitry, could not achieve either this reliability or this accuracy.

A digital computer is a binary-based machine with all numbers coded in the binary number system, as discussed in Appendix 1.

A microprocessor-based computer comprises a **memory** that is used primarily to store the program and data, a **central processor** (the microprocessor) to execute the individual machine instructions that make up the program, and some **input and output (I/O)** devices. These I/O devices form the interface between the computer and the outside world.

The complete combination of microprocessor, memory, and I/O is illustrated in Figure 1.4. This figure also shows the microprocessor's communication bus. The bus structure will be defined and discussed in detail in Chapter Two.

Once a program has been developed for a task, it is loaded into memory and is then executed. To remember which program instruction is to be executed next, the microprocessor uses a register (a storage location in the CPU itself) called the **program counter (PC)**. The contents of the PC identify the address of the next instruction to be fetched and executed. It is said to "point to" the next instruction.

During a typical machine cycle, the next instruction to be executed is read from the address indicated by the contents of the PC. While this instruction is being executed, the contents of the PC are incremented to point to the following instruction. This process is summarized in Figure 1.5.

Often an instruction will require more than one word from the program memory. In such cases the PC will be incremented each time a word

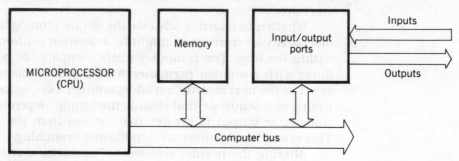

Figure 1.4
A Microcomputer.

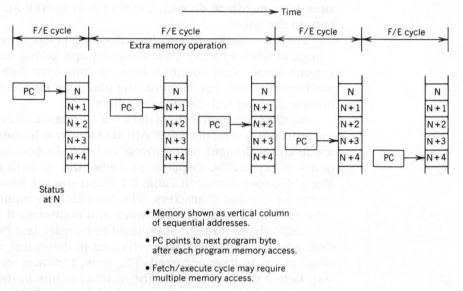

Figure 1.5
Program Counter (PC) Operation.

- Memory shown as vertical column of sequential addresses.
- PC points to next program byte after each program memory access.
- Fetch/execute cycle may require multiple memory access.

is read from the program memory during the instruction. The 8085 requires a single, one-word instruction. Certain instructions must be followed by data embedded in the program, which provide either variable data or addresses.

An instruction consists of a group of binary digits or **bits** (see Appendix 1) forming a digital word. When the microprocessor receives these bits as an instruction, it sets various internal switches so that the instruction will be executed. For many common microprocessors today the instruction and data word are 8 bits long and an address is 16 bits long. The 8-bit binary number is called a **byte**. A 4-bit number is often termed a **nibble**. The term "word" generally refers to any binary number. It is sometimes reserved for 16-bit binary numbers. Thirty-two-bit numbers are often called **long words**.

The capability of a given CPU is often reduced to a specification of the instruction and data word sizes. Thus, the Intel 8085 is termed an 8-bit machine, whereas the Motorola 68000 is called a 16-bit processor and the National 32032 a 32-bit design. This method of specifying CPU performance leaves a great deal to be desired, for many other factors are equally important to a microprocessor's overall capability. In addition, most processors perform their operations using various word sizes. The 8085 includes certain 16-bit capabilities; the 68000 is a 32-bit machine, except for its bus size.

Several 16-bit and 32-bit microprocessors are available. The differences between an 8-bit machine and these generally more powerful devices have mostly to do with the details of operation. The fundamentals remain the same.

The information stored in a microprocessor's memory amounts to groups of related binary bits. These groups, words, are coded as data in various forms. One common form of computer data is, of course, the machine instructions. Second, the data may represent various forms of numbers, as we will discuss elsewhere.

Another common form of data is a standardized method of representing letters and symbols called **ASCII (American Standard Code for Information Interchange)**, pronounced "as key." Most exchanges between such items as keyboards, displays, printers, and so forth are done in ASCII. The ASCII code format in Table 1.1 illustrates the **hexadecimal** representation for various characters. The hexadecimal number system is used extensively in microprocessor work and is discussed in Appendix 1.

ASCII characters are often used to transfer text between computers. Commonly certain tests are performed to determine whether any transmission errors have occurred. The most common test is called a **parity** test. Before the data transfer the number of bits in the data word having a specific polarity—generally one—is determined. A special bit, the parity bit, is set to make this total either even or odd. If the bit makes the total even, we are using **even parity**; if odd, **odd parity**. For the present let us assume that even parity is being used. The parity bit is sent along with

Table 1.1
ASCII Character Set[a]

Lower Bits	Upper Bits							
	0	1	2	3	4	5	6	7
0	@ (Nul)	P̂ (DLE)	space	0	@	P		p
1	Â (SOH)	Q̂ (DC1)	!	1	A	Q	a	q
2	B̂ (STX)	R̂ (DC2)	"	2	B	R	b	r
3	Ĉ (ETX)	Ŝ (DC3)	#	3	C	S	c	s
4	D̂ (EOT)	T̂ (DC4)	$	4	D	T	d	t
5	Ê (ENQ)	Û (NAK)	%	5	E	U	e	u
6	F̂ (ACK)	V̂ (SYN)	€	6	F	V	f	v
7	Ĝ (BEL)	Ŵ (ETB)	'	7	G	W	g	w
8	Ĥ (BS)	X̂ (CAN)	(	8	H	X	h	x
9	Î (HT)	Ŷ (EM)	)	9	I	Y	i	y
A	Ĵ (LF)	Ẑ (SUB)	*	:	J	Z	j	z
B	K̂ (VT)	[̂ (ESC)	+	;	K	[	k	{
C	L̂ (FF)	\ (FS)	,	<	L	\	l		
D	M̂ (CR)	]̂ (CS)	~	=	M	]	m	}
E	N̂ (SO)	^ (RS)	.	>	N	^	n	~
F	Ô (SI)	_ (US)	/	?	O	_	o	DEL

[a] The format is upper bits/lower bits. ASCII "A" is 41 or 01000001. The caret ˆ means control character.

the data. Upon their reception, the bits are counted. Given even parity, the receiver expects always to count an even number of bits. If an odd number is counted, there has been a bit transmission error.

This error-checking technique is quite common. It provides single-error-detecting capability. More extensive error-detecting and even error-correcting schemes are used for transfer of critical data.

1.5 MICROPROCESSOR FAMILIES

Through the years a number of different logic circuit designs and semiconductor active device types have been developed for ICs. The particular combination used for a given IC defines its **technology.** When several chips are used to make a computer system, devices from the same technology are generally used, although exceptions to this abound. The various technologies differ in speed, power required, cost, complexity, and so on.

Microprocessors and their associated families of devices, including memory devices and I/O circuits, are manufactured in a variety of such technologies. Some of these technologies are transistor-transistor logic (TTL or T^2L), Schottky-clamped TTL (STTL), low-power STTL (LSTTL), emitter-coupled logic (ECL), integrated-injection logic (IIL or I^2L), p-channel metal oxide semiconductor (PMOS), n-channel MOS (NMOS), complementary MOS (CMOS), and high-speed CMOS (HSCMOS), among others. The technology chosen will depend on the particular application.

Some typical parameters of digital ICs, constructed with each of the more popular semiconductor technologies, are shown in Table 1.2. Here the trade-off between speed and power is particularly apparent. For example, ECL might be used for large, high-speed computers because of its

Table 1.2
Comparison of Some Device Parameters

| Technology | Typical Parameters, 5-V supply | | | |
	Propagation Delay per Gate, ns	Power Dissipation per Gate	Logic Swing, volts	Noise Immunity, volts
TTL	10	10 mW	3.8	1.0
LSTTL	9	2 mW	3.8	1.0
ECL	2	25 mW	0.8	0.05
IIL	50	100 nW	0.6	0.2
PMOS	200	1.0 mW	3.8	0.9
NMOS	50	0.5 mW	3.8	0.5
CMOS	25	100 nW	5.0[a]	1.7
HSCMOS	8	1 μW	5.0[a]	1.7

[a] CMOS and HSCMOS logic swing is typically the full power supply range.

fast switching (low propagation delay) characteristics, but it would be impractical for many other applications because of its high power requirements and very low noise immunity. CMOS, on the other hand, would be well suited for use in a space satellite or missile guidance application because of its extremely low power consumption and high noise immunity.

Some popular microprocessors are listed in Table 1.3, which shows the technology used along with some of the other characteristics of each device. This table is by no means exhaustive, showing only a small sample of the devices currently available.

One should be very careful in using comparisons such as these. For example, the instruction cycle time listed gives no information about the work accomplished during an instruction or about the number of instruction cycles required to perform a given task. The cycle times shown in Table 1.3 represent the time required for the microprocessor to execute a basic machine instruction that does not require writing or reading data to or from memory. It includes the time required to fetch an instruction from memory and to execute the instruction. These cycle times are given for reference only and do not necessarily reflect the speed of each device in executing a given program. This speed depends on other factors in addition to the cycle time shown. Such factors include the architecture (internal organization) and instruction set for the microprocessor. Moreover, the time required to perform a particular task depends heavily on the programmer's ability to get the best performance from the microprocessor.

TTL, LSTTL, and other technologies offer good speed characteristics but do not have the density or low power dissipation of some of the other technologies. They are, however, often used in a microprocessor type called a **bit-slice** system. A bit-slice system is similar to the more common microprocessor system, except that the operations are divided up into

Table 1.3
Some Representative Microprocessors

Microprocessor	Technology	Typical Standby Power, mW	Typical Instruction Cycle Time, μs
Intel 8008	PMOS	420	10
Intel 8085	NMOS	400	1.3
Intel 80286	HCMOS	2500	0.1
RCA 1802C	CMOS	4.0	6.4
Motorola MC6800	NMOS	600	2.0
Motorola MC68000	HCMOS	1750	0.08
MOS Technology 6502	NMOS	250	3.0
National 32032	HCMOS	1000	0.1
Zilog Z80	NMOS	400	1.3

single or multiple bits. The result is a somewhat more complex system which is significantly faster.

Potentially, the brightest new star in the microprocessor sky is **gallium arsenide (GaAs)**. Gallium arsenide has been used for various applications in infrared systems for a number of years. It offers the potential for complex microprocessor systems of very high speed.

Figure 1.6 is a photograph of a packaged microprocessor, together with an IC memory chip and a programmable I/O device. These three components can be used to form a complete and powerful computing system.

Figure 1.6
Microprocessor (8085), Memory (8755), and Programmable I/O Device (8155), approximately one and one-half times real size.

CHAPTER TWO

MICROCOMPUTER ARCHITECTURE

2.1 INTRODUCTION

Computer structure, or architecture, as it is generally known, was discussed briefly in Chapter One. This chapter develops the subject in more
depth as it applies to microprocessor-based systems, concluding with a
discussion of the 8085 architecture in detail.

Many of the subjects in this chapter will be addressed again in various later chapters. Here each of the elements of microprocessor architecture will be discussed in its relation to the others. Some subjects will
be introduced only in outline form. The detailed discussions will appear
later.

2.2 THE MICROPROCESSOR

At the most basic level, a microprocessor-based system is comprised of a
very large and highly structured collection of digital storage locations
with a central control device. With each machine execute cycle, the contents of a few of these storage locations are moved or manipulated. For
the systems under study, these locations are virtually all 8 bits in size.
The vast bulk of locations form the computer's memory and are simply
called **memory locations.**

Each memory location is identified with an address. The CPU itself,
the microprocessor, performs the central control and has its own structured collection of storage locations, mostly 8 bits long, whose contents
may be moved or manipulated during each machine cycle. These storage
locations within the processor are called **registers.** A register is a temporary data storage location.

Registers

A simplified view of a microprocessor is shown in Figure 2.1. The bus connects the microprocessor to its memory and to its I/O devices, which are used to communicate with the outside world.

The registers within the microprocessor are critical to its operation. Because they are resident on the microprocessor, they can be manipulated rapidly without selecting external chips. Although the details of the internal register architecture vary from machine to machine, certain register types are very common. The PC, which was mentioned previously, contains the address of the next instruction to be fetched. Its size determines the range of memory in which program instructions can be located. For many common machines—for example, the 8080, 8085, Z80, 1802, 6502, or 6800—this is a 16-bit number and gives a range of 65,536 possible locations.

Another critical register is the **accumulator.** It is used extensively for data manipulations. Although exceptions occur, addition, subtraction, and similar instructions commonly use the accumulator for data to initiate the operation and as the destination for the result.

The **flag register** contains various bits of status information. If, for example, the last operation resulted in a zero value, a **zero flag** might be set. By this we mean that a specific bit of the flag register word will be set to a one (a one is most often represented by a positive voltage, whereas a zero is most often simply zero, or near zero, volts). Other common flags are a **carry flag** for addition, a **borrow flag** for subtraction, a flag to indicate the sign of a result, and so forth. The flag register is critical for computer decision making. For example, to cause a branch when a number reaches a given value, we subtract the given value from the number and branch if the zero flag is set. The flag register is often given other names: condition code register, processor status register, program status register, and status register, among others.

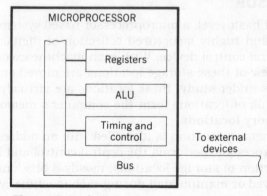

Figure 2.1
A Microprocessor.

Most machines have a few general-purpose registers in which the programmer can store intermediate values and the like. **Index registers**, which are used for counting and certain kinds of memory operations, are also common.

The microprocessor also has an **instruction register**, which is the destination for an instruction during the fetch cycle. The programmer cannot directly manipulate this register; such a register is said to be **invisible**. Registers that can be manipulated by the program are said to be **visible**.

In some microprocessors, a special set of registers is arranged in what is called a **stack**. These registers are connected in such a way that when a word is stored in the first register, the data previously contained in this register are transferred to the next register down in the stack. The previous contents of the second register are transferred to the third, the third to the fourth, and so on. Storing data in this way is called **pushing** the stack. When a read operation is performed, the word that is retrieved is the last word pushed into the stack, and the contents of all the registers in the stack are transferred upward one position. This kind of stack is called a **last-in, first-out (LIFO)** stack. The read operation is called **popping** the stack.

A LIFO stack can also be implemented by using memory locations. Here a CPU register is designated as a **stack pointer (SP)** and contains the address of a free memory location. When the stack is to be pushed, the data are stored in the location pointed to by the SP and the pointer is stepped. Popping the stack involves the reverse operation. The stack thus becomes a stack of free memory locations. The advantage of this type of stack is that many more storage locations become available. The disadvantage is that stack operations may take longer because the data transfers occur external to the CPU.

Other forms of stacks are sometimes used. The LIFO stack, however, is the one most common for microprocessor systems.

Arithmetic Logic Unit

The **arithmetic logic unit (ALU)** and "timing and control" blocks form the central control features of the computer system. At an output register (generally the accumulator), the ALU produces the result of a commanded operation on the contents of its input registers. It might be given two numbers and be requested to add them. The ALU can generally do addition and subtraction along with various logic operations such as AND, OR, exclusive OR, and so forth. It is physically composed of dedicated logic circuits. The ALU also produces flags, such as the carry flag. A typical addition operation might add the contents of the accumulator to the contents of a defined register in the CPU. The result would be placed in the accumulator, and, if a carry presents itself, the carry flag would be set.

The ALU rarely provides a multiplication or division capability for basic 8-bit systems because of the complexity involved. These operations are generally done by programming multiple additions or subtractions. Another approach is to use an external chip, called a **math coprocessor,** which carries out such complex operations.

Timing and Control

"**Timing and control**" in Figure 2.1 refers to a rather complex set of logic functions that synchronize the machine and direct various operations. A high-frequency oscillator provides the basis for timing. During the first cycles of this clock, after the start of the fetch cycle:

1. The memory address of the first program instruction—usually address location zero—is used to excite the memory address lines.

2. An indication is sent that the processor is ready to receive the instruction from this address.

3. The instruction word is moved from memory to the instruction register (which is tied to an instruction decode matrix within the processor).

4. Finally, the memory is told that the instruction has been received.

This view of a fetch cycle is intended to highlight the fact that a number of critical timing conditions must be met if data transmission is to be properly coordinated.

The timing and control block decodes instructions and directs the execute cycle. For example, the instruction word 10001010 is decoded by the 8085 as "add register D with carry to the accumulator." This instruction causes the timing and control block to command the ALU to add the contents of the accumulator to the contents of the internal "D"-register and add to this sum a one if the carry flag is a one. The result of the addition may set or reset the carry flag. The ALU will then store the result in the accumulator, erasing the old accumulator data. The various flags will be changed based on the result of this operation. Again, the function of the timing and control block is to coordinate this activity.

Another important hardware feature of most microprocessors allows **interrupts.** An interrupt suspends the current operation of the processor in response to an external input so that it can attend to a critical request. The microprocessor chip itself will have a pin, or pins, which, when activated, causes the processor to halt the current program and perform a different program intended for the interrupt. At the end of the interrupt routine, processing is returned to the original program. Interrupts are often given levels of priority so that the most critical routine is always performed.

As an example of the use of interrupts, consider a computerized building monitor. The main program might normally check various temperature and light-level sensors so that the heaters and lights can be adjusted. An interrupt initiated by an output of a motion sensor might look at several sensors and monitor the area to see whether an alarm should be sounded. A higher-priority interrupt might be activated by a fire alarm. During these high-priority interrupts, a low-priority interrupt, such as a thermostat changing state would not be serviced until the others were completed. Finally, the microprocessor would revert to its main routine when all the interrupts had been disposed of.

The internal operating details of the timing and control block are not critical to the user. However, various external timing conventions must be followed when interfacing memory and I/O devices to the microprocessor. These timing details will be discussed in this chapter and in later chapters.

The timing and control block also provides a reset function to initialize the CPU along with other components in the computer system.

2.3 BUS STRUCTURE

As should be obvious by now, the microprocessor system performs many data transfers into and out of the CPU. The standard method for such transfers uses a **bus structure.** A bus is a set of conductors over which data, address, control, or other information can be transmitted. A classic 8-bit microprocessor system would include an 8-bit (that is, 8-wire) **data bus,** a 16-bit **address bus,** and a 6- to 8-bit **control bus,** as shown in Figure 2.2. The data and address buses generally portray the data or

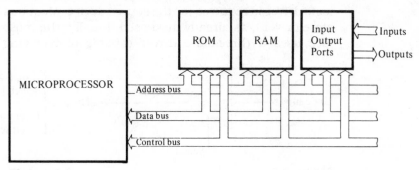

Figure 2.2
Bus Structure.

address word in unison. The control bus, however, is simply a collection of timing and control signals.

All instruction and data transfers use the data bus lines. The address bus identifies any memory location to be activated. The control bus carries all timing and control signals for coordinating data transfers.

For the classic system just mentioned, the data read process starts with the CPU fixing 1 and 0 bits on the address bus and thus selecting a memory location. The CPU then indicates that it is ready for data by changing the state of certain lines on the control bus. It is now the job of the memory location in question to place its stored data on the data bus. The CPU **latches** (that is, holds) this word and proceeds to its next operation. The preceding operation is a memory "read" process, that is, the CPU reads data from a memory location. We refer to the action of the CPU. We do not say the memory "writes" to the CPU; rather, the CPU "reads" the memory.

For a write operation, the state of the control bus would be different. The memory device must discern the write state of the control bus and, thus, take the data off the data bus and store it.

The CPU sets the state of both the address and the control buses for the read or write operations discussed. However, the state of the data bus may be established either by a memory location or by the CPU. Thus, both the CPU and the memory circuits must be able to (1) drive a data bus line to a one, (2) drive a data bus line to a zero, or (3) allow a data bus line to be driven by other devices. For the third state, called the **high-impedance state**, the device does not affect the state of the bus. A device that can achieve these three states is said to be a **three-state driver.** The control bus defines whether the device is to produce data (the first two states) or be passive (the high-impedance state) by some form of **read/write select**, as shown in Figure 2.3.

Devices that attach to the various bus lines have different levels of complexity. The simplest devices only monitor a given line for input. Some bus lines (generally restricted to certain microprocessor control output lines) may always be driven from one device. Then only a good logic driver is required for the source device. Most bus lines require three-state drivers, as already discussed. Finally, the most complex bus interface uses a three-state driver capable of receiving input during the

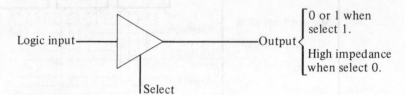

Figure 2.3
Three-State Output Device.

high-impedance state. This would be a three-state, **bidirectional interface** used for a **bidirectional bus,** as shown in Figure 2.4.

The bidirectional bus structure reduces the number of interconnecting wires or printed-circuit runs required in a microcomputer system, and, even more important, it reduces the number of pins required on the IC packages, including the microprocessor itself.

It would seem that the address and control buses would not require three-state drivers since the CPU is normally the only device that drives these lines. However, provision is often made for the microprocessor to change to a high-impedance state so that other devices can address memory. An example is the **direct memory access (DMA)** process, where devices external to the CPU rapidly fill memory, bypassing the processor. Another important example is the 8085, where one-half of the address bus is also used as the data bus. This saves a further eight pins so that additional control functions are possible. This half of the address bus contains address information whenever certain control lines indicate that an address is present on the bus. When data are to be transferred, these eight lines operate as the data bus. Thus, not only is part of the bus structure for the 8085 three-state and bidirectional, but it also changes function from one time to another. It is said to be **time-multiplexed.**

2.4 MEMORY AND I/O

Memory operation has been mentioned often up to this point. It will be discussed in detail in the next chapter. Memory is, of course, a major component of microcomputer architecture.

In a microcomputer system the memory can be divided into **addressable** and **nonaddressable** memory. The addressable memory is

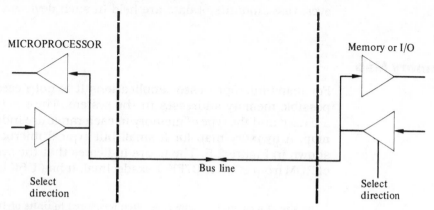

Figure 2.4
Bidirectional Bus Line.

that shown in Figure 2.2. Any byte of this memory can be accessed by the CPU directly. It is considered as an internal part of the microcomputer. In a microprocessor system this memory is usually comprised of two types: **random-access memory (RAM)** and **read-only memory (ROM)**. The terms are somewhat misleading. The difference between the two is that although RAM can be both written to and read from, we can only read from ROM. ROM has information fixed into it either during its manufacture or by special user operations. We can address individual locations in either; that is, both RAM and ROM can be accessed randomly. Perhaps better terms would be read/write random-access memory for RAM and read-only random-access memory for ROM. In any case, RAM and ROM are the universally accepted terms.

For many dedicated microcomputer systems, ROM is used to hold a fixed program. It has the advantage of being **nonvolatile.** This means that when its power supplies are removed, the stored program is not lost. RAM is normally **volatile,** unless the special design features of certain types are exploited.

The basic form of ROM, **mask programmable,** is manufactured with the program fixed in the device. The memory pattern programmed into such ROM during its manufacture cannot be changed. Hence, it is essential that the stored program in it be free of errors. This type of ROM is widely used in large-volume applications because the cost is generally quite low. ROM is also used in many general-purpose applications, such as personal computers. Here the parts of the machine's software that allow it to start and to be operated are held in ROM.

Nonaddressable memory is thought of as memory external to the microcomputer. Its data can be brought into RAM when needed. It generally includes **mass storage** devices, such as disk systems or tape-drive devices. Generally, blocks of data are brought into RAM, byte by byte, from these devices. The operations of reading or writing are slower; however, vast amounts of data are held in such devices.

Memory Map

For many microprocessor applications it is not necessary to use all the possible memory addresses in the system. The range of addresses that are used and the type of memory in each range are indicated by a **memory map.** A memory map for a small but typical microcomputer system is shown in Figure 2.5. The figure indicates that the system has 2K[1] bytes of ROM from 0000 to 07FF, hexadecimal. It has 1.5K bytes (2000 to 20FF)

---

[1] The size of a computer memory is often measured in units of 1024, decimal, locations. This unit is designated 1K. Hence, many microprocessor systems can have a maximum of 64K memory locations since a 16-bit address can define a range of 64K bytes of memory.

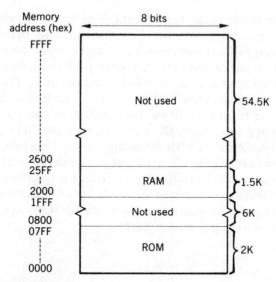

Figure 2.5
A Typical Memory Map.

of RAM. The memory map is an important tool for almost any microcomputer development project.

Another, more detailed, example of a memory map is shown in Figure 2.6. The first 256 bytes are used as temporary storage. We will use the term "page" to indicate a block of memory 256 bytes long. This first page—called the zero page since its hexadecimal address starts with 00— is being used as an extension of the internal registers; that is, it is being

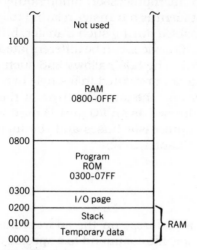

Figure 2.6
A Memory Map.

used for temporary storage of data. The stack is external to the micro-processor and on page one. From there, 256 bytes are assigned for **memory-mapped I/O** devices—input and output devices which the computer can access as though they were part of memory. A program ROM resides in locations 0300 to 07FF, hexadecimal. The top of memory is open RAM for data. This application must be highly data-intensive. Note that the four most significant bits (MSBs) of the 16-bit address are not used. It is apparent from the memory map that all usable memory locations can be identified without using the top four bits. As shown, none of these bits will ever be set to a one for any memory read or write operation.

The reader should notice that part of the memory map shows certain hardware features of the system, such as the location of memory-mapped I/O. Other sections relate to software partitioning, such as the location of program instructions versus data.

Input/Output

Input/output devices allow the microcomputer to transfer data to and from the external world. A simple and common method of dealing with I/O is memory-mapped I/O, as mentioned earlier. Here the I/O devices are connected to the buses in the same way as ROM or RAM. A printer might be assigned a specific memory location so that whenever the CPU sends data to that address, the character would be printed. Memory-mapped I/O is possible with virtually any microprocessor device. Some devices, such as the 6502 microprocessor, use memory-mapped I/O exclusively.

Another method of transferring data to and from I/O is called **I/O-mapped I/O.** The 8085 microprocessor, among others, has special lines on the control bus that identify a transfer relating to I/O-mapped I/O. The memory devices are disabled during such transfer, but the I/O devices are activated. The various I/O devices can be differentiated by normal address data on the address bus. The 8085 allows 256 such I/O-mapped I/O devices. The address data are presented in a single byte, which is repeated in both the high-order and the low-order byte of the address bus. Normally, a special device known as an **I/O port** is used to provide the interface between the microprocessor buses and the input or output device itself, as discussed in Chapter Seven.

Address Decoding

When the CPU sends an address on the address bus, this information must be turned into a specific command to a specific device. The **address decoding** does this operation. It uses the address bus information to determine the device to be accessed.

Because there are a number of devices connected to the computer buses—RAM and ROM, I/O, and so forth—it is necessary to ensure that only the device intended for the data transfer responds when a request is made by the microprocessor. ROM and RAM devices cover large blocks of memory. They usually have direct pinout to the address bus for some number of bits. These lines are internally decoded by the memory devices to access the individual data bytes. A 1K-byte RAM device, for example, will generally have 10 address pins to access 1024-byte storage locations. Address decode circuitry must be added to decode the remaining lines on the address bus.

Each RAM or ROM memory chip will have an input, called **chip enable (CE),** or some similar name. The memory CE input must be activated before the chip will respond. This scheme is shown in Figure 2.7. We can see the evolution of a memory map. The MSBs used for the address decoder allocate a block of data for the device. The memory map is used to keep track of these allocations.

If the system does not use the upper reaches of the available memory, some of the address lines will never be used. As mentioned previously, Figure 2.6 shows a memory map in which the four MSBs are not used. In such systems some savings are possible since the address decode circuitry will be simplified.

The address decoder for a single-byte location, as might be used for memory-mapped I/O, must decode the full address bus in use by the system. This decoding then determines the specific address for the I/O device.

Timing

The control bus incorporates the timing signals that are generated by the microprocessor to synchronize information transfers between the micro-

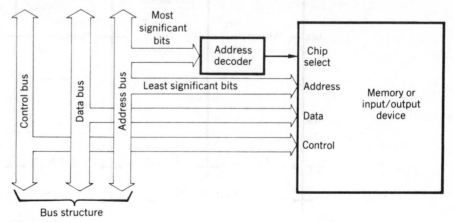

Figure 2.7
Address Decoding.

processor and a memory location or I/O port. Consider the timing diagram shown in Figure 2.8. The figure illustrates the two control signals—**read (RD)** and **write (WR)**—generated by the microprocessor during two successive instruction cycles. The example assumes that both are single-byte instructions, requiring only one instruction word to direct the CPU operation: the first is a memory (or input device) read and the second is a memory (or output device) write. The type of transfer—memory or I/O—will be determined by the memory map, the specific address generated by the microprocessor, and the state of the control bus during each execute cycle.

Memory data transfer timing will be discussed in greater detail in Chapter Three. The timing considerations for I/O-mapped I/O will be discussed in Chapter Seven.

2.5 THE 8085 MICROPROCESSOR

Throughout this book we will use the Intel 8085 microprocessor as a vehicle to demonstrate principles of hardware organization and programming. Once the reader gains familiarity with one microprocessor, he or she will find it easy to transfer the knowledge that has been gained to other devices and systems by studying manufacturers' literature and other references. The Intel 8085 evolved from the popular 8080. These 8-bit processors have much in common with certain other 8-bit devices, such as the Zilog Z80. The Z80 will operate successfully using 8080 instructions. Further, many other devices share much with the 8080

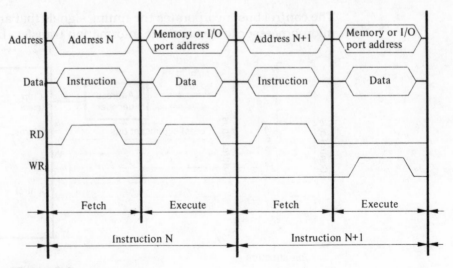

Figure 2.8
Instruction Cycle Timing.

series. Although expanded in performance, the 8086 and 8088 microprocessors have many features similar to the 8080 and 8085. Such similar-
ities remain for the advanced 80186, 80286, and even the 80386 devices.

We shall now examine the architecture and characteristics of the
8085. A block diagram of the internal architecture is shown in Figure 2.9.
The microprocessor is made up of an ALU, various registers, and several
control blocks. The functions of these blocks have been described in
general terms in previous sections. Here the sections of the 8085 and
their operating characteristics will be described in more detail.

The ALU and Associated Registers

The ALU in the 8085 accepts inputs from two registers, the **accumulator
(A-register)** and the temporary (TMP) register. The accumulator, in addition to acting as one of the sources for the ALU, also serves as the
destination for the output of the ALU for all operations. The TMP-register
is filled with data from another location during the execute cycle. The
specific instruction determines the source of this byte. For example, an
instruction to add the contents of a memory location to the accumulator

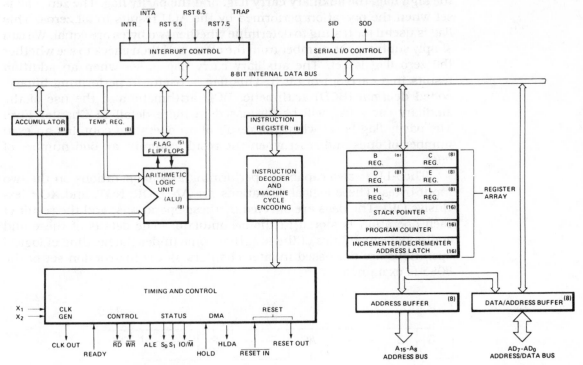

Figure 2.9
8085 Internal Block Diagram. (Reprinted by permission of Intel Corporation, copyright
© 1980.)

would cause the contents of the specified location to be moved to the TMP-register before the actual addition process. The programmer cannot directly access the TMP-register; thus, it is called an **invisible register.**

The ALU performs dedicated addition, subtraction, and logical operations on the pair of input bytes from the A- and TMP-registers. In addition, it generates **flag bits** that are stored in a flag register, as shown in Figure 2.10. This figure shows the bit location of each flag in the flag register. All register bits are numbered from zero, the least significant bit (LSB), to 7, the MSB.

When an ADD is performed, the carry flag is set if the addition results in a carry. Subsequent operations may make use of the carry flag. This feature makes it possible to add numbers that contain more than 8 bits by performing several 8-bit additions. The carry flag provides the link between these operations. When a subtract operation is performed, the carry flag becomes a borrow flag, in effect. If the number subtracted is greater than the number in the accumulator, the carry flag is set after a subtraction. Thus, subtraction of numbers longer than 8 bits becomes viable.

Other flag bit changes that are generated by the ALU are the **zero flag,** the **sign flag,** the **auxiliary carry** flag, and the **parity flag.** The zero flag is set when the operation performed by the ALU results in all zeros. This flag is useful for testing to determine whether two bytes are equal. We can simply subtract one number from the other and then check to see whether the zero flag is set. The auxiliary carry flag is set when an addition results in a carryout of bit 3. This flag is useful in performing **binary-coded decimal (BCD)** arithmetic. BCD arithmetic and the use of the auxiliary carry flag will be discussed in more detail in Chapter Five. The parity flag is set when the result of an operation contains an even number of ones and reset when the result contains an odd number of ones.

The ALU is also capable of performing logical operations on the two input bytes. These logical operations are **AND, OR, NOT,** and **XOR** (exclusive OR). The flags are affected by these operations, and the result of each operation is stored in the accumulator. The details of these and additional capabilities of the ALU that come under the heading of logical operations are discussed in later chapters as the instruction set of the 8085 is examined.

MSB   LSB

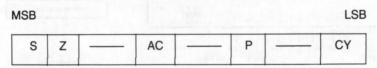

| S | Z | —— | AC | —— | P | —— | CY |

Figure 2.10
8085 Flag Register: S, sign flag; Z, zero flag; AC, auxiliary flag; P, parity flag; CY, carry flag.

Register Section

The register section contains several 8-bit registers with six general-purpose registers arranged in pairs. Several 16-bit address pointer registers are also available.

Six general-purpose registers can be used individually for temporary storage of individual bytes or in pairs to store 16 bits—usually memory addresses. This makes these registers very versatile and enhances the power of the microprocessor. The **H-** and **L-registers** are often used as a pair to store a memory address used for indirect addressing. (Addressing methods, including indirect addressing, will be discussed in detail in Chapter Four.) The **DE-register pair** is often used to store another address for use in indirect addressing—the contents of DE and HL can be swapped with a single instruction. The B- and C-registers are often used for temporary storage of individual bytes of data, such as the intermediate results of a series of arithmetic operations.

The stack pointer (SP) is a 16-bit register that points to the stack located in RAM. The 8085 does not have an internal register stack, but instead uses a section of RAM. Thus, the length of the stack is not fixed but can be as long as necessary.

Any area of memory can be designated as a stack simply by storing an address in the SP at the beginning of a program. The stack grows downward from this location, that is, the SP is decremented before each push operation and incremented after each pop. The address pointed to by the SP is assumed to be the last-in value in the stack. A push involves decrementing the SP and then storing the byte. The address that is initially stored in the SP is the highest-numbered address location to be used for the stack, plus one. The 8085 always does two-byte push and pop operations.

The purpose and operation of the program counter (PC) were discussed in Chapter One. It contains the address of the instruction in memory to be executed next. At start-up, the 8085 is normally reset by external hardware, that is, an external pin named **RESET** is activated. After this action the 8085 PC has memory address zero. Thus, the 8085 start-up—and reset—address is zero.

The "incrementer/decrementer address latch" handles the transfer and manipulation of address data before they are used. The user cannot directly access this device.

Timing and Control

When an instruction is fetched from memory, it is stored in the instruction register (IR) and subsequently decoded to determine the required operation. This **instruction decoder** controls the action of all the microprocessor registers and the ALU through the timing and control section.

Interrupt processing is controlled within the microprocessor using several interface signals. The 8085 microprocessor also contains a **serial I/O port.** The timing and control section is synchronized by an external clock or by an internally generated clock using an external crystal. In addition to generating all the control signals, this section also generates several status-state and cycle-timing signals which are available at the pins of the microprocessor.

EXERCISES

2.1 Determine the maximum memory space for 8-bit microprocessors that have the following address word sizes. Express your answers in K bytes:

    (a) 14 bits.
    (b) 11 bits.
    (c)   8 bits.
    (d) 24 bits.
    (e) 19 bits.

2.2 Given the following memory requirements, determine the minimum number of address bits required. Show, in hexadecimal, the highest addressable location.

    (a) 27K bytes.
    (b) 48K bytes.
    (c) 1.5K bytes.
    (d) 9K bytes.
    (e) 14,800 decimal bytes.

2.3 A microprocessor system requires 4K bytes of ROM and 256 bytes of RAM. Determine the beginning and end addresses of each memory block if the two memories are to occupy contiguous blocks of memory starting at address 0000. Express your answer in hexadecimal notation. Draw a memory map.

2.4 If the microcomputer system in Exercise 2.3 requires four additional I/O ports, define suitable addresses for the ports, assuming memory-mapped I/O.

2.5 A microcomputer has the following memory map:

4000 to 400F	I/O
2000 to 21FF	RAM
0000 to 0FFF	ROM

Determine the amount of ROM and RAM memory and the number of I/O ports in the system.

2.6 Determine which address lines are not used in the system shown in Figure 2.5.

2.7 Determine the amount of ROM (program storage), RAM, and memory-mapped I/O available in the system shown in Figure 2.6.

2.8 A microprocessor system used in an automobile has as one of its inputs an eight-bit word which bit-maps into the status of each of eight lights. That is, if a light is operating properly, its bit will be high. Each bit indicates the status of a particular light. If we assume that only one light fails, which state of the parity flag will indicate the failure?

2.9 The 8085 uses 16 pins for its data and address buses by multiplexing 8 bits. How many additional pins would be needed were no multiplexing used and were the data bus not bidirectional?

2.10 Develop a memory map for a high-resolution video graphics system whose screen has 256, decimal, points of resolution (pixels) per line and 128 lines. Each pixel requires one byte in memory; the byte defines such things as intensity and color. How many address bits are required to address this memory-mapped video?

CHAPTER THREE

MEMORY

3.1 INTRODUCTION

For a computer to function, it must have a program to execute. The program must be stored in such a way that the computer can access each instruction in sequence. In addition, there is usually a need to store data temporarily during the execution of a program. The types of memory used for these applications should be fast because they directly affect the speed of execution. Since these memories hold a relatively small number of bits of information, the cost per bit is not an overriding consideration.

On the other hand, there is often a need to store large blocks of information over long periods of time. Here, some type of **mass memory** is needed for which the cost per bit must be very low, even at the expense of longer access times. Therefore, more than one type of memory is needed for most applications.

Some of the more common types of memory devices used with microcomputers are discussed in this chapter. This chapter also provides a brief introduction to memory access timing and control using the 8085 operations for examples.

3.2 READ ONLY MEMORY

In most microprocessor applications there is a fixed program that does not change from one use to another. In a dedicated application, such as a traffic light controller, the microprocessor normally has only a fixed program to execute. Even in general-purpose applications, such as a home computer, a fixed program exists, which is executed to perform functions like initializing the microcomputer, scanning the keyboard, and so forth.

Since these programs are fixed, they can be stored in a read only memory (ROM). Another application for ROM is a look-up table. In such tables fixed data, rather than program instructions, would be stored. Examples of commonly used look-up tables are trigonometric functions, logarithms, and multiplication tables.

The advantages of ROMs over read/write memories for the applications mentioned earlier are low cost, high density (a ROM cell takes only about one-fourth the area on an integrated circuit), and nonvolatility—the stored data do not vanish when power is removed. The disadvantage of using a ROM is that any changes that must be made to the stored information are difficult and time-consuming. For factory-programmed ROMs, a change can be expensive and require turnaround times of several weeks, or more.

Diode-Matrix ROM

The simplest form of solid-state ROM is a **diode matrix,** as shown in Figure 3.1. The horizontal lines are the input lines, and the vertical lines are the outputs. Only one of the input lines is high at any one time. Address decoding logic is required, which raises one input line high for each address within the ROM. The ROM shown is a 4-bit by 6 array. In

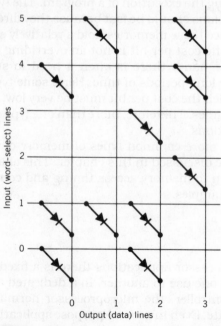

Figure 3.1
Diode-Matrix ROM. (Pull-down loads are assumed.)

other words, it holds six four-bit words. Consider what happens if input line 4 is high while all other input lines are held low. The diodes connected to line 4 will be forward-biased, allowing ones to appear on output lines 0 and 3. Assuming each line is loaded to ground, the output pattern is 1001. The other diodes (not connected to input line 4), which are connected to output lines 0 and 2, are reverse-biased and act as open circuits. Without the diodes to block the voltage, these lines would be loaded by the other input lines. To store a particular pattern of ones and zeros in a diode matrix, we simply connect a diode wherever we want a one to appear on the output.

Although the diode matrix is a very simple and inexpensive type of ROM, it is rarely used in practice today because the input lines must supply the current to all the output lines. Not only does it cause difficulties with input drivers, but it also reduces the speed of performance and causes output drive problems. Although diode-matrix ROM may be used in special applications or embedded in ICs, other ROM types offer better performance today.

Mask-Programmed ROM

When large quantities of ROM devices are required, the least expensive form of ROM is the mask-programmed type. For this type of ROM, the data are stored by the manufacturer during the fabrication of the IC. Although there are a number of methods of storing data in mask-programmed ROMs, only one example will be discussed in detail here.

Figure 3.2 shows an array of MOS transistors in which some of the gates are connected; others are left floating. The resistors shown on the column lines would normally be MOS transistors—either depletion-mode devices or forward-biased, enhancement-mode devices. The memory cell transistors are enhancement-mode devices. Assuming n-channel technology, a positive voltage would be applied to the gate of a given transistor in order to turn it on. The transistors with no gate connections cannot be turned on. Suppose that a positive voltage—logic 1 level—is applied to word-select line number 2, with all other lines held at ground potential—logic 0 level. The transistors connected to output lines 1 and 2 would be turned on, pulling these lines to ground potential while the transistors connected to output lines 0 and 3 would remain in an "off" or high-impedance state. Lines 0 and 3 are left at V_{DD} or logic 1 state. The binary word on the output lines will thus be 1001.

The production process starts when the data to be stored in masked ROM are developed and carefully checked. These data are then sent to the ROM manufacturer where the masks are made and the devices are actually fabricated.

Mask-programmable ROMs can be manufactured at low cost for

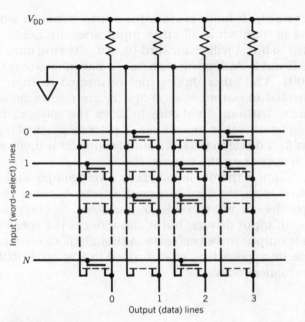

Figure 3.2
Mask-Programmed ROM.

high-volume applications. However, the cost of making and checking the mask makes this type of device too expensive for low-volume applications—less than, say, 1000 units. For these applications a user programmable device called a **programmable read-only memory (PROM)** is more cost-effective. These devices are discussed in the following sections.

PROM

PROMs can be **erasable** or **nonerasable.** Erasable PROMs are often referenced using names denoting the erasure method. Nonerasable PROMs are simply called PROMs.

Nonerasable PROMs are normally programmed by the user, usually by selectively burning through fuse lines (links) on the PROM IC. This PROM programming is done by passing a strong electric current through the PROM fuse links. Once the devices have been programmed, the program cannot be changed.

A bipolar transistor PROM cell is illustrated schematically in Figure 3.3. A fuse is created in series with the collector of the transistor by depositing nichrome (a nickle–chromium alloy), or polysilicon, on the chip. This fuse link has a notch or narrow spot in which to concentrate current. Programming is accomplished by selecting the desired word via the address lines on the chip and injecting a current into the output lines

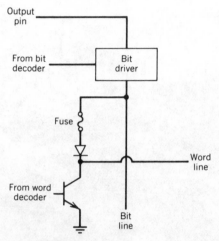

Figure 3.3
Bipolar PROM Cell.

on which the fuses are to be blown. Under normal operating conditions, the current through these fuse links is well below the fusing threshold.

PROMs can be programmed with relatively simple circuits which can be constructed with a few switches and interface circuits. However, programming with switches can be a tedious and time-consuming task. For this reason manufacturers of microprocessor hardware make available more sophisticated **PROM programmers.** This allows the programming process to be automated, relieving the user of the tedium of hand programming and eliminating many of its inherent errors.

A universal PROM programmer, shown in Figure 3.4, is called universal because it allows the user to program a wide variety of different devices. This adaptability is accomplished through various plug-in **personality cards.** Each personality card modifies the programmer's pulse generation functions in a specific way, which then matches the programmer to the PROM type being programmed. Such pulse generation functions apply current for a specific length of time to specific pins so that the PROM can be programmed.

EPROM

For many applications, such as during the development of a new product prior to making masked ROM, it is necessary to change the program periodically. For these applications a memory device that can be erased and reprogrammed, but still retains the nonvolatility of a ROM, is desirable. Such devices are available and are called **erasable programmable read-only memories (EPROMs).**

The most popular type of EPROM is the ultraviolet type, or **UV EPROM.**

Figure 3.4
Universal PROM Programmer and a UV EPROM (Intel 2708). (Reprinted by permission
of Intel Corporation, copyright © 1980.)

After being programmed electrically, these devices may be erased by exposure to a high-intensity ultraviolet light. Specially designed erasure
lights are available for this purpose. They should be used with great care
because ultraviolet light levels are quite high. A quartz window is provided on the EPROM package to allow ultraviolet light to fall on the chip
during erasure. Figure 3.4 includes a picture of a typical EPROM, in
which the window is clearly visible. This window is normally covered with
an opaque label during use to prevent accidental erasure by exposure to

fluorescent lighting or sunlight. Brief exposure to these sources of ultra-violet light will not normally have an adverse affect on UV EPROMs; very long-term exposure may cause a loss of data. For example, it takes about three years of exposure to room-level fluorescent lighting to erase the Intel 8755A EPROM, whereas direct sunlight will erase it in about one week.

The physical mechanism for storing information in a UV EPROM involves trapping a charge in the gate region of a floating-gate MOS transistor through what is known as avalanche injection. This charge will remain trapped for years because of the extremely high resistance of the gate-to-channel region. The short-wavelength photons of the ultraviolet light used for erasing the EPROM interact with the molecules of the oxide layer, knocking charge carriers loose from the atoms in the material and rendering it conductive. The trapped charge is then able to leak off.

Another type of EPROM that can be reprogrammed even more conveniently than the UV EPROM is the **electrically erasable read only memory,** or **EEROM** (sometimes called "electrically alterable" ROM, or EAROM). EEROMs allow bit-by-bit erasure and rewrite when certain electrical conditions occur. The new data are then nonvolatile. The time required for reprogramming operations is much longer than the time required to read information. A typical (Intel 2816A) read access time for such a device is less than 0.5 microsecond. The erasure time is on the order of 10 milliseconds, and the write time is about the same. Erase/write cycles are limited to 10,000 for this device. The EEROM is well suited for applications in which the stored information is accessed frequently but changed only rarely—thus, the nickname "read mostly memories."

EXAMPLE 3.1   EPROM Programming (8755)

Each PROM type has its own method of programming. In this example, the Intel 8755A will be used to illustrate the process of programming a PROM. The 8755A is designed to be used with the 8085A microprocessor. In addition to a 2K-byte EPROM, it contains two programmable I/O ports, as discussed in Chapter Seven. The programming operation is performed by a host programmer, which may be a computer itself.

Erasure of the 8755A causes all bits to be set to a one. The part is delivered in this state when purchased. One of the possible trouble-shooting checks would be to verify that the part contains only ones prior to programming.

The programming procedure amounts to forcing selected bits to zero. The process is to program one byte, check it, program the next, check it, and so forth. Figures 3.5 and 3.6 show the pinout and the signal timing for the program mode. When the **address latch enable (ALE)** input goes high, various command data are allowed to enter the chip. When this line goes low, the data are held, or latched, in the 8755A. It is critical that the

PIN CONFIGURATION

BLOCK DIAGRAM

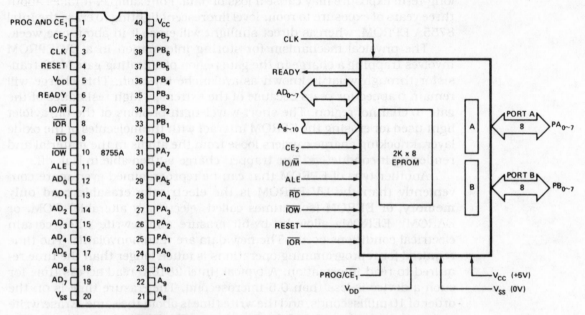

Figure 3.5
8755 Pin Configuration and Block Diagram. (Reprinted by permission of Intel Corporation, copyright © 1980.)

data be properly set up when this trailing edge occurs. The input lines used to latch data into the chip are the lower 11 bits of the address bus, which must have the address of the byte to be programmed, the chip enable (CE) inputs (the $\overline{CE}_1$ must be low and the CE_2 must be high), and the input-output versus memory (IO/$\overline{M}$) input, which must be low to indicate a PROM operation.

Next, the byte to be programmed should be set up on the data bus, which is, of course, the lower eight bits of the combined data and address bus. The $\overline{CE}_1$ input is also used to signal a programming operation. This input should be set to a one when the byte is ready. The V_{DD} input should then be raised from its normal +5 volts to +25 volts. This input must be held for 50 milliseconds while the byte is programmed. Voltage V_{DD} is returned to +5 volts and then $\overline{CE}_1$ is returned to a zero.

The verify operation amounts to a normal read cycle. The ALE line is used again to latch in the address, CE, and IO/$\overline{M}$ data. $\overline{CE}_1$ is now held low. The $\overline{RD}$ line is brought low to tell the 8755A to drive the data bus with the byte from the addressed memory location. This byte should now be compared with the original programming data to verify that the 8755A has been properly programmed.

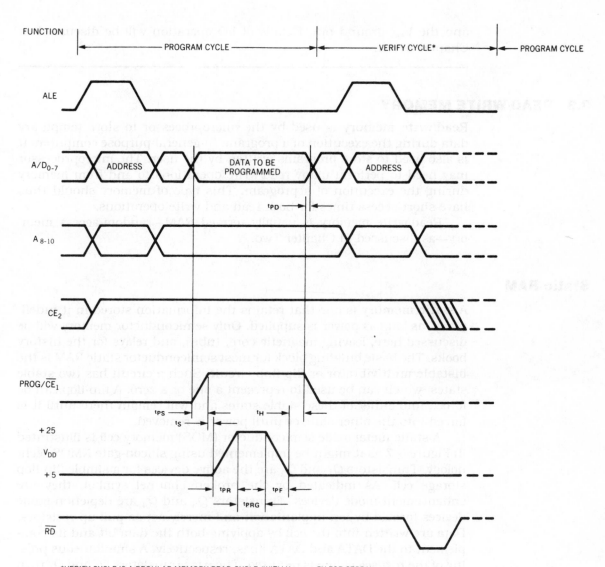

FUNCTION

PROGRAM CYCLE — VERIFY CYCLE* — PROGRAM CYCLE

ALE

A/D$_{0-7}$ — ADDRESS — DATA TO BE PROGRAMMED — ADDRESS

t_{PD}

A$_{8-10}$

CE$_2$

PROG/$\overline{\text{CE}}_1$

t_{PS} t_S t_H

+25 V$_{DD}$ +5

t_{PR} t_{PF}

t_{PRG}

$\overline{\text{RD}}$

*VERIFY CYCLE IS A REGULAR MEMORY READ CYCLE (WITH V$_{DD}$ = + 5V FOR 8755A)

Figure 3.6
8755 Programming Operation Timing. (Reprinted by permission of Intel Corporation, copyright © 1980.)

The IO/$\overline{\text{M}}$, the input-output–write ($\overline{\text{IOW}}$), and the input-output–read ($\overline{\text{IOR}}$) pins are used in conjunction with the I/O port, which resides at the PA$_{0-7}$ and PB$_{0-7}$ pins. The "READY" pin signals the microprocessor that the 8755A has been addressed during normal operation. The CLK input is required to control the timing of the READY line. RESET is used to initialize the 8755A. The +5-volt supply is connected between the V$_{cc}$ pin and the V_{ss}, ground pin. Details of I/O operation will be discussed in Chapter Seven.

3.3 READ/WRITE MEMORY

Read/write memory is used by the microprocessor to store temporary data during the execution of a program. In general-purpose computers it is also used to store programs written by the user. The microprocessor may need to perform many read/write operations to and from memory during the execution of a program. This type of memory should thus have short access times for both read and write operations.

Read/write memory is usually termed RAM—random-access memory—as discussed in Chapter Two.

Static RAM

A **static memory** is one that retains the information stored in it indefinitely, as long as power is supplied. Only semiconductor memory will be discussed here, leaving magnetic core, tubes, and relays for the history books. The basic building block for most semiconductor static RAM is the **bistable multivibrator** or **flip-flop** circuit. Such a circuit has two stable states, which can be used to represent a one or a zero. A flip-flop can be forced into either of these stable states and will remain there until it is forced into the other state or until power is removed.

A static metal oxide semiconductor (MOS) memory cell is illustrated in Figure 3.7 as it might be implemented using silicon-gate NMOS technology. Transistors Q_1 and Q_2 are the active devices for a simple flip-flop storage cell. As indicated by the broken channel symbol, they are enhancement-mode devices. Transistors Q_3 and Q_4 are depletion-mode devices formed by ion implantation and merely act as pull-up resistors. Data are written into the cell by applying both the data bit and its complement to the DATA and $\overline{\text{DATA}}$ lines, respectively. A simultaneous pulsing of the row-select line is required. The pass transistors Q_5 and Q_6 turn on, forcing the cell into the desired state. The row-select line is pulsed with a high impedance on the DATA and $\overline{\text{DATA}}$ lines to read data from the cell. This allows these lines to go to whatever state is present on the drains of the flip-flop transistors Q_1 and Q_2. Other drive circuitry for the DATA and $\overline{\text{DATA}}$ lines must obviously be three-state logic.

Dynamic RAM

To create very dense memory circuits (a large number of bits on a single chip) requires a very small memory cell. One of the smallest is a capacitor

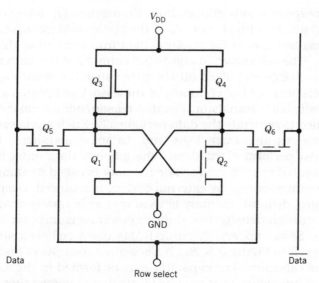

Figure 3.7
Static RAM Cell.

built using MOS technology. The capacitance can be either charged or discharged to give a one or a zero.

It is possible to make use of the small gate-to-channel capacitance to store a logic level because the resistance from the gate to the channel is very large. Any charge stored on the gate capacitance will be retained for some time. Figure 3.8 shows a memory cell that makes use of charge

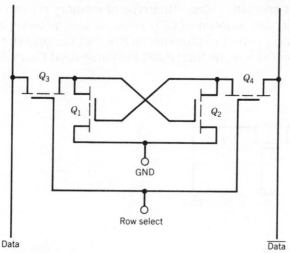

Figure 3.8
Dynamic RAM Cell.

storage to retain information. Transistors Q_1 and Q_2 form a simple latch circuit. As with Q_5 and Q_6 in the static RAM example, Q_3 and Q_4 serve as pass transistors for strobing data into and out of the cell.

The cell shown in Figure 3.8 cannot hold its data indefinitely because the charge will bleed off the gate capacitance through the parallel path consisting of the channels of the associated pass transistor and the opposite latch transistor. For this reason, additional circuitry must be provided to reinstate the data periodically. Such a process is called a **refresh**. This requires extra logic and, in some instances, the microprocessor must perform extra steps. The memory data must be maintained with repeated refresh cycles. The memory is called **dynamic RAM** because active intervention by external devices is required. Despite these disadvantages, dynamic memory is used in a wide variety of applications because of its high-density, low standby power consumption, and low cost per bit.

Some modern dynamic RAMs use a cell even simpler than the one shown in Figure 3.8. Such a cell often consists of just one transistor and one capacitor. The capacitor may be formed in the same way as the gate of a transistor, or it may be fabricated in some other way. An example of a one-transistor dynamic RAM cell is shown in Figure 3.9. Cells as small as 0.5 square mil are available. The trend is toward more bits on a chip and simpler refresh implementation, including self-refreshing memories having the refresh circuitry on the chip with the RAM.

Dynamic RAM usually requires that each cell be refreshed every few milliseconds. The Intel 2117, for example, must be refreshed at least every 2 milliseconds. The refresh process is simplified in that logic on the chip automatically refreshes each cell whenever a read operation is performed. Accessing each address periodically is all that is necessary to perform the refresh operation. Even this type of memory-refresh cycle would tie up a considerable amount of CPU time, as well as being a burden to the programmer, were it not for special ICs that perform the task. An example of such a device is the Intel 8202 Dynamic RAM Controller. This chip is con

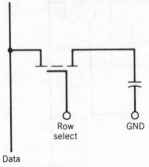

Row
select

GND

Data

Figure 3.9
Single-Transistor Dynamic
RAM Cell.

nected between the microprocessor and a bank of dynamic RAM. It cycles through all the addresses in RAM during times when the RAM is not being addressed by the CPU. This provides a **transparent**—the CPU treats the RAM as though it were static RAM—refresh capability.

The simplified block diagram of Figure 3.10 shows how the 2117 performs its refresh operation. An oscillator on the chip provides clock pulses for a counter that generates the memory addresses. These addresses are fed through a multiplexer to the memory address bus. The multiplexer switches the input address between the refresh address bus and the regular microprocessor address bus under the control of the RAM controller's logic. When the microprocessor requests access to the memory for a read or write operation, the controller temporarily suspends its refresh operation and returns a pulse on the "acknowledge" line to let the CPU know that the memory is available. A timer on the chip provides information on how long it has been since all the cells have been refreshed. A logic circuit, called an arbiter, determines whether to allow the microprocessor immediate access or to continue a refresh cycle. The refresh operation must, of course, take priority if the time limit for data retention is being approached.

EXAMPLE 3.2   RAM Read/Write Cycle (8156)

We touched on the memory read cycle in Example 3.1 using the 8755. Here we use the 8155/8156 devices to develop the memory read and write cycles in more detail.

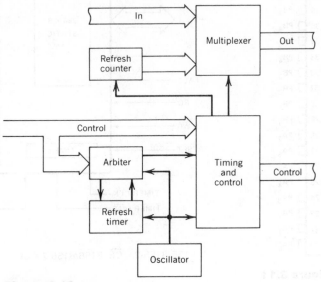

Figure 3.10
Dynamic RAM Refresh Control.

Figure 3.11 presents the pin configuration and block diagram of the 8155/8156. In addition to 256 bytes of static RAM, these devices contain three I/O ports and a timer. Only the operation of the RAM will be discussed here. The one difference between the 8155 and the 8156 is the polarity of the CE input. As will be discussed later in this chapter, the CE input is often used to establish the proper memory structure. By providing both polarities of CE, Intel has allowed the designer to simplify the memory hardware slightly. We assume that the 8156 is being used for this example.

Figure 3.12 is a timing diagram for the RAM read-write operation. The ALE signal from the CPU provides the first critical timing event. At the fall of ALE, the circuits external to the 8155/8156 must have established the IO/$\overline{M}$ line as a zero to indicate a memory operation, the CE input at a one (for the 8156) to tell the chip that it is being addressed, and the proper address within the 256-bit internal RAM using the AD_0 to AD_7 address lines. When ALE falls, the 8155/8156 stores these various commands and prepares for the data transfer. After a delay, the external circuits must now bring either the $\overline{RD}$ line or the $\overline{WR}$ line to zero, indicating the operation required of the addressed memory byte. When the

PIN CONFIGURATION　　　　　　　　　**BLOCK DIAGRAM**

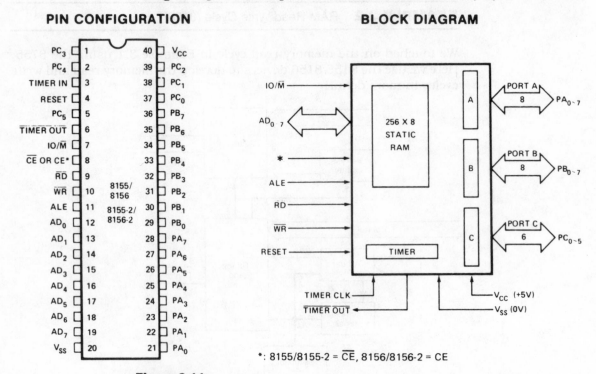

Figure 3.11
8155/8156 Pin Configuration and Block Diagram. (Reprinted by permission of Intel Corporation, copyright © 1980.)

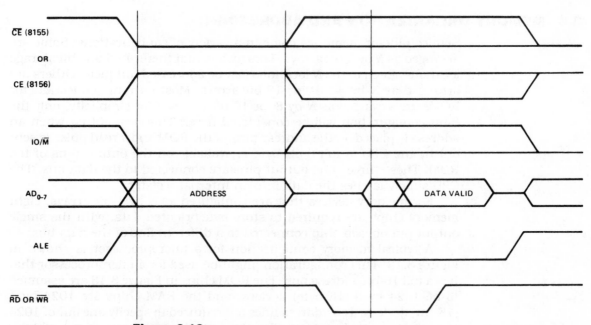

Figure 3.12
8155/8156 Read/Write Timing. (Reprinted by permission of Intel Corporation, copyright © 1980.)

$\overline{RD}$ line rises to a one for a read operation, RAM must have established the valid data on the AD_0 to AD_7 bus. During a write operation, the driving device must have established valid data on the bus when $\overline{WR}$ rises.

The 8155/8156 is designed to operate as fast as the 8085. Some memory devices may be slower. Moreover, dynamic RAM may not be able to respond to the CPU because of an ongoing refresh cycle. In either case, the memory may not be able to respond when the 8085 expects. The 8085 provides an input, called the READY input, which allows memory to signal a delay. The CPU will respond by waiting until the memory is ready. The clock cycles that are lost are called wait states.

The 8080 family uses a memory-fetch cycle that is similar to the one just described. It is termed a **synchronous bus cycle** because the timing is fixed in synchronization with the control bus signals—here the ALE and $\overline{RD}$ or $\overline{WR}$. Other families use asynchronous bus timing. The CPU makes a request, and the memory prompts a response, asynchronously, when it is ready.

3.4 MEMORY ORGANIZATION AND ADDRESSING

Semiconductor memories come in a variety of configurations. Some are arranged as N by 1-bit arrays. This means that there are N one-bit storage locations. Each of the N locations can be addressed uniquely. Others are arranged as N by 4-, 8-, or 16-bit arrays. Most current semiconductor ROMs are arranged as N by 8- or 16-bit arrays. (For simplicity, only the 8-bit configuration will be considered here.) This means that when an address is placed on the address pins of the ROM and a read pulse is sent out by the CPU, a full 8-bit byte is available on the output pins of the ROM. These three-state output pins are connected to the data bus. The CPU simply latches the data into an internal register.

For memory devices that are configured as N by 1-bit arrays, eight memory chips are required to store byte-oriented data, with the single output pin of each chip connected to a different line of the data bus.

A typical memory configuration for a microprocessor is shown in Figure 3.13. This configuration might be used for a microprocessor that has a full 16-bit address bus. The ROM chips in Figure 3.13 are assumed to be 1024 by 8 (1K-byte) devices, and the RAM chips are 1024 by 1 (1K-bit) devices. Ten address lines are required to specify one out of 1024 possible memory locations. Therefore, the lower 10 bits of the address bus are connected to all the memory chips. Some of the upper six bits are connected to a decoder that applies the proper logic levels to the CE pins of the various memory devices.

In this example some control lines are grouped as the control bus for

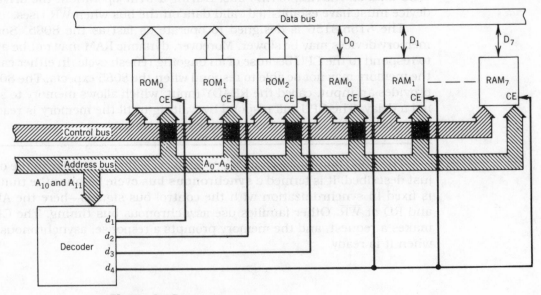

Figure 3.13
Typical Memory Configuration.

the sake of clarity. One important control that must be connected to RAM chips is the read or write command. This logic tells the memory chip whether a read or a write operation is being performed. Each microprocessor family has its own specific control functions. For example, the microprocessor may have a memory-select line that specifies the time at which the read or write operation is to be performed. This line might be connected to an enable pin on the encoder to prevent any of the CE lines from going high until the CPU is ready to allow the memory devices to respond to a read or write command. A common term applied to the bus interface devices is "**bus glue.**"

EXAMPLE 3.3   Address Decode

The decoder in Figure 3.13 can take on many forms. The specific truth table for the decoder will determine which chip is enabled for a given address command. This, in turn, determines the memory structure of the system's memory map. Figure 3.14 shows a truth table which might be used for the decoder. This is a simple one-out-of-four decoder. Notice that at no time should an input address activate more than one of the output lines during a memory read operation. If this were to happen, more than one of the memory chips would attempt to drive the bus at the same time. This might cause damage and would surely present a major problem in the system.

Another choice for the decoder would be simply to attach each memory CE line to a single address bus line. Thus, A_{10} might be attached to ROM_0, A_{11} to ROM_1, and so forth. In such a situation, the programmer must be careful not to address multiple memory devices at the same time; for example, A_{10} and A_{11} should never be high together during the same read operation.

The 8085

The 8085 CPU uses a multiplexed bus system in order to save pins on the package. The 8-bit address bus contains the upper 8 bits of the address, whereas the lower 8 bits are time-multiplexed with the data bus. The CPU

Input		Output			
A_{11}	A_{10}	d_1	d_2	d_3	d_4
0	0	1	0	0	0
0	1	0	1	0	0
1	0	0	0	1	0
1	1	0	0	0	1

Figure 3.14
One-out-of-Four Decoder.

uses various signals on the control bus to demultiplex the address and data. A key line is the ALE (address latch enable), introduced earlier in Examples 3.1 and 3.2. It allows the CPU to signal when the data on the bus are valid address information. This requires that during a read or write operation, when the bus is being used for data transfer, some sort of latch be provided to hold the lower 8 bits of the address.

This latch must be provided as a separate chip when interfacing to standard memory devices, as shown in the block diagram of Figure 3.15. The latch shown could be a TTL device, such as a 74LS373, 8-bit latch. Intel manufactures a special chip, the 8212, which can serve as the address latch. Many common memory devices contain a data-latching capability so that normally no data latch is required. The memory devices in the 8085 family (such as the 8755) contain an internal address latch driven by the ALE signal. They do not require an external address latch.

Several special components that are available for use with the 8085 utilize the multiplexed bus structure. These devices do not require a separate address latch; they combine memory and I/O functions on the same chip. This approach allows the user to design small dedicated computers and controllers with a minimum package count and a minimum PC board area.

3.5 MASS STORAGE

Mass storage devices are used to store large amounts of data and programs that will not fit into the internal memory of the microcomputer all at once. These devices are also chosen because of their nonvolatility.

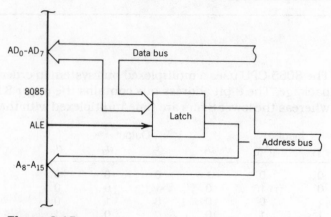

Figure 3.15
8085 Bus Demultiplex: A, address bus lines only; AD, multiplexed address and data bus.

Anything stored in standard RAM is lost when power is removed from the microcomputer.

Some mass storage devices that are commonly used with microcomputers are punched paper tape, magnetic tape (usually cassettes), and floppy disks. Each of these storage media will be discussed in this section. Other mass storage devices that will not be discussed, because they are rarely used with microcomputers, are punched cards, hard disks (although they are popular for the personal computer), reel-to-reel magnetic tape recorders, and magnetic drums.

The microprocessor itself usually sees the mass storage device as an I/O device. The data are passed byte by byte. It is the job of the interface circuitry to coordinate the exchange of the data between the mass storage device and the CPU I/O. The CPU transfers the data on to RAM.

Notice that the mass storage devices do not allow direct addressability of stored data. The data must be loaded into RAM before individual random bytes can be addressed.

In some applications a very fast transfer is implemented using a direct memory access (DMA) process. As mentioned in Chapter Two, DMA refers to data transfer whereby the CPU is commanded to release the microcomputer buses. The external DMA device can then directly transfer data to memory.

Punched Paper Tape

Punched paper tape had been used as an intermediate storage medium for Teletype applications even before electronic computers were invented. Although it is relatively slow, usually 10 characters (or bytes) per second, it is still in use. It is chosen partly because paper tape punches and readers are available at low cost. Many Teletype model ASR-33 terminals equipped with paper tape reader/punches have been purchased by colleges and universities, as well as by individuals for use with home computers. Because of their ruggedness and long life, they will probably be utilized for some time to come. Moreover, a great deal of industrial equipment, mainly numerically controlled machine-tooling equipment, is in daily use and requires paper tape for operation.

Paper tape is a low-cost storage medium that is insensitive to magnetic fields. Data are stored on the tape by means of punched holes and read either electromechanically or optically. Figure 3.16 shows a typical section of eight-level paper tape as used with the ASR-33 Teletype terminal. Seven of the hole positions are used to store data, with the eighth position used as a parity bit (even parity is shown in the figure).

Table 3.1 shows the Teletype paper tape code. Notice that some of the possible combinations are used to control the reader/punch itself. For example, the hexadecimal code 12 turns the punch on. The code shown

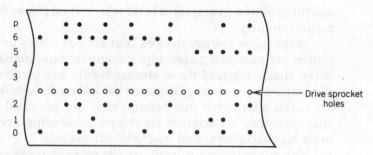

Figure 3.16
Eight-Level Paper Tape.

in Table 3.1 and illustrated in Figure 3.16 is the standard ASCII code used on most paper tape machines. Earlier teletypewriters and paper tape machines used other codes, including a five-level code that did not include lowercase and had no provision for parity checking.

Magnetic Tape

Paper tape provides an inexpensive medium for off-line storage and is still used; however, it is slow and somewhat inconvenient. Most modern systems include some kind of magnetic storage medium. **Magnetic tape** is a medium that provides dense mass storage and higher speed than paper tape. Large computer systems use high-speed, reel-to-reel magnetic tape drives. These large-scale, reel-to-reel tape systems allow very large quantities of data to be stored on a single reel. The computer normally controls the drive to automate file location, recording, and retrieval of data.

Smaller systems sometimes use digital cassette recorders, which allow some control by the computer. Low-cost audio cassette recorders are a more popular method for small personal computers, however. These machines are usually controlled manually. The data must be encoded into a form that falls within the audio frequency range used by the recorder.

The most common method of encoding data for use with audio cassette recorders is **frequency-shift keying** or **FSK**. With FSK two audio tones of different frequencies represent the two binary states. The most widely used FSK technique is called the **Kansas City Standard.** In this form, a one is represented by an 8-cycle burst of tone at a frequency of 2400 hertz. A zero is represented by four cycles of a 1200-hertz tone. This is a byte-oriented coding technique, and the start of a byte is signaled by a single-bit start signal, which is a 1200-hertz tone—a zero. The end of a byte is signaled by a two-bit stop signal—two zeros. At the start of a complete record (program or data), a leader consisting of a burst of 2400-hertz tone, approximately 30 seconds in duration, is provided. At the end

Table 3.1
Paper Tape Coding

Hole Numbers[a]									
O	1	2		3	4	5	6	P	Character
*	*	*	O	*	*	*	*	*	Rubout
*			O				*		A
	*		O				*		B
*	*		O				*	*	C
		*	O				*		D
*		*	O				*	*	E
	*	*	O				*	*	F
*	*	*	O				*		G
			O	*			*		H
*			O	*			*	*	I
	*		O	*			*	*	J
*	*		O	*			*		K
		*	O	*			*	*	L
*		*	O	*			*		M
	*	*	O	*			*		N
*	*	*	O	*			*	*	O
			O		*		*		P
*			O		*		*	*	Q
	*		O		*		*	*	R
*	*		O		*		*		S
		*	O		*		*	*	T
*		*	O		*		*		U
	*	*	O		*		*		V
*	*	*	O		*		*	*	W
			O	*	*		*	*	X
*			O	*	*		*		Y
	*		O	*	*		*		Z
*			O		*	*		*	1
	*		O		*	*		*	2
*	*		O		*	*			3
		*	O		*	*		*	4
*		*	O		*	*			5
	*	*	O		*	*			6
*	*	*	O		*	*		*	7
			O	*	*	*		*	8
*			O	*	*	*			9
			O		*	*			0
	*		O	*	*	*			:
*		*	O	*		*			-
*			O			*			!
	*		O			*			"
*	*		O			*		*	#
		*	O			*			$
*		*	O			*		*	%
	*	*	O			*		*	&
*	*	*	O			*			'
			O	*		*			(

Table 3.1 (continued)

O	1	2		3	4	5	6	P	Character
				Hole Numbers[a]					
*			O	*		*		*	)
	*		O	*		*		*	*
*			O	*	*	*		*	=
*		*	O	*				*	CR
	*		O	*					LF
*	*	*	O	*	*	*			?
*	*	*	O	*		*		*	/
	*	*	O	*	*	*		*	>
		*	O	*		*			.
		*	O	*		*		*	<
	*	*	O	*		*	*	*	'↑
*	*		O	*		*		*	+
*	*		O	*	*	*		*	;
			O						space

* = hole, O = sprocket hole.

of the leader, there are two stop bits followed by another burst of 2400-hertz tone 5 seconds in duration.

The Kansas City Standard recording technique is illustrated in Figure 3.17. The data rate is 27 bytes per second, or three times as fast as paper tape. This method is by no means universal. Many manufacturers chose other coding techniques, often using higher frequencies to increase data rate.

The Kansas City Standard recording method applied at the standard speed for a cassette recorder of 1.875 inches per second achieves a re-

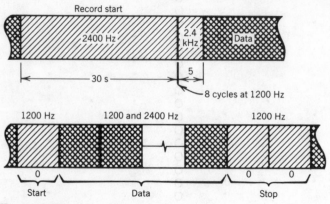

Figure 3.17
Kansas City Standard FSK.

cording density of 116 usable bits per inch. A standard 60-minute cassette will store 96K bytes of information.

Floppy Disks

Many systems use **hard-disk storage** devices which are very fast and can store 100 or more megabytes of information. These high-speed disks are rigid and serve as a magnetic storage medium. The mechanical tolerances are held to tight requirements. With these characteristics hard disks are able to hold a great deal of data.

Because of their original high cost, hard disk storage systems were in the past rarely used with small computers; now with prices lowering they are becoming much more popular. At any rate, a lower-cost alternative was developed by IBM some years ago to fill the need for a drive system for which both the disk drives and the disks themselves are quite inexpensive. These disks are nicknamed **floppy disks** because they are made of flexible Mylar (a DuPont registered trade name), the same material from which magnetic tape is made.

Floppy disks, which are also called **diskettes,** are available in three sizes, 8 inches, 5¼ inches, and 3½ inches in diameter. Figure 3.18 shows the construction of a floppy disk. The disk is driven by a spindle which fits through a hole in its center and clamps it firmly. A plastic jacket encloses the disk, protecting it and helping to position it properly in the drive mechanism. A slot in the jacket provides an exposed surface where the read/write head can make contact with the disk.

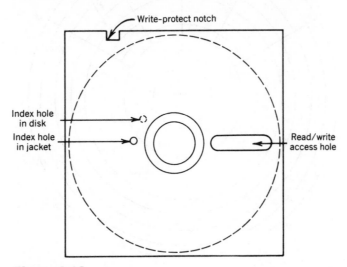

Figure 3.18
5¼-Inch Floppy Disk.

Although the recording head in a hard-disk drive must float on a cushion of air to prevent wear at the very high speeds used, the head in a floppy-disk drive is in contact with the disk. The head is very similar in operation and construction to a home tape-recorder head.

The disk drive typically spins the disk at either 300 or 360 revolutions per minute. The read/write head is movable and is positioned by a stepper motor in the radial direction. Therefore, the information on the disk can be divided up into concentric tracks. It is further divided into sectors within these tracks. A typical disk format, called the IBM soft-sectored standard, is illustrated in Figure 3.19. This format is widely accepted for use with 8-inch floppy disks. There are 77 tracks in this format, and each track is broken up into 26 sectors.

The format for data storage varies from manufacturer to manufacturer. Commonly, a manufacturer will provide higher-density data storage in more expensive drives. These formats typically double the data storage capability and are called **double-density (DD)**, as opposed to **single-density (SD)**, formats. Double-density drives require better-quality disks that are marked as compatible with double-density formats. Some drives have the capability of recording data on both sides of a disk. Again, only disks tested for use on both sides should be chosen when drives are

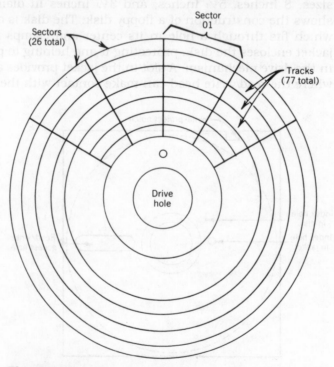

Figure 3.19
IBM Soft-Sectored Standard for 8-Inch Floppy Disks.

double-sided (DS). The disks are generally all made the same, with the various quality levels related to the testing done on the disks. Thus, the least expensive disk, SS/SD, may be the reject from a test for the most expensive type of disk, DS/DD.

To use a floppy disk for data storage, we must be able to locate any sector. Some systems thus use holes in the disk to mark each sector, along with an index hole to mark the first sector. The holes are located inside the innermost track. Such a system has hardware to identify the sectors and is termed a **hard-sectored** system. A second method of identifying sectors uses a single index hole and locates the sectors evenly around the disk. This is known as **soft sectoring** since the sectors are not physically identified by a sector hole.

The most sophisticated sectoring method is not to use any index holes at all. The sector data are recorded onto the disk in a formatting operation. This, too, is called soft sectoring and is used on many personal computers.

A number of cautions should be observed in using floppy disks. They should never be subjected to abuse, such as significant dirt (for example, eraser crumbs or carbon from pencils), temperature extremes, warping, and high magnetic fields. They should be kept in their protective envelopes except when in use. One should never touch the recording surface. Generally, single-sided (SS) drives use the underside of the disk for recording; care should be taken when putting a disk down, for table dirt may contaminate the disk's underside recording surface.

EXERCISES

3.1 Make a table showing the binary words stored in the diode ROM of Figure 3.1.

3.2 Make a table showing the binary words stored in the mask-programmable ROM of Figure 3.2.

3.3 Design a diode-matrix ROM that stores the following four words (0 to 3):

    0001
    0010
    0111
    0000

3.4 Design a mask-programmed ROM that stores the four words given in exercise 3.3.

3.5 Draw a memory map for the memory of Figure 3.13 and the decoder of Figure 3.14. What memory lines are not used?

3.6 If each block of memory in Figure 3.13 is enabled using a single address line, as discussed in Example 3.3, what would the resulting memory map be?

3.7 Draw a diagram showing how the memory chips might be connected to the three buses in a system that uses a 1K-byte ROM chip and four 1K-byte by 4-bit RAM chips. What decoder truth table is needed? How many total bytes of memory are used?

3.8 Decode the section of paper tape illustrated in Figure 3.16.

3.9 Given that the holes in paper tape are one-eighth inch apart, how much tape, in feet, is required to store 128K bytes of data? How many miles? Remember that a 1K byte is 1024 bytes.

3.10 If a sector contains 256 bytes of data, how much data can the floppy disk of Figure 3.19 contain? How much data can be stored using a double-density drive? Using a double-sided, double-density drive? Express your answer in K bytes.

CHAPTER FOUR

INTRODUCTION TO PROGRAMMING AND DATA TRANSFER

4.1 INTRODUCTION

A microprocessor can be considered a device that reads binary-coded information from its input, manipulates this information according to a program stored within its memory, and subsequently produces information at its output. This process is illustrated in Figure 4.1.

With this chapter we begin a detailed look at microprocessor programming. The aim of this chapter is to introduce certain types of machine instructions that are typically available. As in the previous chapters, the Intel 8085 will be used for examples and discussion. Chapters Five and Six will complete the introduction of the 8085 instruction set.

4.2 MICROPROCESSOR REGISTERS

The majority of machine instructions available with a microprocessor affect the state of the various internal registers that make up the microprocessor. Before a program can be written for a particular microproces-

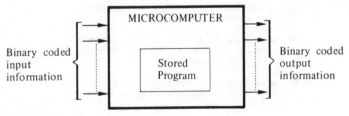

Figure 4.1
Microcomputer Data Flow.

sor, it is necessary to know which processor registers are accessible by the machine instructions. These are the **visible registers.**

In Chapter Two we discussed the architecture of the 8085. Figure 4.2 shows the main registers from this architecture that are visible to the programmer. This is called a programmer's model of the CPU.

Notice that the **B-** and **C-registers** are shown as a pair. Although each can be treated as a separate register, certain instructions treat them as a pair, allowing 16-bit operations. This is also true of the **DE-** and **HL-pairs.** When the data in these register pairs are referenced as 16-bit numbers, the leftmost register (B, D, or H) is the most significant. It holds the left half of the number.

The **IM-register** holds a collection of specialized data used for serial data and interrupt processing, as discussed in Chapters Seven and Nine.

4.3 ASSEMBLY LANGUAGE

The microprocessor uses binary words for its instructions. However, when developing a program, it is quite tedious to represent each machine in-

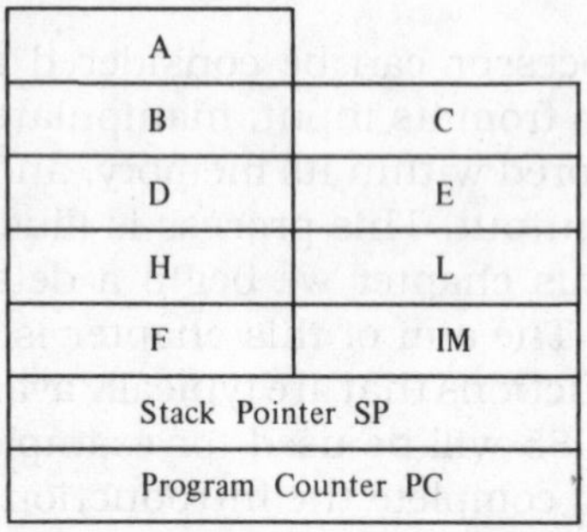

A	
B	C
D	E
H	L
F	IM
Stack Pointer SP	
Program Counter PC	

A	is an 8-bit arithmetic register (accumulator).
B, C, D, E	are four 8-bit general purpose registers.
F	is an 8-bit flags register (modified by ALU operations).
IM	is an 8-bit interrupt control register.
HL	are two 8-bit registers which are normally used to form a 16-bit memory pointer.
SP	is the stack pointer register – this contains a 16-bit memory address which displays (points to) the top of a system stack.
PC	is the program counter register which contains a 16-bit memory address which points to the next instruction to be executed.

Figure 4.2
Programmer's Model for the 8085.

struction in its binary form. A far more convenient representation of machine instructions is what is known as **assembly language.** When each instruction is represented in this form, programs are far more readable and understandable. Each machine instruction is given a simple, short name called a **mnemonic,** or memory aid—from the name of the Greek goddess of memory, Mnemosyne. Because there is a one-for-one correspondence between a basic assembly language instruction and a machine instruction, converting from one form to the other is straightforward.

This one-to-one mapping has an exception for computer-automated assembly techniques. Most such assembly aids include **directives,** which provide the computer with important data. These directives appear in the program as though they were normal mnemonics; however, they are used to define certain features of the assembly process. A list of the assembler directives used here is presented at the end of this section.

All the programs that are presented in this and subsequent chapters will be written in assembly language. An assembly language program can be readily converted into machine instructions. In either form, the program instructions are generally called **code.** The term **source code** refers to the original program, written here in assembly language. The resulting machine instructions are known as **object code.** The method used to convert source code to object code, using 8085 assembly language, is presented later in this chapter.

The simplest use of assembly language is as an aid in manually developing code for a microcomputer. Through the years automated assembly programs that operate in a host computer have been developed to the point that rarely will a programmer directly write object code. Somewhat elaborate assembly programs have been devised. One of the key features of these programs allows a programmer to bring into use whole sections of code with a single command. These programs are called **macroassemblers.** Although these tools are very valuable, they do not directly relate to a knowledge of microprocessor functions. We will use straightforward assembly language for the remainder of this text.

This section and the rest of the book will use Intel's 8085 assembly language. This language is identical, or very similar, to that used with a number of other microprocessors, among them the 8080 and the Z80. Although most assembly languages have different mnemonics and format details, they share many features. Once an understanding of the assembly language for one processor has been developed, learning the language of another processor is straightforward.

As just mentioned, assembly programs that use a host computer to automate the translation from assembly language to object code have been written. These programs require that the source code, the assembly language program, be in a specific format. We will use the 8085 assembly language format from the start, even though the exercises and examples are to be assembled by hand.

A typical assembly language instruction has a closely defined format. One kind of information must always be provided; it details the operation to be performed by the processor. Such operations might require data transfers, manipulations, I/O, and so forth. Assembly language represents these operations by simple code words that reflect the action involved, such as MOV for data transfer or POP for popping the stack. These are the **operation mnemonics** for the microprocessor.

The operation mnemonic almost always requires an object for its operation. We must specify what to ADD (mnemonic for the add operation) or MOV (move), where to JMP (jump), or what to LDA (load to the accumulator). Either a specific value is required, or a register or memory location must be defined. This second term is called the **operand.**

In addition, assembly language instructions may be identified with a **label.** The label is not always needed; it simply gives a name to an instruction. More accurately it gives a name to the address in which the instruction is stored. We will not use labels until the discussion of branch-type instructions in Chapter Six.

Finally, **comments** may be added to help understanding. In effect, the programmer is allowed to make notes that are kept with the program but are never used to generate object code. The area set aside for comments amounts to a scratch pad for the programmer. The comments do not affect the object code after the program is assembled. Comments are much more important than they might appear, especially for programs developed professionally. Good comments allow the software to be easily updated long after it was originally written.

The complete 8085 assembly language instruction may include the following, in the format shown:

LABEL   OPERATION MNEMONIC   OPERANDS   ;COMMENTS

The label, if used, must be placed in the first column. The comments must be preceded by a semicolon. Comments may also be provided on a line by themselves by starting the line with a semicolon.

If a specific number is required in an instruction, it must start with a number symbol, rather than a letter symbol. The hexadecimal number A0, which is 160 in decimal notation, must be expressed as 0A0H. The H is added in 8085 assembly language to indicate a hexadecimal number. We will use hexadecimal numbers exclusively. Most assembly languages, including the 8085 language, also allow decimal, binary, and octal numbers.

The assembly language recognizes the number "0" (zero) only as the null number. The letter "O" cannot be used as a substitute. The same holds for any substitution of the letter "l" for the number "1" (one). The substitution is not allowed.

Finally, what follows is a short list of common assembler directives. Assembler directives appear in the source code as though they were normal mnemonics. We will see, at one time or another, the following assembler directives.

```
        ORG   XXXX   ;STATES THAT THE OBJECT CODE IS TO START
                     ;AT ADDRESS "XXXX."
        DB    XXXX   ;STORES THE VALUE "XXXX" IN THE NEXT
                     ;MEMORY LOCATIONS.
        DS    XXXX   ;RESERVES "XXXX" BYTES OF MEMORY.
YYYY    EQU   XXXX   ;DEFINES THE LABEL "YYYY" TO HAVE THE
                     ;VALUE "XXXX." CALLED AN EQUATE.
        END          ;DEFINES THE END OF THE PROGRAM.
```

Many other assembler directives are used with various assembly languages.

4.4 TYPES OF INSTRUCTIONS

Although a microprocessor may execute many different machine instructions, each instruction can generally be classified as being a member of one of five groups:

Data transfer
Data manipulation
Transfer of control
Input/output
Machine control

We will provide here an overview of each of these groups. The next three chapters are devoted primarily to a detailed development of these groups.

Instructions in the **data transfer** group move data between the various processor registers or between a processor register and a memory location. For example, the 8085 instruction

MOV A,B

causes the contents of the B-register to be transferred to the A-register. Notice that the destination is placed first, with the source shown second. This is typical of 8085 operands.

Instructions in the **data manipulation** group perform arithmetic and logical operations on data that are either in a specified processor register or in a memory location. For example, the 8085 instruction

ADD B

modifies the contents of the A-register, the accumulator, to the sum of its previous contents and the contents of the B-register. All instructions in this group will normally modify processor flags.

The computer derives great flexibility from its ability to transfer from one sequence of operations to another, based on a variety of conditions.

The **"transfer of control"** group of instructions provides this capability. The operation performed is quite simple. When such an instruction is encountered, the PC is changed to the address of the location of the new sequence. The next machine cycle begins execution of the new routine.

Some of these transfer-of-control instructions always force a jump to the new sequence. Others base the jump on machine data. If the jump is always made, it is called an **unconditional branch.** If the jump is based on machine data, such as a specific flag status, it is called a **conditional branch.** Another form of control transfer is the **subroutine call.** Here a group of instructions elsewhere in memory—a **subroutine**—is executed. The PC is returned to its original value, and hence control is returned to the original routine, when the subroutine ends. This return from a subroutine is also a transfer of control.

An example of an 8085 transfer of control instruction is

JMP   0FE3H

This is an unconditional branch to the memory location 0FE3, hexadecimal.

Instructions in the input/output group move data between the various I/O ports of the system and an internal processor register, usually the A-register. For example,

OUT   5H

causes the contents of the A-register to be transferred to output port 5. Microprocessors that use memory-mapped I/O exclusively do not have I/O instructions. Rather, they use memory transfer instructions to access I/O.

Instructions in the **machine control** group affect the state or mode of operation of the processor itself. A common machine control instruction available in most microprocessors is the no operation command:

NOP

It causes the machine to wait through an instruction cycle. NOPs are used for many purposes, including adjustment of timing for certain routines. Notice that for this instruction no operand is needed or generally allowed.

4.5 OPERAND ADDRESSING MODES

The examples in Section 4.4 show that the specific addressing used varies from instruction to instruction. Data movement instructions, for example, utilize the various processor registers or memory locations as source and destination addresses. Other instructions may specify an actual data value, rather than the address of the value.

A data manipulation instruction implies access to as many as three locations: two to specify the location of the values to be manipulated—the **source addresses**—and the third to specify the location for the result—the **destination address:**

Both the CPU itself and the source code are simplified if the number of addresses passed is reduced. If two source addresses are required, the destination address is usually made the same as one of the sources. Consequently, most microprocessors require at most two addresses to be specified.

The type of source and destination addresses utilized by an instruction is determined by the instruction and the instruction addressing mode. All microprocessors provide several addressing modes. The range of addressing modes provided by a particular microprocessor is important, for a variety of addressing modes allow considerable flexibility when writing a program and foster programs that require fewer instructions to implement a given task.

The four main types of addressing modes used in microprocessor systems are

1. Register addressing
2. Immediate addressing

Modes 1 and 2 are used primarily for data transfer and manipulation instructions that use only the internal processor registers.

3. Direct addressing
4. Indirect addressing

Modes 3 and 4 are used primarily for data transfer and manipulation instructions that use the system memory.

Various microprocessor families provide addressing modes in a number of other categories; however, these are generally some combination or extension of these basic modes.

The details of the use of various addressing modes will be discussed along with data transfer group instructions in the next section. Subsequent chapters will introduce instructions from the other groups.

4.6   DATA TRANSFER INSTRUCTIONS

Fundamental to microprocessor operation are the data transfer instructions. They move byte-length data, generally, from one location to another. The heart of each of the data transfer instructions is the definition of the locations where source and destination bytes are to be found. This discussion will, thus, be based on the various addressing modes.

Register Addressing

Register addressing moves data between the internal processor registers. The instruction operand defines which registers are involved in the transfer. The order of the terms in the operand determines which register is the source and which is the destination. For example,

```
MOV   B,A
  |     | └--------- source address
  |     └--------- destination address
  └--------------- operation
```

In this example a label is not used, the operation mnemonic is MOV, and the operands are the A- and B-registers. No comments are included. This instruction causes the contents of the A-register to be moved to the B-register. The contents of the A-register remain unchanged. The ordering of the operands may seem awkward at first because the usual English language formulation would be "Move the data contained in register A into register B" rather than "Into register B, move the data from register A." A common mistake made by beginning programmers is to reverse the operands in this kind of instruction. This format is common, virtually standard, for assembly languages that are derived from 8080 assembly language such as the 8085, Z80, and 8086, among others. It is not universal, however. The 6502 and the 68000, for example, reverse this format.

Virtually standard for microprocessors, in general, is the process of leaving the source register unchanged when a byte is transferred out of it. The operation is not one of truly moving the byte but rather one of copying it elsewhere.

The example given is the assembly language statement for a MOV B,A operation. A common way of representing this operation is

$$(B) \leftarrow (A)$$

The parentheses mean "contents of." In English the statement would be, "Move the contents of the A-register to the B-register."

Another example is

MOV C,B

or

$$(C) \leftarrow (B)$$

which copies the contents of the B-register to the C-register.

The 8085 allows limited 16-bit, address-length, transfer operations. The one 16-bit register addressing mode operation is

    XCHG

No operand is required since only one exchange instruction is allowed. This instruction causes the contents of the combined DE-pair and the HL-pair to be exchanged, that is,

    (H) ⟷ (D)

and

    (L) ⟷ (E)

or

    (HL) ⟷ (DE)

Immediate Addressing

The **immediate addressing** mode allows the programmer to move a specific word into a location. The word is specified in the program itself and is the next immediate byte in the program. With this mode the source is not a register or a memory location. Instead, actual data are contained within the instruction sequence itself. For example,

```
MVI    A,0FEH
 |      |  L----------- source byte
 |      L-------------- destination address
 L--------------------- operation
```

The A-register is set to the value FE, hexadecimal. The proper diction is, "Move immediate FE, hexadecimal, to the A-register," or

    (A) ← FE (hexadecimal)

or

    (A) ← 11111110 (binary)

Notice that the parentheses are not used for the data FE. We have referenced a specific number instead of the contents of a memory location. The parentheses imply the use of the contents of an address. Without them the direct use of the value is implied.

A 16-bit register pair (BC, DE, or HL) may be specified as the destination address. Such an instruction requires two bytes of immediate data. For example,

    LXI H,802DH

This causes the 16-bit register pair HL to be loaded with immediate data, 802D, hexadecimal:

    (HL) ← 802DH

The instruction uses "H" to specify the HL-pair, as is standard for such references with the 8085.

Another example is

    LXI D,0E62H

which means

    (DE) ← 0E62H

As we have mentioned, the leading "0" (zero) is not optional in many assembly languages. As will be discussed in Chapter Six, a label is often used in the operand. Many assembly languages assume that any term beginning with a letter is a label. Thus, when a hexadecimal number begins with "A" through "F," the number is specified as such by inclusion of a leading number "0."

To reference the BC-pair, we would use "B" in the operand.

EXAMPLE 4.1 Register and Immediate Addressing

The following program fragment uses a combination of the previous instructions to load the primary CPU registers of the 8085.

```
;   REGISTER ADDRESSING DATA TRANSFERS
;
        ORG     2000H           ;SDK-85 RAM LOCATION
;
        MVI     A,0FEH          ;REGISTER FILL DEMONSTRATION
        MOV     B,A
        MOV     C,B
        LXI     H,71D3H
        LXI     D,0A071H
        XCHG
```

Address:	Op Codes:	Operations:
2000	3E	
	FE	(A) ← FE
2002	47	(B) ← (A)
2003	48	(C) ← (B)
2004	21	(HL) ← 71D3
	D3	(DE) ← A071
	71	(DE) ↔ (HL)
2007	11	
	71	
	A0	
200A	EB	

The first operation, after the title, is ORG 2000H. This is an assembler directive, as we have discussed. For an automated assembly process, this directive tells the assembly program where in memory to place the object code; here we have used 2000, hexadecimal, the start of the SDK-85 RAM memory—as will be discussed later in this chapter. The SDK-85 is a single-board 8085 microcomputer often used for training. For manual assembly this directive amounts to a note by the programmer indicating where the object code is to be started.

Notice that semicolons are used in the assembly language statements to identify comments, which, in turn, are used to explain the function of the various parts of the code.

The program loads a value into the A-register, using immediate addressing, and then loads this value into two further registers, B and C, using register addressing. This combination fills the A-, B-, and C-registers with FE, hexadecimal. The two register-addressing instructions are used rather than two immediate instructions because they are faster and use less memory. Finally, register pairs HL and DE are loaded, using immediate addressing. Later their contents are exchanged using register addressing.

The program fragment also shows the resulting machine code in hexadecimal format. The details of the operations are also shown. Example 4.4 will discuss the details of the assembly process for this example.

The comments are intended to annotate the purpose of a group of operations. They should not simply repeat the instructions.

Direct Addressing

Register and immediate addressing use locations within the CPU itself. With **direct addressing** a word can be read from or written to a memory location. The address of the memory location is specified in the instruction itself. Our ability to address storage locations now covers the entire memory. Direct addressing is sometimes called extended addressing. An example is

    LDA   20EAH

This causes the A-register to be loaded with the contents of the memory location with address 20EA, hexadecimal, and is expressed as

    (A) ← (20EAH)

Similarly, the contents of the A-register may be stored directly in a memory location:

    STA 20F2H

The contents of the accumulator are stored in location 20F2, hexadecimal.

The register pair HL is frequently used to hold a 16-bit memory address. Consequently, two instructions are provided to enable the two registers, H and L, to be loaded using a single instruction via direct addressing:

LHLD 20A2H

This gives us the contents of the memory location 20A2 in L. Register H is loaded with the contents of the next consecutive location, 20A3, which is expressed as

$$(L) \leftarrow (20A2H)$$
$$(H) \leftarrow (20A3H)$$

Although the reader is cautioned that the details given here apply to the 8085, this "low byte in the first location followed by the high byte in the next location" method of address storage is quite common in various microprocessor families.

The matching instruction is

SHLD 20AFH

Or store HL directly in 20AF, hexadecimal. In another form,

$$(20AFH) \leftarrow (L)$$
$$(20B0H) \leftarrow (H)$$

EXAMPLE 4.2   Immediate and Direct Addressing

The program fragment given here uses a combination of immediate and direct addressing. It first stores immediate data into two consecutive memory locations and later loads register pair HL with these data.

```
;
; DIRECT ADDRESSING DATA TRANSFERS
;
     ORG    2000H    ;SDK-85 RAM ADDRESS
;
     MVI    A,0FFH   ;DATA TRANSFER DEMONSTRATION
     STA    20A2H
     MVI    A,0EEH
     STA    20A3H
     LHLD   20A2H
     SHLD   20A4H
;
```

Indirect Addressing

With direct addressing, only the A-register or the HL-pair can be used to store or load a value to or from memory using the 8085. If a value were to be stored in a memory location from, say, the B-register using direct addressing, it would first be necessary to transfer the contents from B to A. The store operation could then be performed. A more efficient method is possible using register **indirect addressing.** With this mode, data may be transferred between any of the processor registers and the system memory.

Indirect addressing uses the contents of a storage location to point to the address in question. When an internal register is used for indirect addressing, the addressing mode is termed **register indirect addressing,** which is the indirect addressing method used by the 8085 CPU.

Register indirect addressing (with the 8085) either reads the data from or writes the data to the memory location whose address is currently stored in the register pair HL. The instruction does not contain the actual memory address itself. Instead, it implies that the address is currently stored in the HL-pair. The actual address is therefore obtained indirectly through the HL-pair. The high-order byte of the address is assumed to be in the H-register, with the low-order byte in the L-register.

The HL-pair is referenced using the single term "M," for memory:

MOV   A,M

The contents of the HL-pair are used to address a memory location. The contents of this location are moved to the accumulator. We have a double "contents of" situation, for when writing the instruction we know neither the byte to be put in the accumulator nor the address of the byte. Thus, the contents of the memory location whose address is the contents of the HL-pair is brought to the accumulator:

(A) ← ((HL))

Another example,

MOV M,B

is a memory write instruction expressed as

((HL)) ← (B)

The 8085 allows immediate data to be moved into system memory locations. This operation is done indirectly through the HL-pair and is an **immediate register indirect** memory-addressing mode:

MVI   M,0FFH

The value FF, hexadecimal, is stored in the address location pointed to by the HL-pair. Thus,

((HL)) ← FFH

Finally, we can load the accumulator indirectly from a location pointed to by the DE-pair, using

LDAX D

This yields

(A) ← ((DE))

This instruction can use only the BC- or DE-pair for indirect addressing. The associated storage instruction is (this time using the BC-pair)

STAX B

yielding

((BC)) ← (A)

A very important advantage of indirect addressing will become apparent when complex programs are attempted. Often the programmer writes a routine for which the specific memory location of the data to be used or stored is not known; in fact, the required address often changes as the program is executed. For example, a microprocessor that controls multiple robot manipulators might have data regarding each manipulator stored in a separate block of memory. Sections of the program would be written to operate on any of the blocks. The block starting address would be defined before execution of a section. At any rate, the programmer could not have directly defined the source of data when the program was written. The programmer would know only that the starting address of the data is located in, say, the HL-pair.

EXAMPLE 4.3   Data Transfer Operations

Shown here is a demonstration program fragment that loads the DE-pair and the HL-pair with two memory addresses. It then uses these addresses to load AA and BB, hexadecimal, into various registers. The exchange instruction is used. This particular sequence, as it stands, would look a little silly in a program. However, it demonstrates the ways in which the various data transfer instructions can be linked to move data about.

```
;   INDIRECT ADDRESSING DATA TRANSFERS
;
;       ORG     2000H       ;SDK-85  RAM  LOCATION
;
        LXI     D,20D0H     ;DEMONSTRATION OF VARIOUS TRANSFERS
        LXI     H,20A0H
        MVI     M,0AAH
```

```
MOV    B,M
MOV    C,M
XCHG
MVI    M,0BBH
MOV    D,M
MOV    E,M
;
```

4.7 OTHER ADDRESSING MODES

Other important addressing modes are available for some microprocessors. Most of these modes are combinations or extensions of the four modes just discussed. A major example is the **indexed-addressing** technique. A direct or indirect address is selected. Next the CPU steps away from this address by a certain amount. This amount is determined by the contents of some register and is called an index.

As an example of indexed addressing, assume that the address 2000, hexadecimal, has been selected by direct addressing. If a register containing the value 20, hexadecimal, is selected as an index register, the final address will be 2020.

Other more complex versions of indexed addressing are sometimes used. They can provide certain speed or convenience advantages for some programming problems.

The 8085 does not directly support indexed addressing.

Often pages of memory are used for what amount to "extensions" of the CPU registers. These pages can be addressed by single-byte addresses. Single-byte addressing allows very fast access with only one byte of address data stored in memory.

To attempt to illustrate all available instructions not only would yield a book of unneeded bulk but would add little of real value to the text. If a different microprocessor is required for a given application, the reader should become familiar with the details of its addressing modes, in particular, and its instruction set, in general. A good source of this detailed information is the manufacturer's literature.

4.8 THE INTEL 8085 INSTRUCTION SET

The instructions introduced so far are intended as examples of each type of instruction available in the data transfer group. The list of all possible transfer instructions is much longer. For example, there are 49 possible 8085 register transfer instructions of the form MOV r_1, r_2.

The aim of this and subsequent chapters is to introduce the major types of instructions, along with typical examples of each. The reader will then be able to choose the instruction type required for a given application. Selecting the instruction needed to complete a task is a matter of determining in detail the specific registers and memory-addressing modes required. A complete list of the instructions that make up the Intel 8085 instruction set is given in Appendix 2.

4.9 THE ASSEMBLY PROCESS

The instructions that a microprocessor executes are stored in its memory as binary-coded numbers. Before any programs can be executed, including the examples given earlier, the instructions must first be converted from assembly language to object code—the equivalent binary form used by the machine. For the simple assembly language assumed here, the process first involves a translation from assembly language to hexadecimal code. The hexadecimal code is the hexadecimal version of the machine's binary code.

In most general-purpose computers and microprocessor development systems (MDS), various programs are available to perform the generation of object code. Such programs are called **assemblers**. With an assembler we type in the assembly language instructions exactly, as shown in the following sections. The computer will then generate the object code on command. Other programs are used to conduct the transfer of this object code to an I/O port, which is connected, in turn, to a PROM programmer.

There is obviously a chicken-versus-egg problem here since programs are used to write programs. The solution, like that to the chicken-versus-egg problem, is evolution. If we had only the hardware for a computer with no other computer around, we would write a machine code program by hand to let the machine sense, and display, each keystroke of the machine's keyboard. We would design this program so that it would execute specific actions, such as store the last keystroke in memory.

This little program would allow us to type on the keyboard, see the results on the display, and perform primitive actions on the machine, such as storing a byte in a memory location. It would then be necessary to transfer this little program by hand into PROM, using a manual programmer. This type of program is called a **monitor**.

Having a monitor in the machine would allow us to write, in hexadecimal numbers, a simple assembler to translate mnemonics into object code. When the assembler saw MOV A,E it would store 7B, hexadecimal, as the object code, since this is the instruction code for this mnemonic. A complex assembler can be written using our simple assembler. The process could be continued to develop whatever software is needed. Fortunately, this process has already been done for us.

For purposes of this text we assume that the student who is working with real hardware has at least a basic single-board system. The optimum is the SDK-85 from Intel since it uses the 8085 processor. We will use standard Intel assembly language notation for all programs so that the student who goes on to higher-level systems is familiar with the normal programming format.

With a simple system, such as the SDK-85, programs are loaded directly in hexadecimal code. We must convert from assembly language to hexadecimal code manually. The discussion that follows details this process. The hand-assembly process is summarized in Figure 4.3.

Hand Coding

The list of instructions for the Intel 8085 in Appendix 2 shows that each assembly language instruction requires from one to three bytes in hexadecimal form.

For example, the instruction

    MOV A,B

requires a single byte:

          78   (operation)

The instruction

    MVI A,0FEH

requires two bytes:

          3E   (operation)
          FE   (immediate data)

The instruction

    STA   20F2H

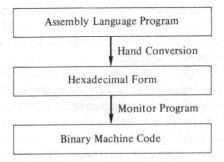

Figure 4.3
Manual-Assembly Process.

requires three bytes:

32	(operation)
F2	(low-address byte)
20	(high-address byte)

Notice that the suffix "H" is used only in the assembly language expression; it is required by the assembler to signify hexadecimal data. Notice too that the address data are loaded in low-order-byte, high-order-byte sequence.

EXAMPLE 4.4   Manual Assembly

As an example of the hand-coding process, Figure 4.4 shows the program in Example 4.1 in both assembly language and hexadecimal form. The program is assumed to be stored in memory, starting at address 2000, hexadecimal.

4.10   SINGLE-BOARD SYSTEMS

Simply reading about the instruction set and programming techniques does not fulfill the needs of the student interested in microcomputers. To understand and retain programming principles, the student must have an opportunity to develop and execute programs on actual hardware. To this end, many manufacturers offer microprocessor **trainers** and **development systems**.

A trainer is intended primarily for educational use. A development system is normally intended for use as an engineering tool during the process of designing a new product that uses a microprocessor. The heart of most development systems is some kind of **single-board computer**. These small computers can also serve as trainers. By the same token, most of the trainers on the market can also serve as design tools. The use of a single-board system for development purposes has the advantage of freeing the designer from the tasks required to build the actual microcomputer system. Instead, the designer can concentrate on the application problems of the overall system.

An example of a single-board system is shown in Figure 4.5. This board is based on the Intel 8085 microprocessor and is typical of such systems. In addition to the microprocessor, it contains the system clock source, a quantity of ROM for holding a system monitor program, a quantity of RAM for holding user programs, a number of I/O ports, a keypad and associated numeric display, and all the necessary bus control logic.

Although in the final system the application program will often be

Line number	Memory		Label	Assembly			Operation
	Address	Byte		Mnemonic	OP1	OP2	
1	2000	3E		MVI	A	FE	(A) ← FE
	2001	FE					
2	2002	47		MOV	B	A	(B) ← (A)
3	2003	48		MOV	C	B	(C) ← (B)
4	2004	21		LXI	H	7103	(H) (L) ← 7103
	2005	D3					
	2006	71					
5	2007	11		LXI	D	A071	(D) (E) ← A071
	2008	71					
	2009	A0					
6	200A	EB		XCHG			(D E) ↔ (H L)

Figure 4.4
Example of Manual Assembly (based on Example 4.1).

stored in ROM, it is advantageous during the development phase for the program to be stored in RAM, since it may then be readily changed if any errors are found. In addition, it is also helpful during program development to be able to control the rate of execution of a program. To these ends, the monitor program in a typical single-board system provides a number of commands that enable the operator to write and store a program into RAM and readily follow the state of the complete system during program execution.

Commands to the monitor of the system of Figure 4.5 are selected by pressing keys on the push-button keypad. The response of the monitor is displayed on the numeric display. The details of operation of the SDK-85 are summarized in Appendix 3.

Figure 4.5
A Single-Board Microcomputer. (Reprinted by permission of Intel Corporation, copyright © 1980.)

Hardware Tests

The programming examples and problems in this text can, with some exceptions, be entered and executed on any 8080A- or 8085-based, single-board computer. The examples assume the memory layout of the SDK-85 (4K bytes of ROM for the monitor starting at zero and 256 bytes of RAM at 2000, hexadecimal). If a different memory map is used, the addresses must be adjusted. The reader is encouraged to work through problems and then try them on the hardware.

If the SDK-85 is used for tests of any of the program fragments, an additional byte, "CF" (RST 1), must be included at the end so that control can be passed back to the SDK-85 monitor.

EXERCISES

Use 8085 assembly language for the following exercises. If you have access to an SDK-85 or other single-board computer, you are encouraged to run the programs and verify your answers. On the SDK-85 you need to add an RST1 (CF, hexadecimal) to the end of each program to return control to the monitor.

4.1 Write an assembly language program fragment to

(a) Load the B-register with immediate data 87, hexadecimal.

(b)   Transfer this value into registers A and C.
(c)   Load the D-register with immediate data 2F, hexadecimal.
(d)   Transfer this value into register E.
(e)   Load the HL-pair with immediate data 8EF2, hexadecimal.

4.2   Write an assembly language program fragment to

(a)   Load the A-register with immediate data FF, hexadecimal.
(b)   Store this in memory at location 20FF, hexadecimal, using direct addressing.
(c)   Load the B-register with the previously stored data, using register indirect addressing.
(d)   Transfer the data in the B-register to registers C and D, using register addressing.

4.3   List the preceding program fragments in a table similar to that shown in Figure 4.4 and obtain the hexadecimal code for each instruction, using the information in Appendix 2.

4.4   Derive the contents of processor registers A, B, and C and the contents of memory locations 2020, 2021, and 2080 after the following program fragment has been run:

```
LXI    H,2020H
LXI    D,2080H
XCHG
MVI    A,2AH
MOV    M,A
MVI    A,20H
MOV    B,A
XCHG
MOV    M,B
XCHG
MOV    C,M
MOV    A,C
STA    2021H
```

4.5   Five sequential two-byte sets of memory locations, starting at 2080, hexadecimal, contain pointers to memory locations where the five bytes starting at location 2090 are to be moved. Write a program fragment to perform this transfer.

4.6   Update the code from Exercise 4.5 to prevent any initial register data from being lost. The page of memory, starting at 2000, hexadecimal, is available as RAM.

4.7   Using a format similar to that of Figure 4.4, assemble the code shown in Exercise 4.4.

4.8   Using a format similar to that of Figure 4.4, assemble the code shown in Example 4.3.

4.9   Using a format similar to that of Figure 4.4, assemble the program fragment of Exercise 4.5.

4.10   Make a memory map of the SDK-85 RAM and ROM capabilities.

CHAPTER FIVE

DATA MANIPULATION

5.1 INTRODUCTION

Microprocessors may be used in a number of applications, and the programmer must be able to represent and manipulate microprocessor data in a number of different ways. This chapter introduces specific data representation methods for microprocessors and then discusses various instructions from the data manipulation group.

5.2 DATA REPRESENTATION

Before considering specific arithmetic instructions, we will examine different ways of representing data in the microprocessor. Appendix 1 reviews the details of number systems and conversions between various number systems. The material in this section is directed toward specific data representations for microprocessors.

For the 8-bit machines we are discussing, there are 256 (00000000 to 11111111) unique possibilities for each word in memory or in a one-byte register. In the most general terms, data representation methods involve the specific coding used to give each word meaning. Different representation formats may be selected for ease of manipulation, interface with I/O devices, compact data storage, and so forth. In general, numbers may be represented in unsigned binary, signed binary, or binary-coded decimal (BCD). Other representation methods, including ASCII and bit-mapped data, are considered in turn.

Unsigned Binary

Unsigned binary is the most direct and, for microprocessors, the most common form of number representation. In this representation all numbers are assumed positive. A byte is simply the direct, 8-bit binary form of the number. Some examples are

2^7	2^6	2^5	2^4	2^3	2^2	2^1	2^0	=	weighting
0	0	1	0	1	0	1	1	=	43
0	1	0	0	0	1	1	0	=	70
1	0	1	0	0	0	0	1	=	161
1	1	0	0	1	1	0	0	=	204

Each bit is usually given the name associated with its **weighting**. Bit zero is thus the least significant bit (LSB) and, in writing, would appear on the right. Bit 7 is the most significant bit (MSB). This convention is virtually always used.

The range of numbers in unsigned binary form—for an 8-bit microprocessor using one byte per number—is 256 (zero to 255) numbers long. Numbers in excess of 255 require additional bits, usually in 8-bit blocks. A two-byte number can therefore cover the range of zero to 65,535.

Binary-represented numbers provide very compact storage in memory since all possible states of a byte are used. They are also easy to manipulate and provide direct interface with a number of I/O devices.

Signed Binary

For some applications it is necessary to represent both positive and negative numbers. Moreover, when performing arithmetic operations, it is often necessary to produce signed results. With a **signed binary** form of number representation, one bit, the most significant, is used to indicate the sign of the number.

The simplest form of signed binary representation might be termed **"sign/magnitude."** In this form the MSB indicates the sign—normally zero for positive and one for negative—and the other seven bits indicate the magnitude. For example,

```
0 0011010 = +26
1 1100100 = -100
```

Here there are 255 possible numbers ranging from 11111111, or −127, to 01111111, or +127; 10000000 and 00000000 form the same number, zero.

The sign/magnitude form of representation is often used for interface with I/O devices and also for many forms of data, in particular when arithmetic operations are not performed.

Unfortunately, with this form it is not possible to perform simple arithmetic operations on numbers and automatically produce correct signed results. If we add directly the two numbers just used, we get 11111110, or −126; this is obviously not the sum of +26 and −100. This problem can be resolved with a different method of coding numbers. This enhanced coding is called **two's complement** representation. Performing ordinary arithmetic operations on two's complement signed numbers automatically produces the correct two's complement signed result.

With two's complement the MSB, called S, of each word is used as a sign bit, as before:

```
MSB                      LSB
 S  6  5  4  3  2  1  0
 S = 0 for positive numbers and zero.
 S = 1 for negative numbers.
```

For positive numbers, the simple binary code is used to represent the number. For zero to 127, the two's complement and straight binary forms are the same. For negative numbers, however, the number is represented in an altered form. The positive, binary number is complemented—each bit is inverted—and the resulting number is incremented by one. For example, the two's complement version of −15 is found by the process

```
 +15 = 00001111  (binary)
                  complement
       11110000
                  increment
 −15 = 11110001  (two's complement)
```

Another example is the two's complement version of −88:

```
 +88 = 01011000  (binary)
                  complement
       10100111
                  increment
 −88 = 10101000  (two's complement)
```

An easier way to find the two's complement of a negative binary number starts with the binary representation of the number without sign. We then retain all trailing zeros and the least significant one-bit and complement all the rest of the bits. This is a simple procedure when doing the conversion by hand. For example,

```
 +76 = 0 1 0 0 1 1 0 0  (binary)
        |_____| |____|
        Complement    Retain
 −76 = 1 0 1 1 0 1 0 0  (two's complement)
```

Each of these processes can be reversed to deduce the binary representation of the value of a two's complement number.

Since zero does not have two codes, we have a total of 256 possible numbers (−128 to +127, including zero) for an 8-bit word. This range is shown in Table 5.1.

Using two's complement numbers, we can now do signed binary arithmetic. Adding −88 to +15,

$$
\begin{array}{rl}
-88 = & 10101000 \\
+15 = & 00001111 \\
\hline
-73 = & 10110111
\end{array}
$$

and adding +76 to the result, we have

$$
\begin{array}{rl}
-73 = & 10110111 \\
+76 = & 01001100 \\
\hline
+\ 3 = & 00000011
\end{array}
$$

The carry would have no meaning for these single-byte manipulations.

When we perform arithmetic operations on 8-bit, two's complement signed numbers, it is important not to exceed the range −128 to 127, or incorrect answers may be obtained. For example, (+68) + (+76) will produce an incorrect answer since the result (+144) exceeds the maximum possible positive number for 8-bit, two's complement representation (+127). Similarly, (−68) − (+76) will also produce an incorrect result. The operation yields −144, which is beyond the maximum allowed negative number, −128. This range can be extended by using multiple bytes for each number in the operation. With two bytes we get a range extending from −32,768 to +32,767.

A rarely used form of signed binary numbers is called **one's com-**

Table 5.1
Two's Complement Representation

Decimal Number	Two's Complement Representation
+127	01111111
.	.
.	.
.	.
+ 3	00000011
+ 2	00000010
+ 1	00000001
0	00000000
− 1	11111111
− 2	11111110
− 3	11111101
.	.
.	.
.	.
−127	10000001
−128	10000000

plement. For this form the negative numbers are simply the complement of their positive counterparts. One's complement is simply two's complement without the increment.

Binary-Coded Decimal

It is sometimes preferable to use a decimal number representation within the microcomputer, for example, if the input data are from a decimal keypad and the subsequent output data drive a decimal display. Most microcomputers provide instructions for performing arithmetic on **binary-coded decimal (BCD)** numbers. BCD representation, similar to the hexadecimal system, is discussed in Appendix 1 and summarized in Table 5.2. Because only four bits are required for each digit, an 8-bit binary number may be used to store two BCD digits. For example,

1000 0110 (BCD) = 86 (decimal)

or

0101 0001 (BCD) = 51 (decimal)

BCD representation allows only 100—zero to 99—possible numbers for each 8-bit word. It is therefore a less efficient coding format than binary formats that handle up to 256 numbers per byte. No signed numbers are allowed in standard BCD representation.

Other Forms of Data Representation

As introduced in Chapter One, a standard coding scheme, known as ASCII, relates a single alphanumeric character—letters of the alphabet

Table 5.2
BCD Code

Decimal Digit	BCD Code
0	0000
1	0001
2	0010
3	0011
4	0100
5	0101
6	0110
7	0111
8	1000
9	1001

and numbers—to a byte. This is a very common data format for certain I/O devices, such as keyboards and video terminals, and for most long-distance transmission links, such as phone connections. We must often translate from an input device's ASCII characters to some other data representation before manipulating the data. At the end of the manipulations, the results may need to be changed again into ASCII for transmission to an output device. For some applications, such as word processing, data manipulations are done directly in ASCII.

Another very important form of data representation is termed **bit-mapped data**. Rather than representing numbers or letters, a byte is broken into individual bits. Each bit then identifies a single element of data. Bit-mapped representation is often used when rather cumbersome or complex input devices are not required. In the example of a building monitor computer, one byte might be used to indicate the status of up to eight lights. Each bit in the byte would signify the on/off status of a specific light.

Certain techniques have been developed for manipulation of bit-mapped data, some of which will be discussed later in this chapter.

In summary, the programmer may choose any one of several possible data representation formats. Sometimes even combinations of the formats are used. It should be stressed that the type of representation is essentially transparent to the microprocessor. A byte is simply treated as 8 bits of binary information regardless of its meaning to the outside world. The programmer has the responsibility of giving meaning to both the data and the operations performed by the CPU.

5.3 ARITHMETIC INSTRUCTIONS

The arithmetic instructions include add, subtract, increment, decrement, and shift. Generally, the add and subtract instructions involve the A-register (the accumulator) and either another processor register or a memory location. The increment and decrement operations can generally be performed on various registers and locations through the use of different addressing modes. Each of these operations can be performed in a number of different ways. The programmer can thus tailor the instruction used to the application.

As usual, we use the 8085 for specific examples of arithmetic instructions. The reader is again advised to consult the manufacturer's literature for the details of other devices.

As discussed previously, the microprocessor contains a number of status bits called flags. Flags are either set or reset, depending on the result of a particular instruction. The programmer is able to use these flags as an aid in data manipulation.

We now discuss various arithmetic instructions. Some details of various addressing modes and flag data are introduced for each of the areas. The 8085 instruction set is summarized in Appendix 2.

Add Instructions

Table 5.3 reviews the process of **binary addition.** Because the sum can be only 0 or 1, a carry will often be generated. It must then, of course, be added to the next higher-order pair of bits. As in all addition, it is necessary to consider not only each pair of bits but also the carry data from the previous pair. The carry from the previous pair is termed the **carry-in bit.** The datum produced as a carry to the next higher order is called the **carry-out bit.**

The truth table, Table 5.4, summarizes all the possible combinations of two bits and a carry-in. It shows the resulting sum and carry-out. The process can be extended to any number of bits. Considering 8-bit addition, for example,

$$
\begin{array}{rll}
A = 10011010 &=& 154 \text{ (decimal)} \\
+\ B = 01010111 &=& \ \ 87 \text{ (decimal)} \\
\hline
\text{Carry} = 00111100 & & \\
A + B = 11110001 &=& 241 \text{ (decimal)}
\end{array}
$$

The carry-out of the final bit, the MSB, causes the overall carry-out from the 8-bit add operation.

Table 5.3
Addition of Two Bits

Bit 1	Bit 2	Sum	Carry
0	0	0	0
0	1	1	0
1	0	1	0
1	1	0	1

Table 5.4
Addition of Two Bits and a Carry-in

Bit 1	Bit 2	Carry-in	Sum	Carry-out
0	0	0	0	0
0	0	1	1	0
0	1	0	1	0
0	1	1	0	1
1	0	0	1	0
1	0	1	0	1
1	1	0	0	1
1	1	1	1	1

The 8085 instructions discussed in this section are used for adding single-byte numbers only. They all use register, immediate, or register indirect addressing to provide one of the bytes to be added. The other byte comes from the accumulator. The result is placed in the accumulator. All relevant flag bits are updated after the addition. None of the instructions is affected by the carry flag status (carry-in).

In later sections we discuss other instructions used for arithmetic involving numbers larger than one byte.

Register Addressing

An example of register addressing is

    ADD B

This causes the contents of the B-register to be added to the contents of the accumulator. The result, as usual, is placed in the accumulator. The B-register is unchanged. Thus,

    (A) ← (A) + (B)

After the ADD instruction, the individual flag bits are affected as follows:

    S   Set if result is negative (MSB of A is 1)
    Z   Set if result is zero (A is all 0s)
    AC   Set if carry is generated from bit 3 (for BCD use)
    CY   Set if carry is from bit 7 (carry-out of MSB)
    P   Set if result is even parity

Immediate Addressing

Immediate data are added to the accumulator. All relevant flags are affected, and the results are placed in the accumulator. An example of immediate addressing is

    ADI 0FH

Here 0F, hexadecimal, is added to the contents of the accumulator. As usual, the result is placed in the accumulator with all relevant flags affected:

    (A) ← (A) + 0F

Register Indirect Addressing

To add the contents of the memory location pointed to by the HL-pair to the accumulator, we use

```
ADD  M
```

That is,

$$(A) \leftarrow (A) + ((H)(L))$$

The result is placed in the A-register. All relevant flags are affected.

Subtract Instructions

The subtraction of two bits is summarized in the truth table of Table 5.5. Both bit 2 and the borrow-in from the previous bit are subtracted from bit 1 to produce the difference and, if necessary, a borrow-out. For example,

```
       A = 10011011 = 155 (decimal)
     − B = 01010111 =  87 (decimal)
            ///////
  Borrow = 1000100
   A − B = 01000100 =  68 (decimal)
```

The subtraction instructions for the 8085 have the same form as the addition instructions. The contents of a location defined by the instruction's addressing mode are subtracted from the accumulator, with the result placed in the accumulator. All flags are affected; the CY-flag is now a borrow flag, being set if a borrow-out is required. Multiprecision subtraction, which uses the borrow-out from previous operations, will be discussed later in this chapter. Examples of register, immediate, and indirect addressing subtract instructions for the 8085 are

```
SUB   B
SUI   0FH
SUB   M
```

Increment Instructions

The **increment instructions** simply add one to the contents of a location. The location is specified by the addressing mode selected. Either register

Table 5.5
Subtraction of Two Bits and a Borrow-in

Bit 1	Bit 2	Borrow-in	Difference	Borrow-out
0	0	0	0	0
0	0	1	1	1
0	1	0	1	1
0	1	1	0	1
1	0	0	1	0
1	0	1	0	0
1	1	0	0	0
1	1	1	1	1

or register indirect addressing can be used. For the 8085, all flags except the carry flag are affected by the INR instructions, whereas no flags are affected by the INX instruction.

Register Addressing

An example of register addressing is

        INR   A

This causes the contents of the A-register, the accumulator, to be incremented by one:

        $(A) \leftarrow (A) + 1$

Pairs of registers taken as a single 16-bit number can be incremented using the INX instruction:

        INX   D

This causes the 16-bit number in the DE-pair to be incremented by one:

        $(DE) \leftarrow (DE) + 1$

Because a register pair is often used to address memory locations indirectly, the INX instruction may be used to address a series of values sequentially in memory.

Register Indirect Addressing

Here the contents of an indirectly addressed memory location are incremented:

        INR   M

This causes the contents of the memory location whose address is contained in the HL-pair to be incremented:

        $((HL)) \leftarrow ((HL)) + 1$

Decrement Instructions

Decrement instructions in the 8085 are very similar to the increment instructions. The contents of the addressed location are decremented rather than incremented. Some examples of the instructions are

        DCR   A
        DCX   H
        DCR   M

EXAMPLE 5.1 Unsigned Arithmetic

The program fragment to be given uses unsigned binary number representation in 8085 code. The two registers A and B are first loaded with immediate data, and their contents are added together. A third number is then subtracted from the contents of A, using immediate addressing. Finally, the resulting contents of the accumulator are decremented once.

The initial numbers are 145 and 58, decimal. The ADD instruction changes the accumulator to 203, decimal. The SBI instruction reduces the accumulator by 72, decimal, to 131. Finally, the accumulator is decremented to 130.

```
;
;   UNSIGNED ARITHMETIC DEMONSTRATION
;
        ORG   2000H    ;SDK-85 RAM LOCATION
;
        MVI   A,91H    ;LOAD AND MANIPULATE DATA
        MVI   B,3AH
        ADD   B
        SBI   48H
        DCR   A
;
```

As has been mentioned, the microprocessor is not affected by the type of number representation being used by the programmer. It simply performs the indicated arithmetic operation. The programmer must represent and interpret the binary patterns in the required way. This can be seen from the following example.

EXAMPLE 5.2 Signed Arithmetic

The program fragment shown here is the same as that in Example 5.1, except that the initial numbers have been changed to represent a positive and a negative value, and the final result is negative. Two's complement signed number representation is used. Particular care must be taken to interpret the signs of the numbers in the correct way.

The immediate data are 35 and -72, decimal. The addition yields -37, decimal. The subtraction of -37 yields zero since $(-37) - (-37) = 0$. The decrement results in -1:

```
;
;   SIGNED ARITHMETIC DEMONSTRATION
;
        ORG   2000H    ;SDK-85 RAM LOCATION
;
        MVI   A,23H    ;LOAD AND MANIPULATE DATA
```

```
MVI    B,0B8H
ADD    B
SBI    0DBH
DCR    A
```

;

5.4 MULTIPRECISION ARITHMETIC INSTRUCTIONS

As mentioned earlier, some applications require more than 8 bits for data representation. Most 8-bit microprocessors, including the 8085, provide a number of arithmetic instructions for manipulating numbers of more than 8 bits.

Sixteen-Bit Arithmetic

Several instructions that operate directly in a 16-bit format have already been mentioned. They include the 16-bit data transfer instructions XCHG, LXI, LHLD, and SHLD. We have also discussed the 16-bit increment and decrement instructions INX and DCX. Another available 16-bit instruction allows a 16-bit addition:

DAD B

This causes the 16-bit contents of the register pair BC to be added to the 16-bit contents of the register pair HL. The result is placed in the register pair HL. Only the carry flag is affected. It is set if there is a carry-out from the MSB of H during the addition operation; otherwise, it is reset:

$$(HL) \leftarrow (HL) + (BC)$$

We have used the BC-pair in this example. The register pair D, for the DE-pair, can also be specified. It will then be added to the HL-pair. We could also use the 16-bit SP for addition to HL:

DAD SP

Finally, the HL-pair can be specified for addition to itself. This is done, using

DAD H

Generally, these 16-bit data manipulation instructions are used, first and foremost, for address manipulations. Although they can be used for general-purpose arithmetic, these instructions do not allow a carry-in. More general forms of arithmetic operations that make full use of the flags are available. These operations are often selected for general-purpose multiprecision arithmetic.

Multiprecision Arithmetic—The Carry Flag

If more than 16-bit accuracy is required, there are no single instructions available. Instead, a number of instructions must be used. For example, consider the addition of two 24-bit—three-byte—numbers. Each number would require three memory locations, and the total addition operation would require three separate 8-bit additions, as illustrated in Figure 5.1.

For these **multiprecision addition** operations it is necessary to add the **carry bit (CY)** when adding together the second and third pairs of bytes. The 8085, as well as most other such devices, provides additional add, and subtract, instructions that use the carry, or borrow, bit.

An example is register indirect addition with carry instruction from the 8085 instruction set:

        ADC   M

The contents of the memory location, pointed to by the HL-pair, are added to the accumulator; in addition, the carry bit is added to the LSB of this sum. The result is placed in the A-register, and all flags are affected:

$$(A) \leftarrow (A) + ((HL)) + (CY)$$

Register addressing is, of course, possible. For example,

        ADC   E

adds the A- and E-registers, along with the carry bit. Immediate addressing is done with the ACI, add-with carry-immediate, instruction.

The **multiprecision subtraction** instructions for the 8085 are the SBB instruction for indirect and register addressing and the SBI instruction for immediate addressing. The addressed word is subtracted from the accumulator along with the borrow bit (CY). Note that CY is either

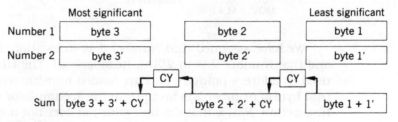

Figure 5.1
Multiprecision Arithmetic.

carry or borrow, depending on the instruction that set the flag and a following instruction, which makes use of it. The result is placed in the accumulator. For example,

    SBB   D

causes

$$(A) \leftarrow (A) - (D) - (CY)$$

EXAMPLE 5.3 Multiprecision Addition

We can now follow the details of the multiprecision addition of Figure 5.1. The 24-bit number called Number 1 might be stored in three consecutive locations in memory; let us assume that the least significant byte occurs first. Elsewhere, three more bytes would hold the 24-bit Number 2. Finally, let us assume that we need to place the result back in the storage location assigned for Number 1. For ease, assume that we know the two storage locations and can load them by an immediate operation. (The alternative would be for the locations to be computed in code, which precedes the addition under study.)

An assembly language code for the process is

```
;
;   MULTIPRECISION (THREE-BYTE) ADDITION DEMONSTRATION
;
;   ORG    2000H       ;SDK-85 RAM LOCATION
;
    LXI    H,20C0H     ;DATA MUST BE SET UP BEFORE EXECUTION
    LXI    D,20D0H     ;LOW BYTE IN LOWEST ADDRESS
    LDAX   D
    ADD    M           ;LOW-BYTE ADDITION
    MOV    M,A         ;HL WILL POINT TO RESULT
    INX    H
    INX    D
    LDAX   D
    ADC    M           ;2ND BYTE
    MOV    M,A
    INX    H
    INX    D
    LDAX   D
    ADC    M           ;HIGH BYTE
    MOV    M,A
;
```

We have assumed that Number 1 is in location 20C0, hexadecimal, and that Number 2 is in 20D0, hexadecimal. The HL- and DE-pairs are used as address pointers and are loaded immediately. The least significant byte of Number 2 is brought to the accumulator with the first LDAX instruction. Notice that the first addition does not use the carry bit since we have chosen the ADD instruction. However, the carry bit is properly set to a one or a zero—depending on the existence of a carry-out—by this instruction. The first sum is stored back where the first byte of Number 1 originated, and the address pointers are incremented. They now point to the second bytes of the two numbers.

The process continues, using the ADC instruction so that any carry-in data are recognized. This routine might be followed with an instruction to test for a final carry-out. Such a test would point out an "overflow" from the 24-bit word. An overflow is a condition in which the result of an operation is too large for the format being used. The conditional branch instructions required for an overflow test is introduced in the next chapter.

Nothing in this process would prevent us from defining the 24-bit word as a signed (or coded in some other way) word. If we did, the whole string of 24 bits would be treated as one, say, two's complement number. Again, the microprocessor simply performs the operations indicated; the programmer assigns a meaning to the results.

5.5 BCD ARITHMETIC

It is advantageous in some microprocessor applications to represent numbers in BCD form. Most microprocessors therefore provide instructions that allow BCD data to be manipulated.

The 8085 uses a two-stage process for **BCD arithmetic.** First, a straight binary operation, such as addition, is performed. This operation is followed by an instruction that adjusts the resulting number into its proper BCD format. The special instruction is then unique to BCD operations. As we will see, it uses the auxiliary carry (AC) flag and the accumulator to make the required adjustment. Consider a first example of BCD addition:

```
      Number 1 = 0110 0010 (BCD) = 62 (decimal)
    + Number 2 = 0010 0101 (BCD) = 25 (decimal)
     Binary Sum = 1000 0111 (CY     0, AC     0)
       BCD Sum = 1000 0111 (BCD) = 87 (decimal)
```

The binary sum and the BCD sum are the same; no correction is needed. The AC flag will be set only if there is a carry-out of bit 3 (the fourth bit above the LSB). AC is used primarily for these BCD operations.

Consider now another BCD sum, example 2, in which an adjustment is required:

```
      Number 1 = 0111 1001 (BCD) = 79 (decimal)
    + Number 2 = 0001 0110 (BCD) = 16 (decimal)
     Binary Sum = 1000 1111 (CY     0, AC     0)
       BCD Sum = 1001 0101 (BCD) = 95 (decimal)
```

Since the sum of 6 and 9 is 15, the BCD operation needs a carry-into bit 4, but the binary addition does not produce the carry. In addition, the binary operation has produced a number, 1111, which does not exist in BCD. An adjustment will be needed. A third example illustrates the situation in which there is a carry-out of bit 3. Again, an adjustment will be needed:

```
  Number 1 = 0011 1001 (BCD) = 39 (decimal)
+ Number 2 = 0100 1000 (BCD) = 48 (decimal)
Binary Sum = 1000 0001 (CY    0, AC    1)
BCD SUM    = 1000 0111 (BCD) = 87 (decimal)
```

All is well except that the second digit of the binary sum, taken as a BCD number, is low by six.

It can be deduced from these three examples that should the normal binary addition of each four-bit group produce an answer that is less than 9 and no AC is generated, the result is correct as a BCD number. However, if the result of the addition is greater than 9 for the low-order BCD digit, or if an AC is generated, an adjustment must be made. It can be shown that the required adjustment is the addition of six to the normal binary sum. Consider example 2:

```
Binary Sum = 1000 1111 (CY    0, AC    0)
Add +6     = 0000 0110
Adjusted Sum = 1001 0101 (BCD) = 95 (decimal)
```

This is, of course, the correct result. The normal binary carry-out of the third bit corrected the high-order BCD digit. Similarly, in example 3, when adding the two low-order BCD digits, an AC is generated and a similar adjustment is required:

```
Binary Sum = 1000 0001 (CY    0, AC    1)
Add +6     = 0000 0110
Adjusted Sum = 1000 0111 (BCD) = 87 (decimal)
```

Again, this result is correct.

One more adjustment might be in order. The same problems noted for the low-order BCD digit can occur when the high-order sum is computed in the binary addition process. The 8085 provides an **adjustment instruction** that acts to adjust both the low- and the high-order digits of the BCD number:

DAA

No operand is required, for only the accumulator can be adjusted. This instruction performs the following operations:

1. If the value of the least significant four bits of the A-register is greater than 9 or if the AC-flag is set, six is added to the A-register.

2. If the value of the most significant four bits of the A-register is now greater than 9 or if the CY-flag is set, six is added to the most significant four bits of the A-register. All flags are affected.

Since both halves of the A-register are corrected and the carry (CY) flag is affected, it is clearly possible to perform multiprecision BCD arithmetic using a chain of binary addition—using the carry—and adjustment (DAA) instructions. This is illustrated in the example at the end of this section.

Because the single-register increment instructions (INRs) are really binary addition instructions, they can be used for BCD data, provided that the incremented byte exists in, or is moved to, the A-register before the DAA instruction occurs. Note that a single increment cannot cause a carry, either AC or CY, prior to the DAA operation. Thus, the fact that the increment operation does not affect the CY-flag is not a concern here.

Subtraction is a bigger problem for BCD arithmetic using the 8085. Some processors, such as the Z80, provide a **postsubtraction adjustment** of BCD data similar to the operation given for addition. With the Z80 the DAA instruction will cause the processor to make one adjustment after an addition and quite another after a subtraction. The processor remembers what was last done and applies the correct adjustment. With the 8085 we must write a special routine to correct the data back to BCD format after subtraction.

The adjustment required when performing BCD subtraction is different from the one required for addition. This adjustment is summarized in Table 5.6. A correction of 00, FA, A0, or 9A—all hexadecimal—must be added to the result, depending on the state of the A-register and the carry flags—CY and AC, which are now really borrow flags—after the normal binary subtraction operation (SUB, SUI, DCR) has been performed.

Two examples are given to illustrate the process.

Example 1

$$\begin{array}{rl}
& \text{Number 1} = 0100\ 0111\ \text{(BCD)} = 47\ \text{(decimal)} \\
- & \text{Number 2} = 0011\ 0010\ \text{(BCD)} = 32\ \text{(decimal)} \\
\hline
& \text{Binary Difference} = 0001\ 0101\ (\text{CY} \quad 0,\ \text{AC} \quad 0) \\
& \qquad\qquad \text{Add } 00 = 0000\ 0000 \\
\hline
& \text{Adjusted Difference} = 0001\ 0101\ \text{(BCD)} = 15\ \text{(decimal)}
\end{array}$$

Table 5.6
BCD Subtraction Corrections

Carry CY	Upper Hexadecimal Digit (Bits 7–4)	Auxiliary Carry AC	Lower Hexadecimal Digit (Bits 3–0)	Correction To Be Added
0	0–9	0	0–9	00
0	0–8	1	6–F	FA
1	7–F	0	0–9	A0
1	6–F	1	6–F	9A

Example 2

Number 1 = 1000 0001 (BCD) = 81 (decimal)
− Number 2 = 0110 1001 (BCD) = 69 (decimal)
───
Binary Difference = 0001 1000 (CY 0, AC 1)
Add FA = 1111 1010
───
Adjusted Difference = 0001 0010 (BCD) = 12 (decimal)

EXAMPLE 5.4 BCD Addition

The following program fragment adds together two four-digit (16-bit) BCD numbers. It forms the adjusted BCD sum. The first number is stored in the two consecutive memory locations starting at address 2080, hexadecimal. The second is stored in the two locations starting at address 2082, hexadecimal. The result replaces the first number in 2080 and 2081, hexadecimal.

```
;
;  BCD ADDITION DEMONSTRATION
;
   ORG   2000H    ;SDK-85 RAM LOCATION
;
   LXI   H,2082H  ;2080 TO 2083 CONTAIN 2, 4-DIGIT
                  ;BCD NUMBERS
   LDA   2080H    ;LOAD, BCD ADD, STORE 1ST TWO BCDs
   ADD   M
   DAA
   STA   2080H
   INX   H
   LDA   2081H    ;2ND TWO BCDs
   ADC   M
   DAA
   STA   2081H
;
```

5.6 LOGICAL OPERATIONS

As discussed earlier in this chapter, the data stored in the computer may not be purely numerical. Often bit-mapped or ASCII data are manipulated. For example, a single bit may indicate the state of a control valve: 0 = valve open, 1 = valve closed. The 8-bit binary value 01100111 may mean that control valves 0, 1, 2, 5, and 6 are closed and control valves 3, 4, and 7 are open. In addition to the arithmetic instructions already introduced, most microprocessors have available a number of data manipulation instructions that are primarily intended to work with nonnumerical data of this kind. These are the instructions of the **"logical operations"** group. Remember that the processor does not know the character of the data being manipulated; often logical operations are applied to numerical data if such a process achieves the objectives of the programmer. Again, we use the instruction set of the 8085 for our examples.

Logical AND

The **logical AND** instructions perform the bit-by-bit AND operation between the contents of the A-register and (1) immediate data; (2) the contents of another processor register; or (3) a memory location, depending on the addressing used.

The truth table for the AND function is given in Table 5.7. A typical application of this instruction is to test the state of a specific bit in a given byte. For example, if we wish to test bit 6 of the accumulator, we use

ANI   40H

This is

(A) ← (A) AND 40H

Since 40, hexadecimal, is 01000000, the AND operation with an arbitrary byte in the A-register—call it XXXXXXXX with each X being either zero or one—yields 0X000000:

```
    (A) = XXXXXXXX
     40 = 01000000
(A) AND 40 = 0X000000
```

If bit 6 of A were a zero, the new contents of A would be zero and the zero flag would be set. We have a means of testing for the status of a specific bit, in this case bit 6. If this bit were a one, the AND with 40, hexadecimal, would yield 01000000; the zero flag would be reset to zero. The next chapter will introduce control transfer instructions, which can be used to take advantage of these bit test data. Another way to make this test, and more complex tests, is to use the parity flag. It indicates the number of ones (even or odd) in the accumulator.

Table 5.7
AND Function Truth Table

Bit 1	Bit 2	Bit 1 AND Bit 2
0	0	0
0	1	0
1	0	0
1	1	1

The 8085 also allows register and indirect addressing of the AND operation, using the ANA instruction. The accumulator is the source of one of the bytes, and the result is always placed in the accumulator. All flags are affected, with CY and AC always being cleared for the AND instructions of the 8085.

Logical OR

At this point it should be obvious that a **logical OR** is simply a bit-by-bit OR operation between the accumulator and the addressed byte. The result is placed in the accumulator; all flags are affected, with both the CY- and AC-flags being cleared. The truth table for the OR operation is shown in Table 5.8. Whereas the AND operation allowed testing of bits in a word, the OR operation allows the setting of selected bits without disturbing the others.

An example of the OR operation is

    ORA   C

This is a register-addressed OR instruction. A bit-by-bit OR operation is performed on the contents of the C-register and the A-register. The result is placed in the accumulator:

$$(A) \leftarrow (A) \text{ OR } (C)$$

Using specific binary numbers in an example, let

$$
\begin{array}{ll}
(A) & = 01100100 \\
(C) & = 10010101 \\
\hline
(A) \text{ OR } (C) & = 11110101
\end{array}
$$

The ORA instruction allows indirect addressing A through the HL-pair. ORI is the immediate OR instruction for the 8085, with the immediate data in the operand.

Exclusive-OR Operation

The **exclusive-OR (XOR)** operation differs from the normal logical OR in that when both bits are logical ones, the result is zero. Put another way,

Table 5.8
OR Function Truth Table

Bit 1	Bit 2	Bit 1 OR Bit 2
0	0	0
0	1	1
1	0	1
1	1	1

two identical bits yield a zero when an exclusive-OR operation is performed on them; the result of an exclusive-OR of two different bits (one with zero or zero with one) is a one. The truth table is given in Table 5.9.

The exclusive-OR operation has all the normal addressing modes; all flags are affected, with the CY- and AC-flags being cleared by these instructions.

Exclusive-OR operations are often used to detect errors in binary data transmission. The received word is returned to the transmitter; if no transmission errors have occurred, an exclusive-OR on the two words will yield all zeros. If an error has occurred, one or more bits will be one after the exclusive-OR operation. Many programmers will use the exclusive-OR instruction to load zeros into the accumulator by performing the exclusive-OR of two identical bytes. It is also commonly used to complement a number by doing an exclusive-OR with FF, hexadecimal.

The 8085 immediate exclusive-OR instruction is

XRI 0FAH

The indirect operation is

XRA M

where

(A) ← (A) XOR ((HL))

Using detailed bytes as an example,

$$
\begin{array}{ll}
\text{(A)} & = 10011011 \\
\underline{\text{((HL))}} & = 11001101 \\
\text{(A) XOR ((HL))} & = 01010110
\end{array}
$$

The exclusive-OR operation is often used in measurement applications to detect transitions in data. If we perform an exclusive-OR between a current byte and the previous byte, the result will be zero if no change has occurred. If any bit has changed, the result will not be zero.

Table 5.9
XOR Function Truth Table

Bit 1	Bit 2	Bit 1 XOR Bit 2
0	0	0
0	1	1
1	0	1
1	1	0

Rotate/Shift

The three instruction types just described, AND, OR, and exclusive-OR, perform bit-by-bit logical operations between two 8-bit words. In addition, the logical group contains instructions to move the bits within a byte. The two primary forms of this operation are the **rotate** and the **shift** functions. The 8085 does not provide a shift instruction; however, it does provide two forms of rotate in two directions. We will first discuss the rotate operation.

The **rotate left** instruction, for example, for the 8085,

RLC

causes each bit in the accumulator to move to the next higher-order location. The MSB is rotated back to the now-vacant LSB position; it is also moved into the CY-flag bit. This operation is shown in Figure 5.2. For the 8085 no operand is required since rotate instructions affect only the A-register byte. Some processors allow addressed rotate—or shift—operations. Only the CY-flag is affected.

Rotate right in the 8085 is initiated by the RRC instruction. Here the LSB is rotated around to the most significant position and the CY bit. This instruction and the other two rotate instructions (RAL and RAR) are also shown in Figure 5.2. The RAL and RAR instructions cause the rotate operation to include the CY-flag in the rotation path. They are the "rotate through carry" instructions.

If the upper or lower bit is not rotated back to the opposite end of the byte, we have the general form of a shift instruction. A shift left generally causes a zero to be entered into the LSB, with the MSB being passed into the carry flag. The old value of the carry flag is lost. The 8085 does not directly support the shift operation.

The 8085 can mimic the shift function by performing a rotation through carry with the carry bit preestablished at zero. The result is a

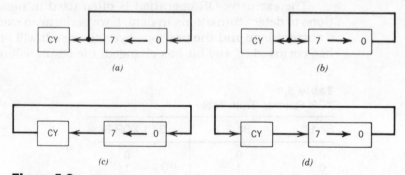

(a)   *(b)*

(c)   *(d)*

Figure 5.2
Rotate Operations: (*a*) rotate left (RLC); (*b*) rotate right (RRC); (*c*) rotate left through carry (RAL); (*d*) rotate right through carry (RAR).

multiplication or division by two. The shift left causes a multiplication by two; if an overflow occurs, it is carried into the carry bit. The shift-right operation causes a division by two with any remainder appearing in the carry bit.

Compare Instructions

The **compare instructions** may at first appear to be of minor value. In reality, they often provide the keystone of computer decision-making operations. As will be discussed in the next chapter, most decision instructions cause one or another result based on the status of the various flags. To select a particular option based on a byte reaching a given value, we might subtract the byte from the value and make the decision based on the status of the zero flag. If the byte and the value are the same, the zero flag will be set; if not, it will be a zero. There can be difficulty because the subtraction causes one of the words to be lost, the one originating in the accumulator. The compare instructions set the various flags as though a subtraction had occurred without actually completing the subtraction. The only states affected are the flags.

For example,

    CMP B

The contents of the B-register are compared with the contents of the A-register. The Z-flag is set to one if the contents are equal; the CY-flag is set to one if the contents of A are less than the contents of B—the equivalent of a borrow. The other flags are also affected as though a subtraction had occurred.

All 8085 compare instructions are performed using the accumulator with the other byte selected, as usual, based on the addressing mode used. The CMP M instruction is the indirect addressing form; the CPI causes an immediate compare operation.

Other Operations

The 8085 instruction set includes three other operations that may or may not be available with other processors. None of the three affects any flags—other than the carry—or requires an operand. The first operation is

    CMA

This causes the bit-by-bit complement of the accumulator with no flags affected. The other two operate on the carry flag only. To complement the carry flag, use

CMC

To set the carry flag, use

STC

Whichever microprocessor is used, the programmer should study such miscellaneous instructions. They are often provided to take advantage of various processor characteristics or to overcome limitations.

EXAMPLE 5.5 Transfers, Arithmetic, and Logic

The program fragment given here illustrates the action of some of the preceding instructions. This block of code would not be used as shown, for it can be greatly simplified and made useful with various branch instructions. Since the rotate instruction provides multiplication by powers of two, we can show that F0 divided by 0F, hexadecimal, is 16, decimal. We do this by repeated multiplication of 0F by two, until the two numbers are equal. Since it takes four of these multiplications, the ratio must be 2^4, or 16.

The A- and B-registers are loaded with immediate data, and the C-register is set to zero. A series of compare, rotate, and increment instructions cause the accumulator to be multiplied by sixteen before the compare instruction sets the zero flag.

Note that a CMC instruction is required because each compare will cause the CY-flag to be set. Without the CMC instruction, this flag would be rotated into the accumulator.

The status of each critical register and the Z-flag for the points in the source code marked with step names are shown below the source code. Diagrams such as this are sometimes valuable in developing very complex routines.

```
    ;   LOGICAL OPERATIONS DEMONSTRATION
    ;
    ;   PERORMS A SIMPLE APPROXIMATION TO A DIVISION
    ;
        ORG     2000H       ;SDK-85 RAM LOCATION
    ;
        MVI     B,0F0H      ;DIVIDE F0 HEX
        MVI     A,0FH       ;BY 0F HEX
        MVI     C,0H
        CMP     B           ;A-REG BIGGER THAN B-REG?
    ;   STEP 1  IF ZERO FLAG SET → FINISHED
        CMC
        RLC                 ;X2
        INR     C           ;1ST TIME
        CMP     B           ;TEST
    ;   STEP 2  IF ZERO FLAG SET → FINISHED
        CMC
        RLC                 ;X4
```

```
        INC   C        ;2ND TIME
        CMP   B        ;TEST
;       STEP 3  IF ZERO FLAG SET → FINISHED
        CMC
        RLC            ;X8
        INC   C        ;3RD TIME
        CMP   B        ;TEST
;       STEP 4  IF ZERO FLAG SET → FINISHED
        CMC
        RLC            ;X16
        INC   C        ;4TH TIME
        CMP   B        ;TEST
;       FINISH  IF ZERO FLAG SET → FINISHED
;
```

The results of executing the program are

Register Contents

	A	B	C	ZERO FLAG
STEP 1	00001111	11110000	0	0
STEP 2	00011110	11110000	1	0
STEP 3	00111100	11110000	2	0
STEP 4	01111000	11110000	3	0
FINISH	11110000	11110000	4	1

As it stands, this fragment would not be used by itself. However, it does demonstrate how we might use the various manipulation instructions to derive data and to set up the flag registers so that critical decisions can be made.

EXERCISES

5.1 Derive the equivalent decimal numbers from the following 8-bit binary words interpreted, in turn, as unsigned binary, two's complement signed binary, and BCD numbers:

(a) 01101001   01110110
(b) 10010011   00101000
(c) 10001000   10000111
(d) 00000000   11111111

5.2 Perform the following operations using unsigned binary number representation:

(a) 103 + 27
(b) 67 + 118
(c) 105 − 94
(d) 56 − 19
(e) 452 + 241

5.3 Perform the following operations using two's complement signed binary number representation:

(a) −105 + 94
(b) −56 + 19

(c) 103 − 27
(d) 67 − 118
(e) 632 − 756

5.4 Perform the following operations using BCD number representation. Do this as the 8085 would do it, that is, perform the binary operation and then apply the required adjustment.

(a) 34 + 52
(b) 19 + 27
(c) 75 − 42
(d) 81 − 39

5.5 Determine the number that is in the A-register after execution of each of the 8085 instructions in the following sequence:

(a) MVI A,13H
(b) ADI   41H
(c) DAA

5.6 Write an 8085 assembly language routine to perform the following arithmetic operation, using two's complement signed binary numbers:
−56 + (−27)

5.7 Determine the result of performing the AND, OR, and XOR operations, using the following pairs of hexadecimal numbers. Express the results in both binary and hexadecimal formats.

(a) AE and 14
(b) 2B and 8F
(c) 37 and 48
(d) A5 and 5A
(e) 00 and AA
(f) FF and AA

5.8 Determine the number that is in the 8085 A-register and the state of the carry, zero, and parity flags after each instruction in the following sequence has been executed.

(a) MVI A,9EH
(b) MVI B,A4H
(c) RLC
(d) ANI C2H
(e) ORA B

5.9 Determine the decimal equivalent of the operations in Example 5.1 if the numbers are assumed to be in two's complement form.

5.10 Determine the decimal equivalent of the operations in Example 5.2 if the numbers are assumed to be in unsigned binary format.

CHAPTER SIX

TRANSFER OF CONTROL AND PROGRAMMING TECHNIQUES

6.1 INTRODUCTION

The idea of computer decision making was introduced in Chapter One. One of the great powers of modern computers is their ability to adapt their operation based on input data or computed information. The function, the "transfer of control" introduced in Section 4.4, is implemented by instructions that shift execution to alternate routines. The shift may be such that it always occurs, or it may be based on internal data. This chapter introduces these instructions in detail, as well as several miscellaneous types of instruction.

With these last instruction categories, we will have discussed the major classifications of machine instructions. We will also have mentioned all the 8085 instruction set. The final sections of this chapter provide an overview of the process of software development. It is included here as a summary of techniques for using the software tools that have been introduced.

6.2 JUMP OPERATIONS/LABELS

Unconditional Jump

A **jump** instruction is used to break normal sequential program execution. The program counter (PC) usually steps one by one through instructions in memory. When a jump instruction is encountered, execution is moved to another part of the program. This is done by replacing the two bytes in the PC with the address of the start of the new routine. The processor is thus forced to fetch the contents of this new location for its next instruction. The PC-register is then incremented, as usual, through the new part of the program. This process is virtually universal for microprocessor program branching. What follows will highlight the details of the 8085's jump operations so that specific examples can be presented.

The new address for execution is included in the instruction statement for many control transfer instructions. For example,

    JMP   20B3H

causes the contents of the 8085's PC to be changed to 20B3, hexadecimal. The old address in the PC is lost. The microprocessor then fetches and executes the instruction at 20B3 where program execution will continue. If this instruction were located at 2000, hexadecimal, the machine code instructions in 2000, 2001, and 2002 would have been

    2000 . . . . C3
    2001 . . . . B3
    2002 20

C3 defines the operation; B3 and 20 define the new PC contents in the standard low-order, high-order address format. The PC is incremented to 2003 when the 20 is fetched. The execute cycle changes the PC to the new address 20B3. The old PC address pointer, 2003, is lost; 2003, hexadecimal, would have been the next instruction fetch address had the PC not been changed.

This 8085 instruction causes a branch to the new routine under all conditions when it is encountered. It is called as an **unconditional jump** instruction. The conditional jump instructions will be introduced shortly.

Labels

The address shown in the assembly language jump instruction operand can be, as just indicated, the direct address of the new routine. However, this address may not be known until the assembly process is completed. When first writing the program, a programmer will almost always use a substitute term, a label, for the address, at least until the specific address can be determined. Although labels are generally used for manually assembled programs, they are almost always used for programs assembled by software assemblers. If the instruction shown were branching to a routine that checks exhaust temperature, for example, we might label the new routine "EXTEMP." The jump instruction would be

    JMP   EXTEMP

We must now attach the label to the proper routine. Upon assembly, each line of the program is given an address, and each line has provision for a label, as discussed in Chapter Four. The label is the first group of characters of the assembly language instruction. Assembler programs often assume that the first space encountered defines the end of the label; if the first character is a space, they assume no label is present. If the new routine starts with an immediate load of the A-register, the first instruction of this routine might be

```
EXTEMP   MVI   A,0FEH
```

The program now looks like

```
         .
         .
         JMP   EXTEMP
         .
         .
EXTEMP   MVI   A,FEH
```

The assembler, manual or automated, will first calculate the address of the EXTEMP instruction and then insert this address into the machine code for the jump instruction.

Labels are used extensively to identify blocks of code. They are also used to give convenient, meaningful names to specific data or to data storage addresses.

Conditional Jump

The unconditional jump instruction just introduced will always branch to the address contained in the instruction. The more flexible jump instructions are from the **conditional jump** group. They cause the processor to branch to a new routine only if a specific condition is satisfied; otherwise, the PC is not changed and execution continues with no branch occurring.

The conditions that may be specified are generally determined by the state of the various flags in the processor flag register. Table 6.1 shows conditional jump instructions for the 8085. Each processor family has its own set of conditional jump parameters. The state of these flags is determined by the operations that have occurred before the conditional jump instruction. It is very important to note that the flags are changed only for certain instructions. The programmer must take care to verify that the flags are established properly before a conditional jump is executed.

Table 6.1
Conditional Jump Instructions

Op Code	Condition	Flag Status
JNZ	Not zero	Z=0
JZ	Zero	Z=1
JNC	No carry	C=0
JC	Carry	C=1
JPO	Parity odd	P=0
JPE	Parity even	P=1
JP	Plus	S=0
JM	Minus	S=1

Table 6.1 shows the power of the conditional jump instructions. For example, the zero flag test allows us to change the computer's operation when two values become equal. We perform a CMP instruction to set the flags as though the two values had been subtracted; we then test to see whether the zero flag is set. If the conditional test is passed, the processor changes the PC and the new routine is performed. If not, the processor does not branch. JZ and JNZ allow an interesting variety of other branching options. We can see that the tests for the C-, P-, and S-flags also provide a number of useful branch conditions. We can test for the relative sizes of various stored numbers or inputs, for bit-mapped data, for overflow conditions, and so on.

A typical conditional jump instruction is

```
TEST    JZ    INTEMP
```

This instruction, labeled TEST, is read "Jump to INTEMP if zero flag is set; otherwise continue." It causes the next instruction to be fetched—by changing the PC-register—from the address associated with the label INTEMP only if the zero flag is set; otherwise, the next sequential instruction after the JZ will be fetched, without changing the PC.

EXAMPLE 6.1   Short Delay

When a microcomputer is interfaced to other equipment, a real-time delay must often be provided. For example, a microprocessor-based traffic light controller needs to provide time delay intervals for the required timing of the light changes. Because each machine instruction takes a known amount of time to be executed (typically a few microseconds), it is possible to provide a specific time delay by repeating a known set of instructions a number of times. By changing the number of repetitions, we can change the time delay.

Shown here is a short routine that uses a conditional jump instruction to establish a delay loop. The routine is labeled SDLY. The delay length is loaded first. The F5 is hexadecimal for 245. The loop will be repeated 245 times before control is passed on to the next part of the overall program. The two-instruction routine, labeled LOOP, is the actual delay operation. This loop is repeated until the conditional jump instruction, JNZ, is not satisfied. This occurs when the C-register has been counted down to zero.

```
;
;   SHORT DELAY ROUTINE
;
        ORG    2080H    ;SDK-85 RAM
;
SDLY    MVI    C,0F5H   ;245 TIMES AROUND
LOOP    DCR    C
        JNZ    LOOP     ;MORE
;
```

To compute the delay time for this routine, we must know the time required for each instruction. Table 6.2 lists the 8085 instruction set, along with delay information. Each instruction requires a number of clock cycles. The SDK-85 uses a 6.144-megahertz clock. After an internal frequency division by two in the 8085, this clock yields a clock period of 325.5 nanoseconds. The crystal frequency, and hence this clock time, is very accurately controlled. Microprocessor routines can thus be used for very well-controlled timing functions.

The clock cycles required for each instruction are listed in Table 6.2. The table also provides the specific instruction times for the SDK-85. The 8085 in the SDK-85 processes certain instructions faster than the older 8080. These times should not be used for 8080, Z80, or other systems, even though they have similar instruction sets.

Figure 6.1 is a detailed computation of the time required to complete the short delay routine shown in this example. We simply add up the total number of clock cycles required for the routine.

6.3 SUBROUTINES

Often a task or computation in a program will be repeated many times over. Rather than the programmer's having to repeat the code for the task each time it is used, provision is made for use of subroutines, which were referred to in Chapter 4. A subroutine is a section of code designed to perform a subtask and then return control to the main instruction sequence. A subroutine execution, called a subroutine call, must allow two critical functions: a transfer of control to the subroutine, and a way to return control back to the original routine, called the calling routine.

Not only do subroutines save program memory, avoiding repeated uses of code, but they provide the opportunity to construct a program

Table 6.2
8085 Instruction Times[a]

Mnemonic	Cycles	SDK-85	Mnemonic	Cycles	SDK-85
DATA TRANSFER			ANA M	7	2.28
			XRA M	7	2.28
MOV r1,r2	4	1.30	ORA M	7	2.28
MOV M,r	7	2.28	CMP M	7	2.28
MOV r,M	7	2.28	ANI	7	2.28
MVI	7	2.28	XRI	7	2.28
MVI M	10	3.26	ORI	7	2.28
LXI	10	3.26	CPI	7	2.28
STAX	7	2.28	RLC	4	1.30
LDAX	7	2.28	RRC	4	1.30
STA	13	4.23	RAL	4	1.30
LDA	13	4.23	RAR	4	1.30
SHLD	16	5.21	CMA	4	1.30
LHLD	16	5.21	STC	4	1.30
XCHG	4	1.30	CMC	4	1.30
			DAA	4	1.30
DATA MANIPULATION					
INR r	4	1.30	**CONTROL TRANSFER**		
DCR r	4	1.30			
INR M	10	3.26	JMP	10	3.26
DCR M	10	3.26	Jcc	7/10	2.28/3.26
INX	6	1.95	PCHL	6	1.95
DCX	6	1.95	CALL	18	5.86
ADD r	4	1.30	Ccc	9/18	2.93/5.86
ADC r	4	1.30	RET	10	3.26
ADD M	7	2.28	Rcc	6/12	1.95/3.91
ADC M	7	2.28			
ADI	7	2.28	**OTHER OPERATIONS**		
ACI	7	2.28			
DAD	10	3.26	PUSH	12	3.91
SUB r	4	1.30	POP	10	3.26
SBB r	4	1.30	XTHL	16	5.21
SUB M	7	2.28	SPHL	6	1.95
SBB M	7	2.28	IN	10	3.26
SUI	7	2.28	OUT	10	3.26
SBI	7	2.28	EI	4	1.30
ANA r	4	1.30	DI	4	1.30
XRA r	4	1.30	NOP	4	1.30
ORA r	4	1.30	HLT	5	1.63
CMP r	4	1.30	RIM	4	1.30
			SIM	4	1.30

[a]Conditional instruction times are given as "not true"/"true."
SDK-85 times are in microseconds (6.144-megahertz clock), r is a single-byte register, cc a conditional test.

using convenient sections that can be written and tested independently and then collected together to perform the overall task. Most modern, large-scale assembly language programs are designed according to this building-block approach.

Outside loop (start): MVI   0.00228 ms
Loop: DCR r   1.30 μs
     Jcc   (true)   3.26 μs

                   4.56 μs $\times$ 244 1.113 ms
     DCR r   1.30 μs
     Jcc   (not true) 2.28 μs

                   3.58 μs   0.00358 ms
                   Total   1.12 ms

Figure 6.1
Delay Calculation.

The two primary instructions provided by the 8085 to **call** a subroutine and **return** from it are

CALL nnnnH

and

RET

where nnnnH is the two-byte starting address of the subroutine. The return (RET) instruction is the last instruction to be executed in the subroutine. It returns control to the calling program at the instruction following the CALL instruction. As may be apparent, the call to the subroutine is generally made using a label in assembly language. The assembler—either the manual or the software assembler—first determines the address of the subroutine's start. This address is placed following the subroutine call in the machine code.

In operation, the microprocessor must remember the address of the calling location for the subroutine. This is done in the 8085—and in most microprocessors—by using the stack. In the 8085 the stack amounts to a group of free memory storage locations addressed so that the last byte stored is the first byte returned. When the 8085 sees a subroutine call, it places its current PC address (both bytes, high byte first) on the top of its stack, as shown in Figure 6.2.

The figure shows the address of the subroutine call instruction, CD, to be HHL2. The PC holds this address at the start of the operation. Because CD is a three-byte instruction, the next instruction address is HHL5. This address is pushed onto the stack. At the start, the SP is pointing at a 16-bit address, sp. After the address HHL5 is pushed onto the stack, the new SP value is sp-2. Since the object code has ll and hh as the two bytes following the subroutine call, the instruction causes the PC to be changed to this address—remembering that the address is given in low-byte, high-byte format. After the call, the PC is pointing at the address of the subroutine, the stack has the return address, and the SP is set to accept new data.

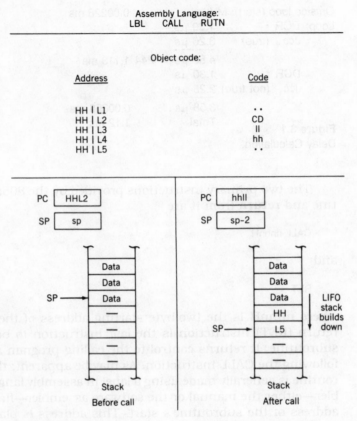

Figure 6.2
Subroutine Call (8085).

Whenever a return instruction is executed, the process is reversed. The PC-register is loaded with the contents of the top of the stack—two bytes. Operation is thus returned to the main program. A return from the situation of the figure places HHL5 into the PC and sp back into the SP.

Both the call to a subroutine and its return can be made *conditional* with the 8085. The conditions are the same as those used for the conditional jump instructions. For example,

    CPO   PODD

causes control to be passed to the subroutine labeled PODD if the parity flag is zero—odd parity. A conditional return might be

    RM

This causes a return—PC set to the top two bytes of the stack—if the sign flag is a one.

EXAMPLE 6.2 Long Delay

The routine shown here provides a much longer delay than the one in Example 6.1. Sixteen-bit arithmetic allows the loop to be repeated up to FFFF, hexadecimal, which is over 65,000 times. In addition, the routine of Example 6.1 is called each time the loop is executed. The combination of the MOV and the ORA instructions allow the 16-bit word in the DE-pair to be tested for zero. If any bit in the DE-pair is a one, the zero flag will not be set by the ORA operation. To show the possible options provided in the 8085 instruction set, we have established the return/loop decision here by using a conditional return with an unconditional jump back to the loop.

```
;
;       LONG DELAY ROUTINE
;
        ORG    2000H    ;SDK-85 RAM LOCATION
;
LDLY    LXI    D,18E3H  ;6,371 TIMES AROUND LOOP
NEXT    DCX    D
        CALL   SDLY     ;SHORT DELAY . . . USES C-REGISTER
        MOV    A,D      ;TRICK TO TEST FOR ZERO IN DE
        ORA    E
        RZ              ;FINISHED
        JMP    NEXT
;
```

In a large program we might adjust the delay parameter of the short-delay loop so that it produces, when inserted into the long-delay routine, a specific delay, say one millisecond. The delay parameter of the long-delay routine could be set to different values in different applications in the program. A 4-second yellow-light delay call might use a delay parameter of 4000—0EA0, hexadecimal. A 30-second green light might then require 30,000—7530, hexadecimal. The next topic, parameter passing, allows the calling program to establish the parameters used in a subroutine.

Parameter Passing

The two delay routines just discussed established the delay count parameter within the routine itself. If we establish this value in the calling program, the delay subroutine becomes a variable delay. For example, the short delay of Example 6.1 sets this count in the first instruction. If the calling routine were to fix the C-register before calling SDLY, the calling routine could specify the delay of the subroutine. The subroutine becomes, after adjusting the labels,

```
SDLY    DCR    C
        JNZ    SDLY
        RET
```

The process is called **parameter passing**. Free memory can also be used for parameter passing. This allows huge amounts of data to be passed to a subroutine. If we use a memory location pointed to by the HL-pair to pass the delay parameter, our little delay subroutine becomes

```
SDLY    MOV   C,M
LOOP    DCR   C
        JNZ   LOOP
        RET
```

Nested Subroutines

It is common for one subroutine to call another subroutine and, indeed, for that subroutine to call a third. The LIFO stack always ensures that the correct return address comes up with each return. Calling a subroutine from a subroutine is termed **nesting**. The depth of nesting is limited only by the memory available to the stack. Such limitations generally occur when the stack overwrites, or is overwritten by, other storage. If the stack location is carefully established, deep subroutine nesting is rarely a problem for processors similar to the 8085.

Some microprocessors use a limited stack located on the microprocessor IC itself. This allows fast stack operations, along with other advantages. However, such stacks are generally very limited in size. When such devices are used, the programmer must be cautious about the depth of subroutine nesting.

6.4 OTHER OPERATIONS

Other instruction types that are commonly provided for microprocessors are discussed in this section. For completeness, we also round out the 8085 instruction set.

Stack Operations

The stack can be used for parameter storage. This is done with **stack push and pop**, sometimes called **pull**, instructions. Most microprocessors have some form of these instructions. For the 8085, either a register pair or flag and accumulator data can be pushed. For example,

    PUSH B

causes the BC-pair to be pushed into the stack. The contents of the B-register are placed in the memory location pointed to by the SP minus one—SP – 1. The C-register byte is placed in SP – 2. The SP is decremented by two.

A similar instruction for the 8085 is

PUSH PSW

This puts the contents of the accumulator into the next stack location, followed by the contents of the flag register. As usual, the SP is decremented by two.

The POP instructions reverse the process. For the 8085,

POP   B

exactly reverses the process just described for the PUSH B. In a similar fashion,

POP   PSW

returns the accumulator and flag data and increments SP by two.

These stack operations may be used to manipulate address data that the CPU has saved in the stack at a subroutine call. More commonly, they are used for saving register data during a subroutine. This technique is called "status saving." Before a subroutine call, any critical register data are pushed into the stack; the calling program then pops these data after the return instruction. When control is returned to the calling program, the status is thus restored.

An alternate, and generally better, status-saving technique is to ensure that all subroutines push the registers at the start of subroutine processing, popping them just before the return. This technique is preferred because it saves code; the subroutine need save only the register data it would otherwise destroy, and only one set of pushes and pops is required.

The stack is not used as often for parameter passing to subroutines because the calling address information is also pushed into the stack. Finally, the stack is commonly used as temporary storage in manipulation and computation routines.

The 8085 HL-pair can be exchanged with the top two bytes in the stack, using

XTHL

The SP value is not changed. The current stack top at location SP is exchanged with the contents of the L – 1-register. The contents of the H-register are exchanged with the byte one step down the stack (SP + 1).

Finally, microprocessors with free memory stacks similar to the one in the 8085 generally require an instruction that establishes the location of the stack. The 8085 instruction moves the contents of the HL-pair to the SP:

SPHL

Free memory stacks do not always require such instructions. The 6502, for example, simply dedicates page 1 (addresses 01XX, hexadecimal) to the stack.

Input/Output

The 8085 and a number of other microprocessors provide specific locations for I/O data. The hardware implications of this feature will be discussed in later chapters. For the programmer, this I/O-mapped I/O gives a group of locations—256 locations for the 8085, numbered zero to 255—that can provide the CPU with data or can accept output data from the CPU. An example of an 8085 input instruction is

IN 6AH

The byte at I/O location 6A, hexadecimal, is moved to the accumulator. To copy the accumulator byte to this location, we would use

OUT 6AH

Miscellaneous

A standard microprocessor instruction is the **no-operation** command. The CPU simply does nothing during the execute cycle. The 8085 no-operation instruction is often used to provide a short delay:

NOP

Almost all microprocessors provide for hardware interrupts. Interrupts will be discussed in detail in Chapter Nine. An external hardware interrupt signals the CPU that some event has occurred that requires the processor to perform some action. Most microprocessors provide instructions that **enable** or **disable** interrupt processing. The 8085 interrupt enable instruction is

EI

Logically, the disable interrupt instruction is

DI

The 8085 instruction set, which we have used for examples, is identical to the 8080 instruction set, except for two additional operations.

Any 8080 program will run on the 8085. If one of these special 8085 operations is contained in a program, the program will not run on the 8080; otherwise it will. The 8085 is said to be software-upward-compatible with the 8080. The two new instructions are the RIM and the SIM, which deal with the interrupt mask and serial I/O; they will be discussed in Chapters Seven and Nine.

The 8085 has two transfer of control instructions that were not discussed previously. The first of these is a **restart** instruction. It pushes the current PC onto the stack. The PC is changed to a number that is eight times the instruction's operand. Thus,

RST 6H

causes control to be passed to location 48 (30, hexadecimal). Again, this instruction is used primarily for interrupt processing. It will be discussed in detail in Chapter Nine. It is mentioned here only to indicate that it is part of the instruction set.

The 8085 also allows an **indirect jump** operation. The address for the jumped is determined during execution of the program and is stored in the HL-pair. This instruction, which moves the contents of the HL-pair to the PC, is

PCHL

Finally, the 8085 allows the processor to be stopped. The fetch/execute cycle is halted, with no registers affected. The instruction is

HLT

This completes the 8085 instruction set. Some of the more advanced instructions will be discussed in later chapters.

6.5   PROGRAMMING TECHNIQUES

Software engineering is a study worthy of a great deal more development than we can provide here. However, any serious look at microprocessor systems should at least touch on good programming practice.

The objective of software design techniques is to develop machine code that works as desired and that does so efficiently; second, this process should be performed quickly and accurately. The design process in a professional environment often involves updating, modifying, or maintaining existing software. Because of this, the design of much modern software must ensure not only efficiency in the coding but also flexibility and maintainability of the software.

The instruction sets of today's microprocessors are very carefully designed to allow efficient code to be developed for a problem at hand. The techniques discussed here are intended primarily to yield software that is readily usable with few errors. They tend to produce software that can be reused for other purposes or updated quickly as requirements change. The cost is that these techniques produce code that is often slightly slower or slightly larger than is absolutely required. This cost is small compared to the gains in development time, fewer errors, and maintainability that these techniques yield.

As usual, we approach this study as though an 8085 assembler were being used. Software that is manually assembled should be designed using the same techniques, although the format need not be as rigid.

Documentation

Good **software documentation** is a must. Documentation refers to comments, notes, and other information added to the program or kept as reference material. It provides the programmer with design and structure information. Other subjects related to documentation, such as labeling techniques, are also discussed in this section.

Documentation should be developed along with the program itself. Each step in the development process requires design decisions that must be documented for later reference.

Requirements   The specific definitions of the requirements for the program are determined. This includes system details, I/O definitions, data format information, timing constraints, and so forth.

Structure   The form of the program must be determined. This may be as simple as direct, line-by-line processing with no subroutines or loops for very simple tasks, or as complex as multiple-level modularized programs with extensive subroutine nesting. At this stage the documentation tasks include defining the allocation of tasks, setting up memory maps in general form for data and software, and defining data formats and parameter-passing structures.

Coding   Coding is the actual setting down of the software. Each of the required tasks is detailed in assembly language code. Much of the detailed documentation is created here. Good software often has many more lines of comments than actual machine instructions.

Testing   The finished program will rarely work as required with no corrections. In the process of debugging a complex program, the software documentation may get its first real use. The program is generally checked in parts. Each section is verified and corrected as necessary. The documentation provides the **benchmarks** against which this debugging is done. For example, the programmer may verify that a subroutine actually passes the required parameters in the proper locations. During the testing stage, empirical data may be developed and documented. They might include timing information or memory requirements. The finished program is tested against its initial requirements.

Maintenance The finished program may be updated from time to time to add new features, correct minor errors, or make various improvements; it may even be extensively redesigned. In a professional environment, this is often done by various programmers over time. The documentation is very valuable here. Software that is poorly documented is difficult to maintain, and undocumented software is essentially impossible to maintain.

Embedded documentation—documentation contained as comments in the source code itself—is critical to clarity. The rule is that the code and documentation together should be brutally clear. The comments should explain the purpose or function of the code in the context of the program's structure. At the start of a subroutine, the comments should define the parameter passing both into and out of the routine. The routine's purpose should be briefly described and data that are lost during the routine noted.

Documentation should not repeat the message of the mnemonics. The reader of the documentation is assumed to be very familiar with the mnemonics. A very poorly documented version of the long-delay routine in Example 6.2 would be

```
LDLY    LXI     D,18E3H    ;LOAD 18E3 HEX INTO D
NEXT    DCX     D          ;DECREMENT D
        CALL    SDLY       ;DO SDLY
        MOV     A,D        ;PUT D INTO A
        ORA     E          ;E OR'ED WITH ACCUMULATOR
        RZ                 ;IF ZERO, RETURN
        JMP     NEXT       ;OTHERWISE JUMP BACK TO NEXT
```

All these words do no good at all. A better version might be

```
;
;
;
;**** LDLY *****
;
; → LONG-DELAY ROUTINE ←
;
;   YIELDS A FIXED DELAY OF XXXX SECONDS FOR EACH LOOP COUNT
;   A, C, D, E, AND FLAG DATA LOST
;
LDLY    LXI     D,18E3H    ;6,371 TIMES AROUND LOOP
NEXT    DCX     D
        CALL    SDLY       ;SHORT DELAY . . . USES C-REGISTER
        MOV     A,D        ;TRICK TO TEST FOR "0" IN DE
        ORA     E
        RZ                 ;LONG DELAY COMPLETED
        JMP     NEXT
;
;
;
```

Clever coding tricks shoud be avoided unless they can be easily described in the comments. It is generally better to use a few more bytes of memory or a few more microseconds of execution time than to produce undecipherable code.

Break long routines into small functional blocks that are documented individually. When a long routine is broken into blocks, the blocks should be separated physically with white space—blank lines. Moreover, extensive use of jump instructions should be avoided. They can make the program confusing, leading to greater numbers of programming errors.

Labels should be used extensively. They should be as clear and meaningful as possible, particularly those associated with major blocks of code. Labels used for references over short distances within a routine may be more cryptic. A good approach is to use a very descriptive label to identify a major routine and simpler, but related, labels within the routine. For example, a sorting routine might be labeled SORT, whereas the internal labels might be SRT1, SRT2, and so forth.

Data and data storage locations should also be labeled. If a program puts data on a digital-to-analog converter (DAC, discussed in Chapter Eight) in several places and if the DAC is located at I/O location 5C, do not use OUT 5CH to send data to the port each time. Define the term DAC to be 5C as a label and use the instruction OUT DAC for transferring data to the DAC. When the code is read later, the term DAC will be understood. A 5C has little meaning in itself.

These label references for addresses and data should be clearly defined at the start of the program. Many large programs have pages of these label definitions, called **equates.** If, long after the program was written, the DAC is moved from location 5C to location 5D, only the one label in a known location needs to be changed. Without the use of labels, a number of I/O instructions would have to be found and changed. If the label definition were buried in the program, the programmer would have to search through pages of code to find it.

A storage location is labeled using the equate, an assembler directive. A typical equate might be

```
DAC    EQU  5CH    ;DAC I/O-MAPPED OUTPUT LOCATION
```

Again, the comment is critical for later understanding. Here the comment tells us that this is really a DAC and that it is an I/O-mapped output, rather than a memory-mapped output.

Modular Design

Modular program design takes the concepts just introduced one step further. Program modules are developed and tested independently. When individual operation is verified, the modules are connected together either in sequence or, more often, with various subroutine calls.

A common technique is to use **utilities,** which are routines developed to perform standard functions. Various arithmetic functions are often developed as utilities, such as multiplication or division utilities or multiprecision arithmetic utilities. Many programmers develop a repertoire of commonly used utilities which can be added as required to modular programs. Sets of standard utilities are often purchased commercially.

As long as reasonable care is used to interface the modules carefully and to document them well, modular design generally produces programs that can be debugged more easily than would normally be true. The modules can be debugged individually; the task of troubleshooting is thus reduced to a series of small steps. The programmer is not faced with a large program that may have a number of interrelated errors.

Special assemblers, the macroassemblers, support modular programming. They allow modules to be inserted into a program by referencing a single label. When large, complex programs are being written, these assemblers can be quite valuable.

Modular program design is often extended to a somewhat more formal process called "**top-down programming.**" The overall task is divided into a distinct set of major subtasks. The main program is then written to call major subroutines which are to perform the subtasks. The subtasks are then treated as unique programs and, perhaps, broken again into smaller units. The process is thus one of dividing the effort, from the top down, into smaller units until the specific program modules can be written.

Top-down techniques have a number of advantages. If the programmer is careful with documentation, he or she produces a very ordered and maintainable program. The software can usually be debugged step by step as the overall program is written. This is possible because the main structure of the program exists from the start. With the program clearly divided into major tasks, updates can be performed with a minimum of difficulty.

Today most programs are developed using elements of various techniques. A very common approach for large programs is to use top-down techniques with stock utilities, when they are available. Small programs are sometimes developed in one block with no modularization at all.

Flowcharts

A flowchart is a diagram used to display the details of control transfer and data flow in a program. Flowcharts have been used for many years to document complex program functions. They can be used to communicate the details of a program to others. They are also valuable in the development of complex software.

Through the years a standard set of symbols has been developed for use in flowcharts. These symbols are shown in Figure 6.3. Because flowcharts are often used for communication, it is wise to follow these standards.

Figure 6.4 is a flowchart of the long delay routine from Example 6.2.

EXAMPLE 6.3 Data Conversion

In some applications memory-mapped input data are present in a range of memory locations. For example, an input keypad often loads data into an input buffer. These data are then available to the CPU. It may be necessary to modify the format of the data for use elsewhere.

This example uses a number of the 8085 instructions to translate a block of input data into other formats. The code moves the data to other storage locations for later use.

We assume that locations 20B0 to 20BF, hexadecimal, contain the input data that are contained in a table of ASCII decimal numbers. The end of the table is marked by the byte FF, hexadecimal. In other words, the ASCII numbers start at 20B0 and end when an FF is encountered, or at 20BF, whichever occurs first. The ending character is called a **delimiter**. The program must translate these ASCII numbers to straight binary numbers, which are to be stored at 20A0, hexadecimal. The program must also translate the numbers to BCDs, which must be stored in another table starting at 2080, with the end of the table marked by the value F, hexadecimal. Of course, two of the binary numbers form one BCD byte.

The format for this program will be used throughout the rest of this

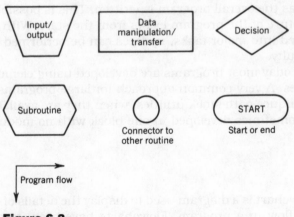

Figure 6.3
Flowchart Symbols.

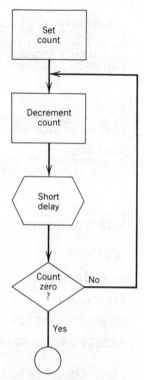

Figure 6.4
Flowchart from Example 6.2.

text. The first part of the program is devoted to equates, the assembler directives that define any important labels for constants and data storage areas. The first instructions set the starting location for code, establish the stack, and jump the CPU to the main part of the program which follows the equates.

The main body of the program calls any utility subroutines that are placed after the main loop. Finally, the stack is established an adequate number of memory locations past the end of the last subroutine. The code ends with the END directive.

Programmers use many different formats for assembly language source code. We use this format because of its relatively direct flow of code, its ease of hand assembly, and its ease of maintenance. Later we will discuss variations when we must consider RAM versus ROM allocation, start-up and reset requirements, as well as other memory management issues.

```
ORG     2000H       ;SDK-85 RAM
LXI     SP,STACK
JMP     MAIN
   .
   .
   .
```

```
        ;EQUATES
INPUT    EQU   20B0H        ;LOCATION OF INPUT ASCII NUMBERS
FULL     EQU   20BFH        ;LAST POSSIBLE INPUT LOCATION
BINARY   EQU   20A0H        ;BINARY RESULT STORAGE LOCATION
BCD      EQU   2080H        ;BCD RESULT STORAGE LOCATION
EOD      EQU   0FFH         ;END OF DATA DELIMITER
;
;
MAIN     LXI   H,INPUT      ;POINT TO INPUT
         LXI   D,BINARY     ;POINT TO BINARY OUTPUT START
         LXI   B,FULL       ;LAST INPUT STORAGE LOCATION

MAIN1    MOV   A,M          ;NEXT ASCII
         SUI   30H          ;CHANGES ASCII TO BINARY
         XCHG               ;STORE BINARY OUTPUT
         MOV   M,A
         XCHG
;
         CPI   EOD          ;LAST?
         JZ    STOP         ;STOP BASED ON EOD
;
         CALL  DONE         ;FULL?
         JZ    STOP         ;YUP
;
         INX   H            ;POINT TO NEXT
         INX   D
         JMP   MAIN1        ;LOOP AGAIN
;
STOP     MOV   B,D          ;RESET FILL LIMIT FOR BCD FILL
         MOV   C,E
         LXI   D,BCD        ;RESET POINTERS FOR BCD FILL
         LXI   H,BINARY

STOP1    MOV   A,M          ;LOAD LOW-ORDER BCD BYTE
         XCHG
         MOV   M,A
         XCHG
;
         CALL  DONE         ;FINISHED?
         JZ    FINI         ;YUP
;
         INX   H            ;LOAD HIGH-ORDER BCD BYTE
         MOV   A,M
;NEXT TWO ARE REQUIRED FOR THE SHIFT OF THE NIBBLE TO THE FOUR
;HIGH BITS OF THE BCD FORMAT
         CMP   A            ;TRICK—CLEARS CARRY FLAG
         ANI   0FH          ;ZEROS TOP FOUR BITS—YIELDS 0000XXXX
;
         RAL                ;SHIFT NIBBLE
         RAL
         RAL
         RAL
;
         XCHG               ;PLACE NIBBLE IN UPPER MEMORY BCD SPOT
         ORA   M
         MOV   M,A
         XCHG
;
         CALL  DONE         ;FINISHED?
         JZ    FINI         ;YUP
;
         INX   H            ;NEXT
         INX   D
         JMP   STOP1
;
```

```
FINI      RST   1             ;SDK-85 RETURN-TO-MONITOR INSTRUCTION


;***********************SUBROUTINES***************************
;DONE
;CHECKS 16-BIT ADDRESS IN HL VERSUS LIMIT IN BC
;RETURNS WITH FLAG ZERO SET IF HL = BC
;A-REGISTER AND FLAG DATA LOST

DONE      MOV   A,H           ;16-BIT COMPARISON—HL VS BC
          CMP   B
          RNZ   MAIN2         ;NOT FINISHED YET
          MOV   A,L
          CMP   C
          RET

;************************************************************
;
          DS    10H           ;16-BYTE STACK SPACE
STACK     END                 ;STACK STARTS HERE - 1
```

The equates define the key parameters for the program, followed by the main loop, which first sets internal registers as memory pointers to the input data, the binary table, and the top of the data table. At MAIN1, which is labeled for later use, the program gets the first ASCII character from the input list. The simple subtraction of 30, hexadecimal, from the ASCII-coded decimal number converts it to binary. The next two instructions store the number in the binary table.

The program then checks to see whether it is finished by comparing the current byte to EOD. At assembly, EOD will be changed to the value in the equates, FF. If the current character matches EOD, the JZ instruction causes a transfer of control to the code at STOP. Let us assume that this does not happen at this time.

The next instruction calls the subroutine DONE. DONE will return with the zero flag set if the HL- and BC-pairs have the same values stored in them, that is, if the input pointer has reached the end of the table labeled FULL. Therefore the JZ instruction will cause a jump to STOP if we are finished. Again, let us assume that the branch does not occur.

The next three instructions move the pointers to the next byte and return the CPU to MAIN1 for another byte. The end address then becomes the old value from the binary pointer. This is the last valid binary byte location.

When an exit occurs from the main loop, control is passed to STOP. Here the pointers are set to point to the binary and BCD table starting locations. The next instruction directly loads the first binary byte into the BCD table. After a check for the end of the data, the INX instruction moves only the binary pointer to the next number. The next BCD location is the upper nibble of the current address.

The program uses the RAL instruction to move the latest byte to the upper nibble. For this to work we must make sure that the carry flag is zero and that the upper nibble of the data byte is zero. The latter will always happen except for the EOD delimiter byte. After the number has been moved to the upper nibble, an ORA operation places it into the proper byte, which is stored.

The BCD fill routine ends with an incrementing of the pointers and a check for the end of the table. FINI has the instruction required to return to the SDK-85 monitor.

The subroutine is straightforward. It simply compares HL and BC on a byte-by-byte basis. The stack is only used for the subroutine call. Two bytes would have been adequate. We have provided 16 bytes to allow for growth. The object code requires 56 bytes of storage, excluding the stack and table storage areas.

EXERCISES

6.1 Find the final contents of the A-register after the following assembly language program fragment has been run:

```
        MVI   A,0FFH
LAB1    DCR   A
        JNZ   LAB1
        RST   1
```

6.2 Determine the number of instructions executed in the following assembly language program:

```
        MVI   A,00H
LAB2    INR   A
        JM    LAB2
        RST   1
```

6.3 Write an assembly language program to sum together the even numbers from zero to twenty. Draw a flowchart for your program.

6.4 Manually assemble the source code from Exercise 6.3 into hexadecimal format.

6.5 Modify the program of Example 6.1 to provide for parameter passing.

6.6 Write a properly documented assembly language program that produces a delay by incrementing a register until a limit is reached. Use parameter passing through RAM to establish the delay. Draw a flowchart for your program.

6.7 Modify the program of Example 6.2 to call the new program of Exercise 6.6.

6.8 Determine the parameter required to adjust Example 6.1 to provide a delay of one millisecond.

6.9 With the new delay time of one millisecond developed for the short delay, determine the delay provided by Example 6.2.

6.10 If the SP is initialized at 8000, hexadecimal, and if each subroutine does two PUSH operations, how deep can subroutines be nested before the stack fails? The memory map is filled with RAM from 7500 to 7FFF, with ROM above and below this range.

6.11 Modify the code of Example 6.3 as follows:

(a) Use location 3400, hexadecimal, for input data with up to 256, decimal, bytes of data. You must also move the BCD and binary result tables. Memory from 3000 to 33FF is open for this purpose.

(b) Use DD, hexadecimal, as a delimiter.

(c) Add all the input numbers together and end with this value in the DE-pair.

CHAPTER SEVEN

DIGITAL INPUT AND OUTPUT

7.1 INTRODUCTION

Computers have often been described as digital devices in an analog world. Although this may be true in the most general sense, all I/O of the CPU itself is digital in nature. In addition, much of the communication is inherently digital in that it involves transfers between digital devices. Examples of this include communication between computers, data from a keyboard, output to digital display devices, such as video terminals along with a number of other I/O interfaces. Therefore, the subject of I/O naturally breaks into two parts: digital I/O, for which the designer establishes a link with inherently digital devices; and analog I/O, which the designer must interface with nondigital devices. This chapter discusses digital I/O; Chapter Eight is devoted to analog I/O.

This chapter first reintroduces the basic I/O interfaces with the CPU. These were touched on earlier and are always digital in nature. The chapter then discusses the two major classes of digital I/O, parallel and serial.

7.2 CPU I/O INTERFACE

If we were to observe the voltage on a single data bus line of a microcomputer, the scene would be one of chaos. The line would change state about every microsecond, with a single bit of an instruction, a data word, or, possibly, an address flashing by. This would be interspersed with short periods during which no device is driving the line and the voltage floats to some intermediate level.

Internally, the flow of data is orchestrated by the timing and control section of the CPU. External devices rarely have the ability to find valid

133

output data because they are not synchronized with the CPU timing. Furthermore, if an external device were to drive data onto the bus without regard to proper timing and address conditions, it would probably damage parts of the microcomputer. Clearly, a standard **interface** between the CPU and external devices is required.

The I/O interface for a microcomputer generally brings a single byte into or out of the machine. The device that performs this interface is called a **port**. A port may handle only input, an **input port**; only output, an **output port**; or both, an **I/O port**. The direction always refers to the flow of data to or from the microcomputer in question. If data are transferred out of a microcomputer, we use an output port, even though the data may be used as input elsewhere.

A port can provide an interface that looks very much like a normal microcomputer memory address. As we have mentioned earlier, a port may be designed to reside at a given memory location, with all the normal address decoding and control bus interfaces. This is the memory-mapped I/O scheme that is available for any microcomputer system. The I/O process is quite simple. If the program directs the CPU to bring in data through a memory-mapped port, the CPU will set up the address bus with the address assigned to the port and fix the control bus lines for a transfer into the CPU. The port's address decoding and control bus interface will signal the port to drive the input word onto the data bus at the proper time. The machine instruction is a normal load-from-memory operation, such as the 8085's LDA instruction. For the internal hardware and for the machine's software, this appears to be a normal memory operation. For the environment outside of the microcomputer, however, the operation is one of transfering data into the computer.

Memory-mapped output is similar in operation, the program instruction used being a normal store-in-memory type such as the 8085's STA.

Memory-mapped I/O is quite common. Some microprocessors, such as the 6502, use this type of I/O exclusively. The popular Apple II computer uses the 6502 and devotes over a page of memory to each of its eight interface slots. Another popular version of memory-mapped I/O, which also happens to be used in the Apple II, has normal RAM in the memory-mapped locations. This RAM is made into I/O by special circuits that monitor the contents of the RAM without interfering with normal CPU operation. This amounts to a window on the mapped RAM. The most popular use of this scheme is for memory-mapped video.

Memory-mapped I/O has certain disadvantages. One is simply that such I/O schemes take up system memory. This is generally not a significant problem. Even if several hundred memory-mapped I/O locations are used, this is a small fraction of the total 65,536 locations available to a basic microprocessor such as the 8085. A greater disadvantage is that a single memory-mapped I/O device can complicate memory allocation and decoding.

Modern RAM devices provide system memory in large blocks. A common configuration for a 64K-byte memory is eight chips, each having 64K-bit addresses. These eight devices, in parallel, form a continuous block 64K bytes long. Because we never allow two input devices to reside at the same location, not only must any memory-mapped input port have address decoding to turn it on, but it must have the ability to turn off RAM when its address is called. We are faced with using more RAM devices in smaller blocks or more bus glue to direct input from a port. Finally, with memory-mapped I/O, the I/O ports must have decoding for the whole address bus range in use since the ports occupy only discrete address locations in the memory map.

To assist the designer when some of these difficulties arise, certain microprocessors allow I/O-mapped I/O. Here two alternate address spaces are established. One is designated for normal memory, including memory-mapped I/O, if desired; the other is designated as I/O space. The programmer specifies I/O-space-versus-memory-space transfers by using special I/O instructions, for example, the IN and OUT instructions for the 8085. A specific pin on the microprocessor—the IO/$\overline{\text{M}}$ pin on the 8085—tells the memory and I/O ports which is being accessed. Thus, if the 8085's I/O$\overline{\text{M}}$ pin is low, normal memory calls are processed. If this pin is high, the I/O devices must decode the address lines to determine the active device; the system memory is told to remain idle. Because I/O data transfers are initiated by program instructions, I/O-mapped I/O techniques are sometimes termed programmed I/O.

With I/O-mapped I/O, the I/O space is almost always much smaller than the memory space. For the 8085, 64K of memory is addressable using the sixteen address lines. I/O is allocated only eight address lines (the 8-bit I/O space address is placed on both the upper and the lower bytes of the address bus) for a total of 256 possible ports. The I/O space is thus less than one-half of one percent the size of the address space. However, 256 ports are generally more than enough. Another example is the 8086, which has a basic memory address space of 1024K bytes (one megabyte) and an I/O space of 64K bytes.

EXAMPLE 7.1   I/O-Mapped I/O

This example demonstrates the typical simplifications in memory management and addressing that I/O-mapped I/O can provide. Suppose we wish to design a microprocessor system having 8K of RAM, 8K of ROM, and four I/O ports. If we place the RAM as shown in Figure 7.1, it will use the first thirteen address lines (address lines 0 to 12) to select one byte out of its 8K total. A one on the next address line (called number 13 in the range of 0 to 15) can be used to select the RAM. This line is zero for addresses 0 to 1FFF, hexadecimal; it is a one for addresses 2000 to 3FFF,

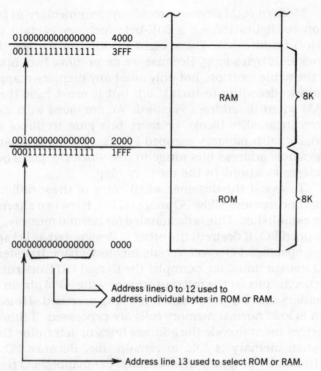

0100000000000000 4000
0011111111111111 3FFF

RAM } 8K

0010000000000000 2000
0001111111111111 1FFF

ROM } 8K

0000000000000000 0000

→ Address lines 0 to 12 used to address individual bytes in ROM or RAM.

→ Address line 13 used to select ROM or RAM.

Figure 7.1
Memory Map for Example 7.1.

hexadecimal. It is also a one for other ranges in higher memory—6000 to 7FFF, A000 to BFFF, and E000 to FFFF. We are not using these ranges, so no harm comes from this multiple addressing.

The 8K ROM also uses the lower 13 address lines for internal addressing and is selected when the RAM is not selected, that is, when address line 13 is a zero. The memory address decoding is quite simple. Each major block uses the minimum number of address lines to decode its internal locations, and the number 13 (starting at zero) address line is used as a select between ROM and RAM. ROM is in locations 0000 to 1FFF, hexadecimal; RAM resides in locations 2000 to 3FFF, hexadecimal. Figure 7.2a shows this simple address scheme without I/O.

If four memory-mapped I/O ports are added to this memory system, additional logic must be included. There is no place in memory that is not being addressed as our design now stands. All locations in upper memory above RAM are addressed by either RAM or ROM calls. Additional devices are required to provide memory addressing for this I/O. If we add logic, we can prevent the ROM or RAM from being addressed when the address line 14 is high. Figure 7.2b shows a method of doing this. The truth table for

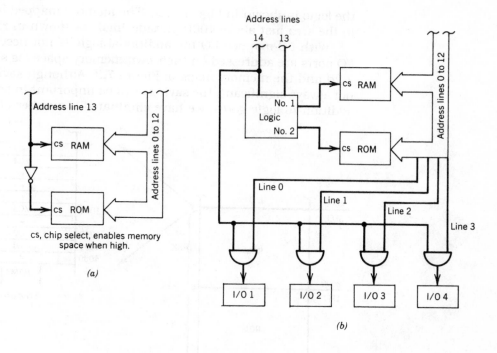

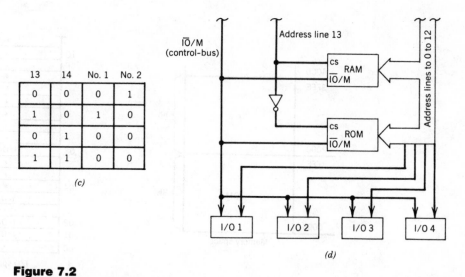

cs, chip select, enables memory
space when high.

(a)

(b)

13	14	No. 1	No. 2
0	0	0	1
1	0	1	0
0	1	0	0
1	1	0	0

(c)

(d)

Figure 7.2
Memory-Mapped and I/O-Mapped I/O for Example 7.1: (*a*) memory address decode with
no I/O; (*b*) memory address decode with memory-mapped I/O; (*c*) logic truth table for
part *b;* (*d*) memory address decode with I/O-mapped I/O.

the logic is shown in Figure 7.2c. The memory-mapped I/O would reside in the area just above 4000, hexadecimal, as shown in Figure 7.3a.

With I/O-mapped I/O the additional logic is not necessary since the I/O ports are addressed on their own memory space, as shown in Figure 7.2d and the memory maps of Figure 7.3. Although saving this logic is not always significant, the savings can be important in small systems. In addition to logic gates, we have eliminated a number of hardware con-

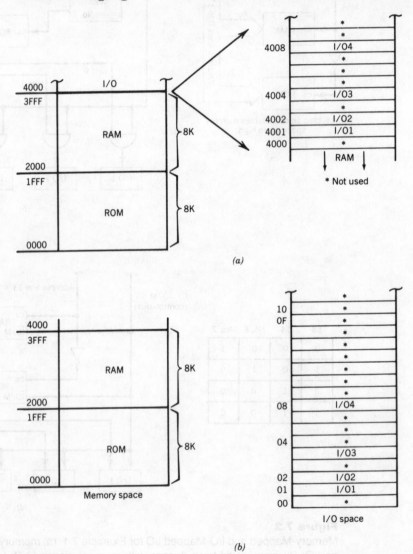

(a)

(b)

Figure 7.3
Memory Mapping for Example 7.1: (a) memory-mapped I/O; (b) I/O-mapped I/O.

nections by using I/O-mapped I/O. However, we have assumed more complex I/O devices designed for I/O-mapped I/O.

I/O-mapped I/O can be useful; however, it is not generally critical that it be available. Whole families of very powerful microprocessors—the 6502, as mentioned earlier, and the 16- and 32-bit 68000 family of microprocessors—do not provide this feature.

7.3 PARALLEL PORTS

In its simplest form, a **parallel port** amounts to the I/O interface that we have been describing. An output port presents the contents of the data bus as output whenever it is addressed and a write operation is indicated. It is said to latch the data off the bus. The input operation moves the data from the outside world onto the computer's data bus whenever the port is addressed and a read operation is requested by the CPU. Almost all the I/O operations that will be discussed in this and the following chapters use such a parallel port. The port may be buried in a much more complex device.

The following example illustrates the use of a simple parallel port.

EXAMPLE 7.2 Simple Output Port (8212)

We will deviate slightly from our normal process of using for illustration devices designed around the 8085. The 8085 devices are more complex than simple parallel ports and will be discussed later. Here we describe the Intel 8212 I/O Port, which is part of the 8080 family. It can be used with the 8085 if desired.

Figure 7.4 shows the pinout of the 8212. The data output (DO) pins are three-state outputs. The function of the chip is to latch the data present on the data input (DI) pins when required; on command, at some later time, it presents the latched data actively at DO. The device includes several control functions that allow for proper timing of the data transfers. It also includes interrupt processing logic.

Application of the 8212 as a simple output port is shown in Figure 7.5. The mode (Md) input is tied to a logic one to set the device's internal operation for this output mode. The three-state output drivers will now always be turned on, transmitting the internal latch data to the outside world. The 8212 DI lines are attached to the microcomputer's data bus. Its DO lines are used externally as output from the microcomputer.

For this output port the address decode logic drives the device select (DS) inputs whenever the CPU dictates that valid output data for this port are present on the data bus. Through the use of the control bus, the

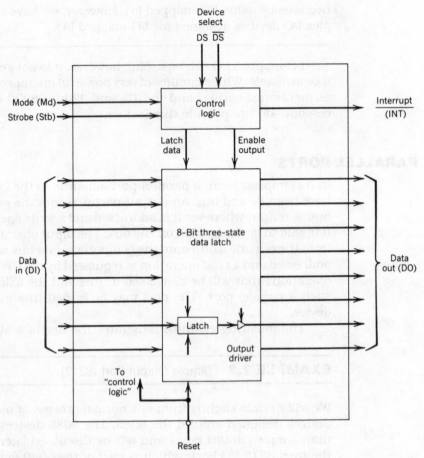

Figure 7.4
I/O Port (8212) for Example 7.2.

address decode design determines whether this is to be I/O-mapped I/O or memory-mapped I/O and the exact timing of the output operation. The decode logic also determines the port's specific address. Notice that the 8212 requires two DS inputs, DS and $\overline{DS}$. These inputs must be a one and a zero, respectively, for a device to be selected. In the timing discussion that follows, assume that $\overline{DS}$ has been fixed at logic zero so that DS alone controls device selection.

The microprocessor's data bus must remain stable with the valid output data for the time required for the 8212 to complete its latching operation. Within, at most, 25 nanoseconds of the rise of the DS signal, the 8212 will latch the bus data to the port's output. We must therefore keep the DS signal at a logic one for at least this 25 nanoseconds to ensure that the output operation will be completed. The actual appearance of the data at the output may take as long as 40 nanoseconds. The

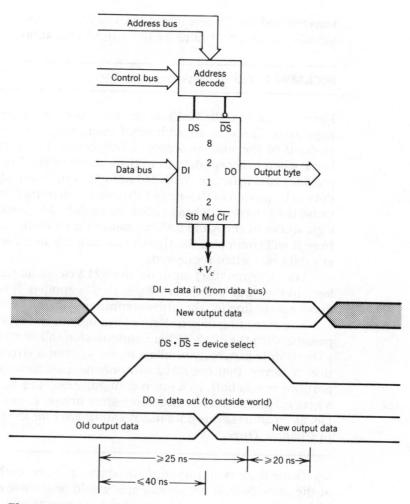

Figure 7.5
Output Operation for Example 7.3.

8212 requires no more than 20 nanoseconds to latch itself after the DS input falls to a logic zero. Therefore, the data bus must remain stable for at least 20 nanoseconds after the fall of the DS input.

The DS and $\overline{\text{DS}}$ lines work together to cause device selection in the 8212. The device is selected when the DS line is at a logic one and the DS line is at a zero. If the decode logic design is simplified by the use of inverse logic, we can simply tie the DS input to a logic one and use $\overline{\text{DS}}$ as the device selection input with a logic zero indicating selection. Additionally, we can use both DS inputs. For example, the $\overline{\text{DS}}$ line might be forced to a zero when the address decoding indicates that this port is being selected and the DS line might then be made a one when the control bus signals the proper timing for the output operation.

EXAMPLE 7.3   Simple Input Port (8212)

Figure 7.6 shows the 8212 as an input port. Here the Md line is tied to logic zero. There is an additional complexity. Not only must the port respond to the microprocessor's bus commands properly, but it must know when to accept data from the outside world. The strobe (Stb) input provides this function. With Md at logic zero, a one at Stb causes the DI data to be passed to the output three-state drivers. A logic zero at Stb will cause the internal latches to hold the DI data. Meanwhile the device select logic works in the same fashion as discussed earlier for the output port. Here it will command the three-state outputs to drive the microcomputer's data bus when requested.

The clear-not (Clr) input on the 8212 clears all the latches and other logic in the 8212 whenever a logic zero is applied. It is normally tied to a master reset line for the microcomputer system.

The preceding discussion applies only to two types of I/O operations possible with the 8212. Other configurations allow an output port to have a three-state capability or allow input without a strobe requirement. Notice, however, that the 8212 can only be used as an input or an output port but not as both in a given configuration. The 8212 is often used as a general-purpose latch and three-state driver. It can be used, for example, as an address bus/data bus demultiplexer for the 8085, as mentioned in Chapter Three.

Some devices can be configured as a port for both input and output at the same time. A simple example would be the use of two 8212 devices in inverse parallel, that is, two tied to the same address, one as output and one as input. A write or an I/O output command (such as STA or OUT for the 8085) would excite the output side of such a port. In turn, the port's address decoding would be set up to direct an input operation whenever a read or an I/O input command occurs. More complex devices integrate the input and output port functions into one component. These devices can often be configured for specific applications by use of special commands from software. Such programmed devices will be discussed in more detail later in this chapter.

Handshake Techniques

In its simplest form, digital I/O amounts to nothing more than the latching operation just discussed. However, additional communication

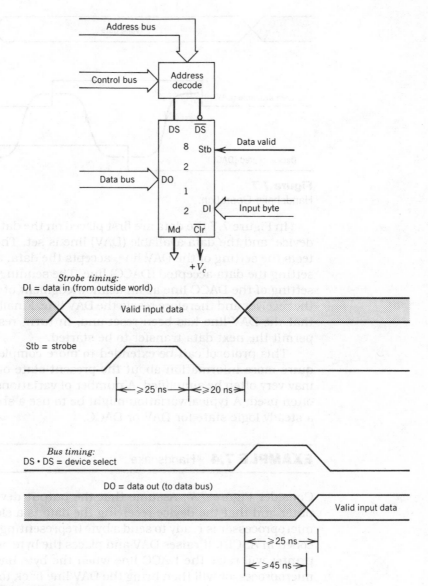

Figure 7.6
Input Operation for Example 7.4.

schemes are often used. For some applications it is necessary to synchronize the transfer of data between the microprocessor port and an external device. This synchronization is accomplished by means of some sort of handshake procedure. A **handshake** transfers the status of a communication process. The overall procedure is termed a protocol. A typical handshake protocol is shown in Figure 7.7.

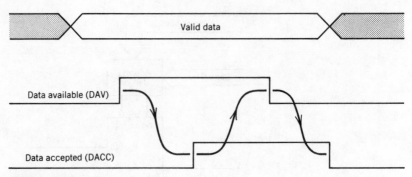

Figure 7.7
Handshake Operation.

In Figure 7.7 the data are first placed on the data lines by the sending device, and the data-available (DAV) line is set. The receiving device detects the setting of the DAV line, accepts the data, and then responds by setting the data-accepted (DACC) line. The sending device interprets the setting of the DACC line as an acknowledgment of receipt of the data by the receiver and therefore resets the DAV line. Finally, the receiver detects that the DAV line has been reset and, in turn, resets the DACC line to permit the next data transfer to be started.

This protocol can be extended to more complex operations that require more information about the present state of the data transfer. It may very often be simplified. A number of variations are possible and are often used. A typical variation might be to use a short pulse rather than a steady logic state for DAV or DACC.

EXAMPLE 7.4 Handshake

Consider Figure 7.7. Assume that the output device is our microcomputer and that the device receiving the data is a slow printer. When the microprocessor is ready to send a byte (representing a printable character coded in ASCII), it raises DAV and places the byte on its output port. The printer will raise the DACC line when the byte has been accepted. The microprocessor will then bring the DAV line back to zero, indicating that the output port no longer has valid data. When the printer has finished printing the character, it will pull DACC back to ground and the microprocessor, sensing this, will be allowed to transmit another byte.

Another type of printer handshake illustrates how this general procedure might be extended. This interface adds a busy line that is high any time the printer cannot accept data for any reason. The DAV logic state is replaced with a strobe pulse. Thus, if busy is low, the microprocessor will produce a short pulse—say 5 microseconds long—telling the printer to accept the data on the output port. The DACC signal is replaced with an acknowledge pulse, which the printer returns when the byte has been received.

The hardware for a handshake operation is usually implemented as a port dedicated to the handshake with a second port dedicated to data transfer. Since each of these ports can be controlled by the CPU, the actual handshake protocol is established in the software coding. A very flexible system design is thus possible; the hardware is designed to place an I/O port at some specific location, with the handshake ported at another address. The software controls the entire system operation. It determines the data for I/O and the complete handshake procedure. The system can be changed from one configuration to another without any changes in the hardware.

Programmed Devices

Powerful I/O devices are possible using **programmed I/O** device techniques. These general-purpose I/O devices are designed to attach to the microcomputer bus. Such a port will often have two addresses. One of these addresses is the normal I/O-mapped or memory-mapped data transfer address; the other is a special command/status address. By sending a specific byte to this command/status address, the microcomputer can configure the programmed I/O device in a specific fashion. This command byte is normally bit-mapped. Each bit in the command byte establishes one particular function in the I/O port. For example, one bit might fix a port as output, whereas another might establish a certain kind of handshake.

These programmed I/O devices often provide status data. The most common implementation is for the microcomputer to request a read from the command/status address. The programmable I/O device will then return a bit-mapped word, indicating the status of the I/O operation. Examples of such status bytes might be the state of the handshake—whether the port is ready to accept another byte, or whether any new input data have arrived.

Large and complex programmed I/O devices are very popular. The details of their operation vary greatly from device type to device type. As usual, our example uses a device from the 8085 family.

EXAMPLE 7.5 Programmed I/O (8755)

We will use the Intel 8755 introduced in Chapter Three as an example of a programmed I/O port. In Chapter Three we discussed its use as an EPROM. The following discussion also applies to the 8355, which is the

masked ROM version of this device. Figure 7.8 repeats Figure 3.5 and
shows the pinout and block diagram of the 8755. The address, data, and
control bus connections are similar to those used for the EPROM. The
hardware connection of the port to the outside world is provided on pins
24 through 39. The control bus uses IO/$\overline{\text{M}}$ or one of the lines $\overline{\text{IOR}}$ or
$\overline{\text{IOW}}$ to select the I/O port rather than the EPROM.

If I/O has been selected, the port presents four usable addresses, as
shown in Table 7.1. These addresses are specified through the use of the
two lower address lines, AD_1 and AD_0. The addresses of the two ports are

PIN CONFIGURATION **BLOCK DIAGRAM**

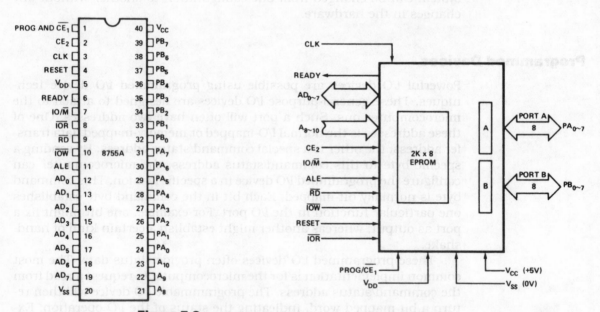

Figure 7.8
8755 Pin Configuration and Block Diagram. (Reprinted by permission of Intel Corporation, copyright © 1980.)

Table 7-1
8755 Internal Addressing

AD_1	AD_0	Function
0	0	Port A
0	1	Port B
1	0	Port A programming
1	1	Port B programming

00 and 01, and 10 and 11 are used to address the programming locations for ports A and B.

The 8755 I/O ports are programmable as either input or output. Each bit is programmable within a port. Therefore, either port can be used for input or for output; in addition, a given port can have some of its pins configured as input and the others dedicated to output. The programming is done by passing a bit-mapped word to the port's programming address. A zero at a specific bit location of a programming command will establish the associated port's bit to be input; a one will fix the port bit as output. These direction commands are stored by the 8755 in data direction registers (DDRs), one for each port. The DDRs cannot be read. If we attempt to read either programming address of the 8755, no meaningful data will result.

Figure 7.9 shows the effect of DDR programming on a single bit of port A. Suppose a programming command that directs this bit to be output is applied. Suppose, in addition, that the port had previously been established as input by either a reset or an earlier programming command. When the output programming command is received, the DDR latch will change state to a one and the output three-state driver will present the current contents of the output latch to the I/O port pin. Any subsequent change in the contents of the output latch will be reflected as output until the bit is reprogrammed. Note that we may send output data and a bit programming command in either order; however, if we first

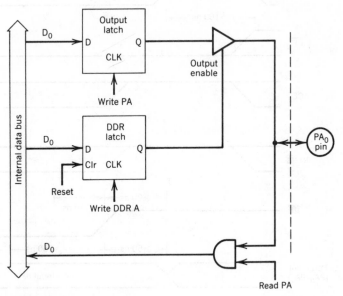

Figure 7.9
Single-Bit Model for 8755 I/O.

program the bit as output, the current contents of the output latch will appear first, before our desired output bit.

When a bit is programmed as input, the output driver is turned off and an input command simply brings the bit from the outside world onto the data bus. Note that if we request an input from a bit programmed as output, the current output state of the port bit will be returned.

Figure 7.10 is an example of the microprocessor interface for the Intel 8755. It shows the timing required for an input operation using the $IO/\overline{M}$ line to direct the 8755 to perform an I/O read. The falling edge of the ALE input causes the AD_1 and AD_0 address lines to be brought into the 8755 along with the chip enables—address decoding outputs that select this particular chip—and the $IO/\overline{M}$. The $\overline{RD}$ line then directs that an input operation is to occur, and the data are driven onto the data bus.

EXAMPLE 7.6 Printer Interface Program

Assume that an 8755 is to be used to implement a printer handshake similar to that mentioned in Example 7.4. Assume that the normal data-

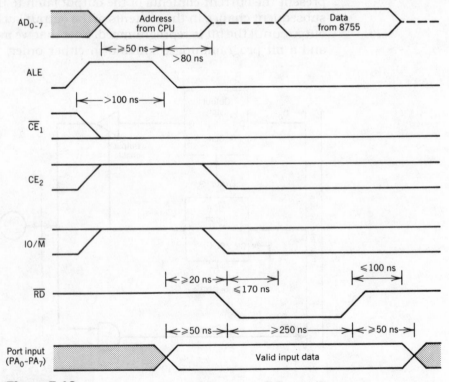

Figure 7.10
8755 Input Port Timing. (Reprinted by permission of Intel Corporation, copyright © 1980.)

available and data-accepted lines are used along with a busy line. When the busy line is a one, the printer cannot be accessed. The address decoding and control bus interface are designed to place the 8755 I/O as memory-mapped I/O above the memory boundary where the MSB of the address word becomes a one. Thus, the two ports, A and B, are located at 8000 and 8001, hexadecimal, respectively. The programming ports are located above this at 8002 and 8003. The following subroutine (called PTXT for print text) will direct a string of characters to the printer observing the proper protocol.

```
;EQUATES——LOCATED NEAR THE START OF THE SOURCE CODE

PRINT     EQU    8000H          ;PRINTER PORT
PRINTC    EQU    8002H          ;PRINTER PORT PROGRAMMING ADDRESS
HANDSK    EQU    8001H          ;HANDSHAKE PORT
HANDSKC   EQU    8003H          ;HANDSHAKE PORT PROGRAMMING ADDRESS
;
PTCNFG    EQU    FFH            ;PRINTER PORT CONFIGURATION
HSCNFG    EQU    01H            ;HANDSHAKE PORT CONFIGURATION
;
DAV       EQU    01H            ;DATA-AVAILABLE HANDSHAKE
DAVNOT    EQU    00H            ;DATA-NOT-AVAILABLE HANDSHAKE
DACCM     EQU    80H            ;DACC-BIT MASK
BUSYM     EQU    20H            ;BUSY-BIT MASK
;
ENDC      EQU    1AH            ;END CHARACTER—CONTROL-Z
                                —————
                                —————
                                —————
;
;PTXT
;
;PRINT TEXT STARTING AT H/L AND ENDING WITH END CHARACTER (ENDC)
;ALL INTERNAL REGISTERS ARE MODIFIED
;
;INITIALIZE:
PTXT      PUSH   H              ;H/L IS TEXT START
          LXI    B,PRINT        ;PRINTER PORT
          LXI    D,HANDSK       ;HANDSHAKE PORT
;
;CONFIGURE THE PORTS:
          LXI    H,HANDSKC      ;HANDSHAKE PORT COMMAND ADDRESS
          MVI    M,HSCNFG       ;CONFIGURE HANDSHAKE PORT
          LXI    H,PRINTC       ;PRINTER PORT COMMAND ADDRESS
          MVI    M,PTCNFG       ;CONFIGURE PRINTER OUTPUT PORT
;
          POP    H              ;TEXT OF START
PTXT1     LDAX   D              ;IS PRINTER BUSY?
          ANA    BUSYM          ;GET BUSY BIT
          JNZ    PTXT1
;
          MOV    A,M            ;NEXT CHARACTER
          CPI    ENDC           ;END OF TEXT?
          RZ                    ;YES, RETURN TO CALLING ROUTINE
          STAX   B              ;PRINT IT
;
          MVI    A,DAV
          STAX   D              ;HANDSHAKE—DATA READY
PTXT2     LDAX   D              ;LOOK FOR ACKNOWLEDGE
          ANA    DACCM          ;GET DACC BIT
```

```
            JZ      PTXT2       ;NOT ACKNOWLEDGED YET
    ;
            MVI     A,DAVNOT
            STAX    D           ;HANDSHAKE—DATA NOT READY
    PTXT3   LDAX    D           ;HAS PRINTER RESET HANDSHAKE?
            ANA     DACCM
            JNZ     PTXT3       ;NO
    ;
            INX     H           ;POINT TO NEXT CHARACTER
            JMP     PTXT1       ;HERE WE GO AGAIN
```

This code is written as though it were embedded in a much longer program. All parameters are grouped together as equates, which would be placed in the source code together with other related equates so that any later changes could be easily made.

After the equates, the program saves the HL-pair, which passes the text start address to the routine. This PUSH H operation is required because the following code must use HL for port configuration. After the configuration operations, the text address data will be popped back to HL. The code then sets the BC- and DE-pairs as memory pointers. Because the old contents are lost in this operation, the warning at the start of the routine states that the registers will be modified. The calling program must account for this by storing any valuable data prior to the subroutine call. Alternately, the subroutine could have pushed all registers onto the stack, popping them at the return.

The program next configures the ports using data from the equates.

After popping the text start pointer, the routine interrogates the handshake port and uses a logical AND to screen out the busy bit. The mask is 00100000 as established in the equate statement BUSYM EQU 20H. Thus, after the ANA BUSYM statement, the accumulator will be 00100000 if the busy bit is a one. It will be zero if the bit is a zero. The PTXT1 loop is continued until the busy bit falls to a zero.

Next, the character to be transferred is moved to the accumulator and compared with the character ENDC from the equates. This character has been set in the equates as a 1A, hexadecimal. In ASCII this is a control-Z. We see that the text is to be printed, character by character, until this ending character is encountered. If the character pointed to by the HL-pair is not 1A, hexadecimal, the RZ test will fail and the CPU will proceed to the STAX B instruction, which sends the character to the printer. If the character pointed to by the HL-pair had been 1A, hexadecimal, the RZ instruction would have returned us to the calling routine.

Through the PTXT2 and PTXT3 labels, the routine sends handshake data and looks for handshake responses from the printer. Finally, the HL-pointer is incremented to the next character, and the main body of the routine is rerun.

Since the SDK-85 does not include a printer, this routine is not directly applicable to it. With hardware additions to the SDK-85 and any necessary changes to the equates, it could be used with the trainer.

The printer interface is controlled by this software. If some element of the printer interface protocol were to be changed, the software could be changed to match it in most instances. An example might be a requirement that the DACC output be held for a minimum number of microseconds. To do this we would add a wait loop before the DACC search.

7.4 SERIAL PORTS

Serial data communication is significantly different in data transfer format from parallel I/O. Rather than transferring all the bits of a word at once over parallel lines, each bit is transferred one by one over a single line. Because fewer wires are required, serial transmission is the preferred mode for long-distance data transmission. However, for a given line quality, serial data transmission is several times slower than parallel transmission. Therefore, parallel interfaces are used for short-distance transmissions, especially where high speed is required. Serial data transfers are common for long-distance communication and are often used for shorter-distance communication when ultimate speed is not critical.

As discussed earlier, virtually all I/O operations from a microcomputer start as parallel I/O because internal data transfers are done using parallel techniques. For serial I/O the word latched off the data bus is converted to serial format within a serial I/O device. In general, such a serial I/O port will also develop any necessary serial handshake signals.

Serial Communication Formats

Serial data communication was used commonly many years before the development of the practical digital computer. This communication format is the basis for the teletype transmissions used for wire service news communication, as well as for telegraph transmission. Out of this history, fairly standard formats have been developed for serial data transfers.

The most common serial interface format is the **RS-232** convention. Here a specific electrical connector is defined, along with the function of each of the pins on the connector. In addition, various electrical requirements are defined, such as the voltage levels associated with the two logic states. The RS-232 interface allows a number of handshake lines from those that indicate the "Busy/Ready" status to lines that indicate whether a ring has occurred on a telephone line. In any given application only selected handshake lines are used. The serial I/O device connected to the microprocessor often has interface connections established specifically for the RS-232 format.

RS-232 allows for **full-duplex** data transmission, that is, it allows data to be transferred in both directions of a two-way interface at the same time. It does this by providing two active data transmission lines in addition to two sets of handshake lines. A **simplex** or a **half-duplex** communication scheme can be established using only parts of the RS-232 interface. Simplex communication allows transmission in only one direction. Half-duplex interfaces provide communication in both directions but in only one direction at a time.

A common serial communication technique uses telephone lines for long-distance transmission. Because of certain limitations, the logic signals cannot be sent directly over the telephone network. Rather, the ones and zeros must be converted to tones of distinct frequencies—one frequency for a logic one and a different frequency for a logic zero—which can then be carried on the telephone lines. The device that translates the digital data into the telephone-compatible signals is called a modulator. The device that converts these signals back is called a demodulator. The device used both to modulate and to demodulate the telephone signals is thus called a modulator/demodulator or, as commonly shortened, **modem.** Table 7.2 shows a standard format for a full-duplex modem. Notice that the full-duplex operation is achieved by using two different frequencies for the two directions of data transfer.

Serial data transfer rates are often given as baud rates. The **baud rate** of a communication channel is the rate of the fastest bit transfer. The net channel bit transfer rate is normally somewhat slower than the baud rate. This slowing occurs because some extra bits are often added to provide timing information. In very high-speed systems the transfer may also be slowed by processing delays.

Serial data must be transferred in such a way that the receiver can determine the timing of the received bits. Without some sort of timing information, the receiver could not determine the difference between one bit 10 milliseconds long, and 10 bits one millisecond long. Moreover, timing is required to ensure that bits are not evaluated during a transition from one bit to another. Finally, serial data are normally transferred in words. The timing information must allow the receiver to determine the start and stop points of these words. This bit- and word-level timing information is required in addition to any "I'm ready, are you?" handshake operations.

Of the two classes of methods for timing serial data transfers, **syn-**

Table 7.2
Standard Frequencies for Full-Duplex Modem

Direction of Communication	Frequency for a	
	One	Zero
Originate device to answer device	1270 Hz	1070 Hz
Answer device to originate device	2225 Hz	2025 Hz

chronous techniques are more direct but are probably less popular. Synchronous transfer techniques require one of the devices to establish timing signals that are communicated along with the data. These synchronous schemes require additional wires, additional communication channels, or additional modulation/demodulation processes for a modem. They are commonly used for very high-speed transfers, often in large computer systems.

The second class of serial communication is called **asynchronous** data transfer. A common form of asynchronous communication will be described here. Variations on this theme are sometimes used.

For asynchronous serial communication, the baud rate is established beforehand so that the time for the arrival of each bit is known at the outset. The data transfer then proceeds with timing information inserted into the serial data stream, as shown in Figure 7.11. The transmitting device is designed to send a steady digital one whenever the channel is idle. This is termed "**marking.**" The first one-to-zero transition signals the start of the transfer of a word. The transmitter will send one or more zero signals. These are called **start bits.** A predetermined number of data bits are sent. This is commonly a full byte, although 5-, 6-, or 7-bit transfers are also sent. Some designers add a parity bit to help detect errors. The transmitter will then send a predetermined number of ones as **stop bits.** If no new data are ready, the transmitter will continue this one signal as further marking until new data can be sent.

The total number of bits sent, both control and data, along with the baud rate, determines the total time required for a single word to be transmitted. This then determines the maximum data transfer rate, which is usually measured in data words per second. The maximum rate is simply the reciprocal of the time required to transfer a single data word. The actual transfer rate may be slower if marking states must be inserted to accommodate delays at either end of the transmission.

This start/stop-bit format allows the channel to be self-timed. Certain conditions must occur with each transmission. Many communication channels include checks to see whether these conditions are met. If they are not, an error must have occurred and steps can be taken to correct the difficulty. The most common of these tests is for parity. Any single-bit

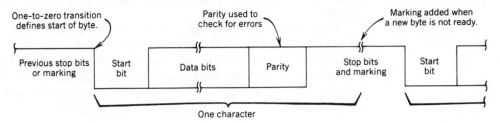

Figure 7.11
Asynchronous Data Format.

errors can be found by using a parity check. That is, if a single data zero or one is detected as a one or a zero, the error will be found.

Another common error—the **framing error**—will be detected if the stop bit is missing. The stop bit should always occur a certain length of time after a start bit, and it should always be a one. If this one is not present, the receiver has lost track of the timing, the transmitter is making some form of an error, or the received data are in error; in any case, there is a problem.

An additional common error that can be detected is the **overrun error.** Most serial communication devices have little or no receiver data memory. In addition, the receiver cannot prevent the transmitter from sending a new character. An overrun error occurs when the serial I/O device must drop data because new data arrived before the old data were transferred out of the serial receiver device.

Example 7.7, in the next section, will provide specific details of a common serial I/O port implementation.

Programmed Devices

Common serial I/O devices provide a selection of data transfer formats. The specific format is established by programming the I/O port. For example, one such device is a universal asynchronous receiver/transmitter, known as a **UART.** It allows various baud rates, various numbers of start and stop bits, and a selection of parity formats. Normally, such a device will also have a status output available. This byte will provide information about the status of the receive and transmit buffers; it will specify whether the transmitter is ready for new data or whether the receiver has new data. This status byte will also specify whether any errors have been detected. As with many manufacturers, Intel takes the idea of a UART one step further in its universal synchronous/asynchronous receiver transmitter (**USART**). Such a device can be programmed to operate asynchronously or synchronously. Beyond this selection, the specific communication protocol is also programmable. The terms UART and USART are far from universal. We use them here because they are common terms for such devices in the 8085 family.

Serial communication devices can become quite complex. An example is the Zilog Z8530 serial communications controller (SCC). It contains two programmable channels. Either of these can be used synchronously or asynchronously, with a number of protocols, at up to one megabit per second. Such programmable serial I/O devices may be as complex internally as the microprocessor itself.

EXAMPLE 7.7   Programmed Serial I/O (8251)

Figure 7.12 shows a block diagram of the 8251 USART from Intel. The 8251 is commonly used as a programmable serial I/O port for the 8085. Both the transmitter and the receiver have a buffer and a control function. The actual serial transmit line is the TxD output. The RxD input receives the serial data for the port. The transmitter ready (TxRDY) and transmitter empty (TxE) outputs are available for use either as input into the host computer or as information to the outside world regarding the state of the transmitter. The transmitter clock input ($\overline{TxC}$) is used by the USART to determine the transmitted baud rate. The receiver has a receiver ready (RxRDY) output and receiver clock ($\overline{RxC}$) input that function in a fashion similar to the transmitter signals. The receiver also has a "sync detect/break detect" (SYNDET/BD) line that is bidirectional. It is used for synchronous communication protocols.

For this example, we will assume that the status data on the TxRDY,

PIN CONFIGURATION

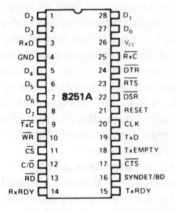

BLOCK DIAGRAM

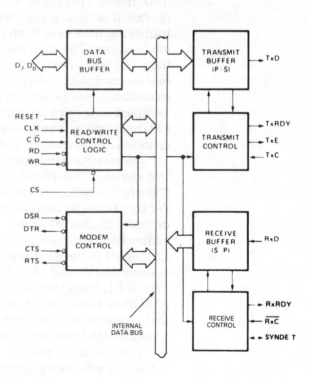

Figure 7.12
Pin Configuration and Block Diagram of the 8251 for Example 7.6. (Reprinted by permission of Intel Corporation, copyright © 1980.)

TxE, and RxRDY are not used. We will obtain the data via the programming/status port and assume asynchronous communication. The SYNDET/BD interface is thus not used.

The "modem control" block provides the key elements of an RS-232 serial interface with a modem. The four signals provided, data set ready ($\overline{\text{DSR}}$), data terminal ready ($\overline{\text{DTR}}$), clear to send ($\overline{\text{CTS}}$), and request to send ($\overline{\text{RTS}}$), are standard RS-232 handshake control lines. Notice that the functions provided are actually inverse logic. That is, a zero on the $\overline{\text{DSR}}$ line indicates that a data set ready condition has occurred. All these pins, except $\overline{\text{CTS}}$, have no direct effect on the USART. They are simply passed through to the command/status port where the CPU can use them to direct the serial handshake. The $\overline{\text{CTS}}$ input must be low, a logic zero, for the transmitter to be enabled. The handshake protocol will often use this line to disable the transmitter when the receiving device is not ready for data, thus avoiding overrun errors.

The blocks named "data bus buffer" and "read/write control logic" provide familiar bus interface lines for the microprocessor system—the normal data bus interconnects along with reset, clock, read, write, and chip select ($\overline{\text{CS}}$) inputs. In addition, the 8251 has a command/data ($\text{C}/\overline{\text{D}}$) input. This input tells the 8251 whether the current read or write operation is to be a transfer of programming command/status data or a transfer of data to or from the communication channel. Four conditions are possible. The first two conditions occur if the $\text{C}/\overline{\text{D}}$ input is driven high. If a byte is written to the port, it will accept the byte from the data bus as command information. If a read operation is requested, status information will be sent to the bus. When $\text{C}/\overline{\text{D}}$ is low, the bus transfer is assumed to involve an actual serial data transfer; data driven from the CPU by a write will be transmitted over TxD; a read operation will take the contents of the receiver buffer and place it on the data bus.

Address-decoding logic is required to establish the various chip control signals. This decoding logic must be designed to activate $\overline{\text{CS}}$ and $\text{C}/\overline{\text{D}}$ when preselected addresses are specified by the host microprocessor. For this example, assume that this logic places the data port at 00, hexadecimal, in the I/O space. This means that when the microprocessor addresses 00, hexadecimal, and the $\text{IO}/\overline{\text{M}}$ control line is low, the $\overline{\text{CS}}$ and $\text{C}/\overline{\text{D}}$ inputs to the 8251 must both be driven low by the decoding. Further, assume that the decoding has been designed to place the command/status port at 01, hexadecimal. When an I/O access—as indicated by the 8085 $\text{IO}/\overline{\text{M}}$ line—occurs at 01, hexadecimal, the decoding must now draw the $\overline{\text{CS}}$ line low to select the chip while drawing the $\text{C}/\overline{\text{D}}$ input high to indicate a command/status port selection.

The coding of the command data for the 8251 is shown in Figure 7.13a. We will discuss this coding using the following example command sequence.

A typical command sequence for the 8251 is shown in Figure 7.13b.

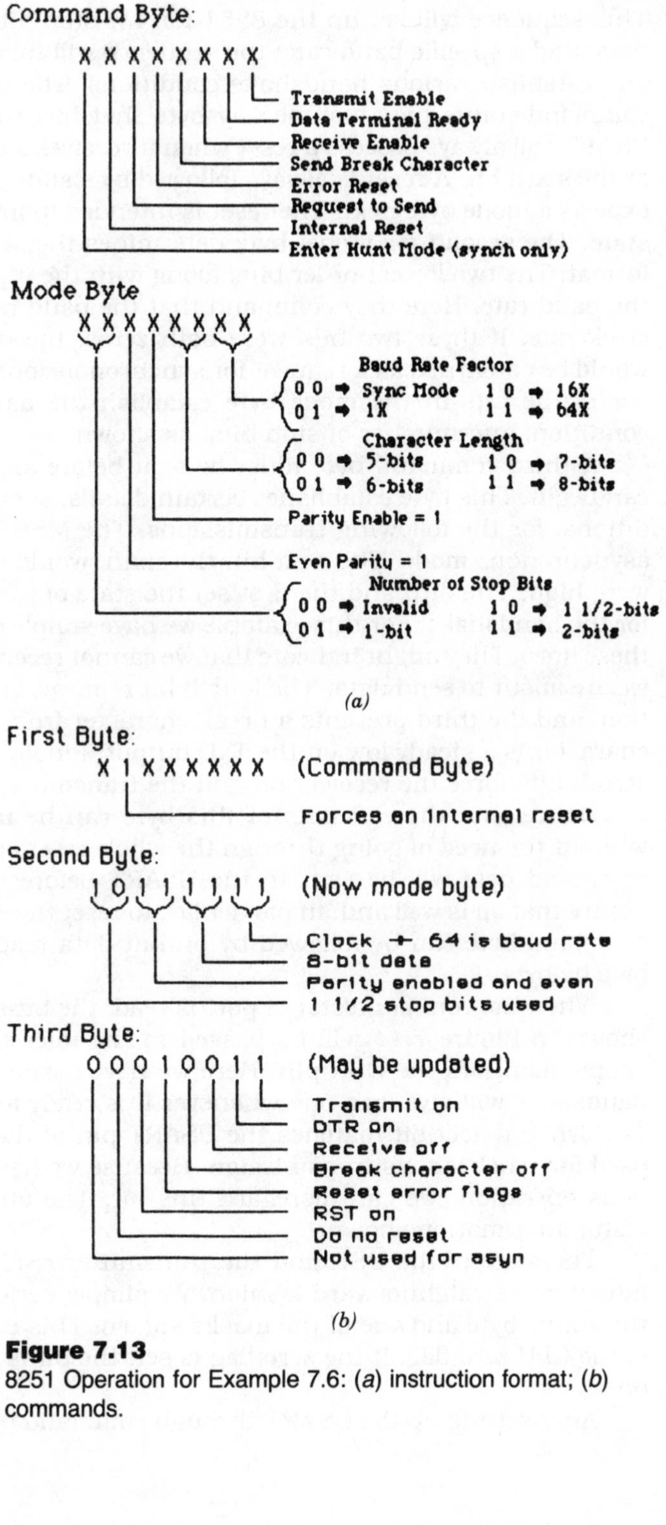

Command Byte:

```
X X X X X X X X
                  Transmit Enable
                  Data Terminal Ready
                  Receive Enable
                  Send Break Character
                  Error Reset
                  Request to Send
                  Internal Reset
                  Enter Hunt Mode (synch only)
```

Mode Byte

```
X X X X X X X X
                  Baud Rate Factor
                  0 0 → Sync Mode   1 0 → 16X
                  0 1 → 1X          1 1 → 64X
                  Character Length
                  0 0 → 5-bits      1 0 → 7-bits
                  0 1 → 6-bits      1 1 → 8-bits
                  Parity Enable = 1
                  Even Parity = 1
                  Number of Stop Bits
                  0 0 → Invalid     1 0 → 1 1/2-bits
                  0 1 → 1-bit       1 1 → 2-bits
```

(a)

First Byte:

```
X 1 X X X X X X  (Command Byte)
    Forces an internal reset
```

Second Byte:

```
1 0 1 1 1 1 1 1  (Now mode byte)
                  Clock ÷ 64 is baud rate
                  8-bit data
                  Parity enabled and even
                  1 1/2 stop bits used
```

Third Byte:

```
0 0 0 1 0 0 1 1  (May be updated)
                  Transmit on
                  DTR on
                  Receive off
                  Break character off
                  Reset error flags
                  RST on
                  Do no reset
                  Not used for asyn
```

(b)

Figure 7.13
8251 Operation for Example 7.6: (*a*) instruction format; (*b*)
commands.

This sequence will set up the 8251 for 1½ stop bits, even parity, 8-bit data, and a specific baud rate; the sequence will turn the transmitter on and establish various handshake conditions. The first byte sent to the command/status port may be any byte that has the sixth bit on. The USART will always process a reset when it receives a command with a one at the sixth bit. A reset is always followed by a state in which the USART expects a mode byte next. The reset is intended to invoke this mode-next state. The second, or mode, byte determines the serial communication format. The two lowest-order bits, along with the input clock, determine the baud rate. Here they command that the baud rate will be ¹⁄₆₄ of the clock rate. If these two bits were both zeros, the mode-byte command would be construed as a request for synchronous operation. The remainder of the bits in the mode byte establish the data word size, parity condition, and number of stop bits, as shown.

A third command byte must be sent before any data transmission can begin. This byte establishes certain details, such as handshake conditions, for the following transmissions. The MSB has no effect in the asynchronous mode. The next bit, the sixth, would reset the USART if it were high. The fifth and the first set the state of the $\overline{\text{DTR}}$ and $\overline{\text{RTS}}$ pins for the handshake. For this example we have simply picked two states for these lines. They might indicate that we cannot receive data now and that we are about to send data. The fourth bit removes any old error information, and the third prevents a break character from being sent. A break character is a steady low on the TxD output. Finally, the second and the zeroth bits force the receiver off and the transmitter on.

Notice that the elements of this byte can be updated at any time without the need of going through the whole reset operation. Often, this command byte will be sent to the USART before each output byte to assure that all is well and, in particular, to reset the error flags. The third command byte can be followed by output data ready for transmission, byte by byte.

When the command/status port is read, the bit-mapped information shown in Figure 7.14 will be passed to the microprocessor. The MSB simply monitors the $\overline{\text{DSR}}$ pin. Here we have assumed that the receiver handshake will give us a one whenever it is ready for our transmission. The synch detect bit matches the USART pin of the same name and is used for synchronous transmission. Because we have assumed asychronous operation, we can disregard this bit. The other bits provide the status information shown.

The state of the $\overline{\text{DSR}}$ and the transmitter ready bits can be determined in a straightforward fashion. We simply perform a logical AND of the status byte and one of the masks shown. This is followed by a check of the CPU zero flag. If the zero flag is set, the bit is a zero; if not, it is a one.

After setting up the USART through command port writes, we might

	D$_7$	D$_6$	D$_5$	D$_4$	D$_3$	D$_2$	D$_1$	D$_0$	
	DSR	Syn Det	FE	OE	PE	Tx Empty	Rx RDY	Tx RDY	
	Data set ready	Synch detect	Framing error	Overrun error	Parity error	Transmitter empty	Receiver ready	Transmitter ready	
8 0 =	1	0	0	0	0	0	0	0	DSR mask
0 1 =	0	0	0	0	0	0	0	1	Tx ready mask

Figure 7.14
Status Byte Format for Example 7.6.

have the program check for the proper handshake condition with a status read. This check would be made by an AND with 80, hexadecimal, followed by a check of the zero flag in the CPU. If the zero flag is found to be set, the logic state of the $\overline{\text{DSR}}$ line was zero at the time of the read, and the receiver is not ready. When the program finds that the zero flag is not set, that is, DSR is a one, it would then determine whether the transmitter is ready for more data. This would be done using the transmitter ready mask.

Once the CPU has determined that the transmitter is ready for data and that the receiver handshake is in a ready state, the data can be transferred. The transfer is initiated when the CPU sends a byte to the port. The CPU, having done this, might be instructed to gather the next byte and restart the DSR and transmitter ready search. This process would be continued until the serial data transfer is completed.

Programmable serial I/O devices are generally used in a fashion similar to that described in Example 7.7. The manufacturer's data sheets should be consulted for specifics of other devices.

8085 Serial Port

The 8085 contains a very simple serial port, which is composed of two pins on the device. Pin 5, named SID, for serial input data, forms the serial input port. Any time the RIM instruction is performed, bit 7 of the accumulator will be loaded with the state of this input pin. The other bits of the accumulator are loaded with data related to interrupt processing, as discussed in Chapter Nine.

The serial output port is formed by pin 4, named SOD, for serial output data. The SIM instruction is used here. It is also used for interrupt processing. If bit 6 of the accumulator is a one when this instruction is invoked, bit 7 of the accumulator will be sent to the SOD pin. Bit 3 of the accumulator should be established at a zero to avoid changing the state of interrupt processing, as discussed in Chapter Nine.

The process of setting the serial output line is thus one of setting the accumulator to a value and then executing the SIM instruction. To set the SOD pin to a one without changing the interrupt processing, we set the accumulator to

11XX0XXX

where X can be either a one or a zero. To clear the SOD pin to zero, we set the accumulator to

01XX0XXX

and then perform an SIM.

The serial communication protocol must be developed in software. This includes the establishment of the proper baud rate. If additional handshake lines are required, normal I/O ports must be used.

EXERCISES

7.1 Someone has inadvertently tied an 8-bit digital driver to the microcomputer data bus on the 8085. Could any damage result? If so, what might be damaged?

7.2 In Example 7.1 and Figure 7.2b, address line 14 is used to select between ROM/RAM memory and memory-mapped I/O. Figure 7.3a shows the resulting memory map. Redraw this map, assuming that address line 15 is used in place of address line 14 in Figure 7.2b.

7.3 How many total I/O-mapped I/O devices can be used by applying the simple scheme of Figure 7.2d? How many total memory-mapped I/O devices can be used by applying the scheme of Figure 7.2b?

7.4 The hardware used with the source code in Example 7.6 has changed. What steps are required to move the printer output port to location 2000, hexadecimal, and the associated programming port to 2004, hexadecimal?

7.5 The interface requirements for Example 7.6 have changed. What source code changes are required to (*a*) Make the data-available handshake a zero and the data-not-available handshake a one in bit position?

(*b*) Change the DACC bit to position 6?

(*c*) Change the polarity of the busy bit, that is, make the program recognize a zero as a busy indication rather than a one?

7.6 Again, using the program of Example 7.6, what changes are required to prevent the original contents of the BC- and DE-pairs from being lost during this subroutine?

7.7 Data words of 5, 6, 7, and 8 bits are common formats for serial data communication. If byte wide communications allow coding of 256 distinct terms with each word sent, how many distinct terms can be sent with the other formats? Why might the smaller formats be used?

7.8 A serial communication channel uses two start bits, a seven-bit data word, even parity, and no stop bits. How many total bits must be sent for transmission of one seven-bit word? If each bit requires a 0.833-millisecond time period (1200 baud), how long does it take to transmit a single seven-bit word? What is the data rate, in seven-bit data words per second, assuming transmission occurs as rapidly as possible?

7.9 Modify the 8251 command sequence of Figure 7.13*b* for the communication parameters listed in Exercise 7.8.

7.10 What are the advantages of using a UART rather than the 8085's SID/SOD serial port? What are the advantages of using the 8085's SID/SOD serial port rather than a UART?

CHAPTER EIGHT

ANALOG INPUT/OUTPUT

8.1 INTRODUCTION

Although the interface to the internal microprocessor structure is virtually always a digital process, the derivation of data for the microcomputer and the use of its output involve a variety of interface techniques. A full study of these interesting topics would fill many chapters. Several elements of the analog interface warrant treatment here because they are common to many of these I/O structures. We discussed the interface with the microprocessor bus architecture in the last chapter. This chapter will concentrate on methods of converting between digital data and analog signals. An outline of simple, bit-mapped I/O techniques introduces this discussion.

8.2 BIT-MAPPED I/O

Bit-mapped I/O provides a very simple and often powerful interface method. A simple digital input to a microcomputer can be produced by a single pole switch. Figure 8.1 shows how a logical low or high voltage can be presented to the microcomputer based on switch position. The switch can, of course, represent a variety of mechanical or electrical conditions. In a chemical-process control system, the switch might represent an overpressure condition or the level of fluid in a tank. The switch in a thermostat might indicate the temperature in a refrigeration system.

When we group several switches together, we form a bit-mapped status word. We might bit-map the status of each of the filaments of the lights on a car into a light status word. A device to sense current in each filament would be required. Each of these inputs—from four headlights,

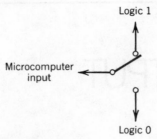

Figure 8.1
Single-Bit Input.

two taillights, and two brake lights—would then be bit-mapped onto an
8-bit status word by connecting them to an I/O port. In a similar fashion,
each of the light-switch positions could be bit-mapped into the microcomputer at another I/O port.

EXAMPLE 8.1 Auto Light Monitor, Bit-Mapped Input

Assume that the filament status word just mentioned is available at an
input port located at I/O address 04 and that the light-switch status word
is at I/O address 08. The following program fragment (written using the
8085 instruction set) will bring each of the status words into the computer, determine whether an error has occurred, and provide subroutine
calls for the various error conditions. This code is more complex than
would normally be required for the task. Example 8.2 will present a simplified version of the program.

```
FILMT    EQU    04H           ;BIT-MAPPED FILAMENT STATUS INPUT
LITESW   EQU    08H           ;BIT-MAPPED LIGHT-SWITCH STATUS INPUT
LITERR   DS     1             ;BIT-MAPPED LIGHT ERROR WORD
                              USED FOR PARAMETER PASSING TO SUB'S
;
;MAPPING:
;    LEFT HEADLIGHT HIGH.BEAM . . . . . BIT-7
;    LEFT HEADLIGHT LOW.BEAM . . . . . BIT-6
;    RIGHT HEADLIGHT HIGH.BEAM . . . BIT-5
;    RIGHT HEADLIGHT LOW.BEAM . . . . BIT-4
;    LEFT TAILLIGHT . . . . . . . . . . . . . . . . . . BIT-3
;    RIGHT TAILLIGHT . . . . . . . . . . . . . . . . . BIT-2
;    LEFT BRAKE LIGHT . . . . . . . . . . . . . . . BIT-1
;    RIGHT BRAKE LIGHT . . . . . . . . . . . . BIT-0
;                                . . . . . .
;                                . . . . . .
;                                . . . . . .
;
;LIGHT OPERATION CHECK . . . DESTROYS A- AND B-REGISTER DATA
;                            . . . CALLS ERROR MESSAGE ROUTINES
LIGHTS   IN     FILMT         ;FILAMENT CONDITION, ON IS A HIGH
         MOV    B,A
         IN     LITESW        ;SWITCH CONDITION
         XRA    B             ;A IS NOW A BIT-MAPPED ERROR WORD
         RZ                   ;LIGHTS OK
```

```
STA     LITERR
CALL    MASTERR    ;MASTER ERROR WARNING SUBROUTINE
LDA     LITERR
ANA     0F0H       ;HEADLIGHT MASK
CNZ     HLITERR    ;BAD HEADLIGHT SUBROUTINE
LDA     LITERR
ANA     0CH        ;TAILLIGHT MASK
CNZ     TLITERR    ;BAD TAILLIGHT SUBROUTINE
LDA     LITERR
ANA     03H        ;BRAKE LIGHT MASK
CNZ     BLITERR    ;BAD BRAKE LIGHT SUBROUTINE
RET
```

This fragment is written as a subroutine, which would be embedded in a larger program. The introductory labels should, of course, be included with other equates at some location in the source code. The XRA B instruction compares the switch commands with the results at the filaments. A zero word from this instruction indicates a match and, hence, no errors. Each of the ANA instructions tests for an error within a block of the bit mapping. The block is specified by the mask used, as shown in Figure 8.2. For example, F0H forces the last four bits resulting from the ANA operation to be zero. On the other hand, ANA F0H forces the resulting high-order bits to match the four high-order bits of the error word. An error subroutine call thus is made if an error bit associated with it is set.

Notice that the masks are specified without using labels. This is acceptable for small programs. If this fragment were part of a larger program and if we elected to change the bit mapping at some later time, we would be forced to search out each of these masks so that they could be modified. In a large program it would be better to establish these masks

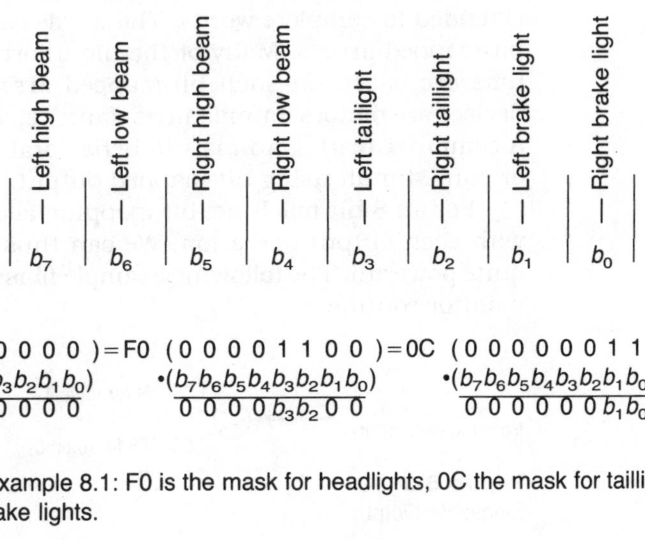

$$(1\ 1\ 1\ 1\ 0\ 0\ 0\ 0) = \text{F0} \qquad (0\ 0\ 0\ 0\ 1\ 1\ 0\ 0) = \text{0C} \qquad (0\ 0\ 0\ 0\ 0\ 0\ 1\ 1) = \text{03}$$
$$\cdot (b_7 b_6 b_5 b_4 b_3 b_2 b_1 b_0) \qquad \cdot (b_7 b_6 b_5 b_4 b_3 b_2 b_1 b_0) \qquad \cdot (b_7 b_6 b_5 b_4 b_3 b_2 b_1 b_0)$$
$$\overline{b_7 b_6 b_5 b_4\ 0\ 0\ 0\ 0} \qquad \overline{0\ 0\ 0\ 0\ b_3 b_2\ 0\ 0} \qquad \overline{0\ 0\ 0\ 0\ 0\ 0\ b_1 b_0}$$

Figure 8.2
Masks for Example 8.1: F0 is the mask for headlights, 0C the mask for taillights, 03 the mask for brake lights.

with labels in the source code along with the other equates and, in particular, along with the bit-mapped definitions.

Other applications of bit-mapped processing rely on thresholding techniques. Here an analog signal is classified by simple voltage threshold circuits. These threshold data are then bit-mapped into the microcomputer for processing. An example might be an infrared intrusion alarm. Here an infrared heat sensor would be scanned across a room, producing information on the temperature of various objects, the current rate of change of temperature as the sensor scans (i.e., contrast), and the position of the sensor. Thresholds would classify the sensor data. If we used three thresholds, four states could be discerned: no threshold (a cold object), low-level threshold (an object at room temperature), warm (a possible intruder), and hot (a possible fire). We could add contrast thresholds to sort distinct objects from general warm areas and position microswitches to indicate the right and left ends of sensor travel.

With these thresholds, which might total eight, we would have enough information to make good estimates of what is happening in the room. By knowing the time between the sensor's start of movement from one end of its scan and a threshold crossing, the microcomputer could determine position. Knowing the positions where various threshold words were seen, the microcomputer could compute sizes. With a history of these data, it could compute movement. Thus, with nothing more than a few thresholds and the microcomputer, a somewhat crude image-processing system is created.

Bit-mapping output is the inverse of the bit-mapped input just discussed. The simplest example of bit-mapped output is the light attached to an output port, as shown in Figure 8.3. The output can, of course, be extended to complete words. The words can, in turn, form parts of large bit-mapped arrays. Many of the big information displays at large stadiums are based on such bit-mapped arrays. Other bit-mapped output devices are motors for machines, fans, refrigeration units, and solenoids. A computer testing animals in behavioral research might issue pleasure or pain stimuli using bit-mapped output.

For an 8-bit machine, bit mapping allows eight devices to be excited with each output operation. We can thus write compact code which is quite powerful. The following example illustrates this for our simple light-monitor routine.

Figure 8.3
Single-Bit Output.

EXAMPLE 8.2   Monitor with Bit-Mapped Input

The LIGHTS routine for Example 8.1 can be simplified to

```
FILMT       EQU    04H        ;BIT-MAPPED FILAMENT STATUS INPUT
LITESW      EQU    08H        ;BIT-MAPPED LIGHT-SWITCH STATUS INPUT
WARNLTS     EQU    02H        ;BIT-MAPPED WARNING LIGHTS OUTPUT
;
                               ......
                               ......
;
LIGHTS1     IN     FILMT      ;FILAMENT CONDITION, ON IS A HIGH
            MOV    B,A
            IN     LITESW     ;SWITCH CONDITION
            XRA    B          ;A IS NOW BIT-MAPPED ERROR WORD
            RZ                ;LIGHTS OK
            CALL   MASTERR    ;MASTER ERROR WARNING SUBROUTINE
            OUT    WARNLTS    ;BIT-MAPPED LIGHT ERROR INDICATORS
            RET
```

The bit mapping of output takes care of steering the error indicator information to the right warning light. The code becomes quite simple. This application might not require a microcomputer in itself. However, as part of a larger automotive data-processing system, this is a simple, yet very flexible, use of microprocessor technology.

Some microprocessor systems, such as the RCA 1802, provide specific I/O bits, called I/O flags, which operate as one-bit I/O. Such flags can be used as single-bit, bit-mapped I/O. They have the advantage of not requiring I/O port devices to be added to the system. Often special I/O flag instructions are provided to increase the speed and flexibility of a system. The 8085 allows bit mapping through both I/O-mapped I/O and memory-mapped I/O. It does not use I/O flags.

8.3   DIGITAL-TO-ANALOG CONVERSION

In Chapter Five, we discussed various methods of representing numbers as digital data for use in a computer. Let us assume that our microcomputer has converted some input data into a convenient format and has processed these data. The result might be a torque command for a motor or a flow rate command for some refining process. Whatever the use, the designer is faced with the task of converting the digital data from the microcomputer's internal processing into a specific electrical output signal, most often a voltage.

The critical step in the conversion process is the actual production of the analog signal. The device that performs this process has digital data as input and produces the analog signal as output. It is called, logically, a **digital-to-analog converter,** or a **DAC.** Sometimes a DAC will be called a D-to-A, which is often written as D/A.

A DAC will normally be driven by a parallel output port from the microprocessor bus. As discussed in the last chapter, such a port will have a specific address; hence, this address becomes the address of the DAC. It should be noted that some DAC devices include the port on the same chip with the DAC. In any event, whenever the CPU sends data to the port address, the DAC produces the corresponding analog output.

DACs are usually designed to use unsigned binary data as input. The programmer must therefore often convert the internal data into the proper format for the DAC. Since the output port, or the DAC itself, may be a programmed device, the programmer must also provide for the proper command bytes to be sent. Finally, DACs using more bits than eight are common; the programmer must then provide for multibyte output data. The output process will often involve conversion of the data into unsigned binary format, programming the I/O port, and finally transferring multibyte data to the output address or addresses.

In unsigned binary format, each bit has a specific weighting. These weightings range from one to 128 for an 8-bit word. The arithmetic process for conversion is to multiply each bit by its weighting and then add all the results together. Since each bit has either the value one or the value zero, this process amounts to adding together the weightings for all the bits that are at one and disregarding the rest. A crude DAC would mimic this process. It might have eight voltage sources from 1 volt to 128 volts. This would be followed by a summing device which selects the proper voltages based on the byte being converted. In this scheme, any input byte would produce a unique output voltage from 0 volts (byte 00) to 255 volts (FF, hexadecimal).

Common DACs build on this process. First, a DAC used in most modern systems would not produce such high voltages. We must scale the output signal so that the levels are reasonable. A very common way to do this scaling is to provide a reference voltage on the DAC. The DAC is designed to produce a scaled output that is based on this reference. The MSB will be worth one-half the reference, the next bit will be worth one-quarter, and so forth. The weighting of the LSB will depend on the size of the digital word the DAC is designed to use. An 8-bit DAC weights its LSB at 1/256th of the reference; a 12-bit DAC weights it at 1/4096th. Table 8.1 shows the output voltages produced by a three-bit DAC using this scheme.

The internal structure of a modern DAC does not use the aforementioned voltage-summing technique directly. Commonly, some form of resistive ladder is used to produce the output sum. Two methods of designing a three-bit DAC are shown in Figure 8.4. Each digital bit from the output port is used to set the state of a switch. The switch settings determine the output voltage. Since our mission here is not directly re-

Table 8.1

Three-Bit DAC Output

Binary Input			Output Voltage, V_0
B_2	B_1	B_0	
0	0	0	0
0	0	1	$\frac{1}{8} V_{ref}$
0	1	0	$\frac{2}{8} V_{ref} = \frac{1}{4} V_{ref}$
0	1	1	$\frac{3}{8} V_{ref}$
1	0	0	$\frac{4}{8} V_{ref} = \frac{1}{2} V_{ref}$
1	0	1	$\frac{5}{8} V_{ref}$
1	1	0	$\frac{6}{8} V_{ref} = \frac{3}{4} V_{ref}$
1	1	1	$\frac{7}{8} V_{ref}$

lated to analog circuit design techniques, we will not discuss these schemes in detail. Suffice it to say that although the implementation of Figure 8.4a is simpler, it is not commonly used for precision devices. For such devices a rather broad range of resistor values is required in addition to very precise resistor values. The resistance range would be 8192 to one for a 14-bit DAC. The technique of Figure 8.4b requires precision resistors of one value, R, and of nearly exactly twice this value, 2R. Such an "R/2R ladder" is much easier to build in an integrated circuit. This is particularly true for the very popular MOS-based technologies.

Precise constant-current sources are practical for bipolar IC technologies. Many bipolar-based DACs use some form of current summing as the basis for the conversion. These devices generally follow this summation process with a conversion to a voltage output.

The reference voltage shown in Figure 8.4 may be generated internally on the DAC device. The DAC will then produce a unique output voltage for a given digital word. It is possible to provide this reference as an input to the DAC. In such a case the DAC output is scaled to this reference. Mathematically, the process is equivalent to multiplying the reference by a number based on the digital word. For an 8-bit DAC with a digital word from the microprocessor of, say, N, the net voltage output of the DAC would be the product of N/256 times the reference voltage. We have a device that takes the scaled product of an analog voltage—the reference—and a digital word. This multiplying process is very useful in many signal-processing schemes. Devices that have provision for a variable reference voltage are termed **multiplying digital-to-analog converters**, or **MDACs**.

EXAMPLE 8.3 DAC Program/Schematic

The following 8085 subroutine generates an output voltage from a DAC that starts at zero and performs a stepping ramp up to the DAC maxi-

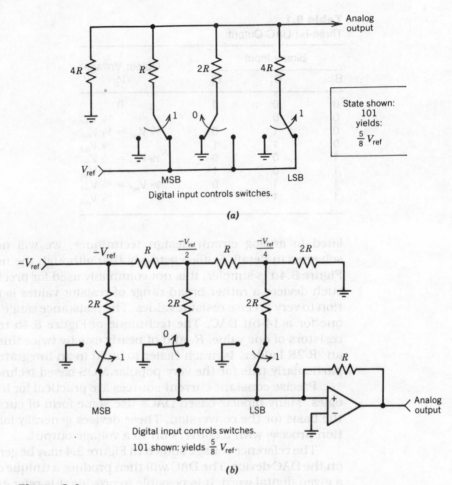

Figure 8.4
DAC Design Types: (a) divider ladder; (b) R/2R ladder.

mum output level. The program assumes a 10-bt DAC accessed through I/O port A of an 8155 for the highest eight bits; the two low-order bits are assumed to be tied to port B. This configuration is shown as a block diagram in Figure 8.5 and as a detailed schematic diagram in Figure 8.6. The 8155 contains three programmable I/O ports, along with 256 bytes of RAM. It also contains a timer, which will be discussed in Chapter Ten. Programming is done port by port; the 8155 does not have bit programming like the 8755. The command/status address of the I/O port is assumed to be located at I/O address 20, hexadecimal. Ports A and B are assumed to be at I/O addresses 21 and 22, hexadecimal.

The Analog Devices 7520 DAC is shown in Figure 8.6. It is a CMOS, 10-bit MDAC based on an internal R/2R ladder. The two operational amplifiers are standard 741-type devices. Since the DAC, with its current

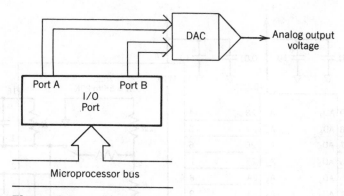

Figure 8.5
DAC Driven from I/O Port.

summer, causes an inversion of the reference signal, an input reference inverter has been provided. If the resistors on this inverter are well matched, the output voltage will be $(N/1024)V_{ref}$ where N is the digital command expressed as a decimal number.

As usual, the software starts with the required equates, which would be located near the beginning of the host program that calls this subroutine. The I/O initialization that is shown establishes ports A and B as output ports, with port C as an input port. Port C will be used in a later example.

```
PORTA   EQU   21H        ;I/O PORT LOCATION IN I/O MAP
PORTB   EQU   22H
CMND    EQU   20H        ;COMMAND/STATUS ADDRESS
                . . . . . .
                . . . . . .
                . . . . . .
;
;RAMP GENERATOR SUBROUTINE
;H/L, D/E, AND ACCUMULATOR ARE ALTERED
;
;CONFIGURE I/O PORTS
RAMP    MVI   A,03H      ;PORTS A & B OUTPUT, PORT C INPUT
        OUT   CMND
;
;INITIALIZE
        STC              ;INITIALIZE CARRY
        CMC
        LXI   H,0        ;INITIALIZE RAMP
        LXI   D,0040H    ;RAMP STEP VALUE
;
RAMP1   MOV   A,H        ;OUTPUT TOP EIGHT BITS
        OUT   PORTA
        MOV   A,L        ;OUTPUT TWO LSB'S
        OUT   PORTB
;
        DAD   D          ;NEXT
;
;CHECK FOR FINISH
        RC               ;ALL DONE
;
```

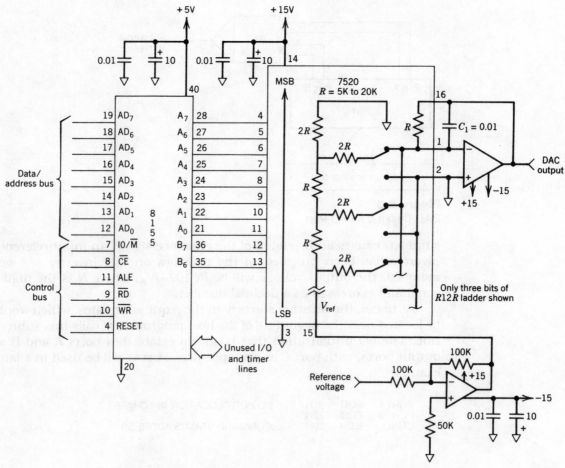

Figure 8.6
Ten-bit DAC for Example 8.3: resistance in ohms, capacitance in microfarads.

```
;DELAY ROUTINE
RAMP2   MVI     A,FFH      ;COUNT DOWN FROM 255
        DCR     A
        JNZ     RAMP2
        JMP     RAMP1
```

This routine generates a transient because the two lowest-order bits are sent to the DAC a few microseconds after the rest of the word is sent. Capacitor C_1 smooths this transient significantly. It could be eliminated if we were to add a 10-bit latch driving the DAC. The latch could be controlled by port C. The output sequence of the subroutine would have to be modified so that the latch at port C gets a latch command at the proper time. The modification would be something like

```
;
        LXI     H,0
```

```
RAMP1   MOV  A,H         ;OUTPUT TOP EIGHT BITS
        OUT  PORTA
        MOV  A,L         ;OUTPUT TWO LSB'S
        OUT  PORTB
        MVI  A,01H       ;PULSE LATCH
        OUT  PORTC
        MVI  A,0H
        OUT  PORTC
;
```

The equates would have to include port C, of course. In addition, the I/O initialization would change to 0F, hexadecimal. This would enable port C as an output port.

Example 8.3 produces a ramp starting at zero and going in only one voltage direction. The DAC is not configured for signed data. Various hardware designs that interface with different data formats are available. One simple but common example is the use of a very accurate offset. A DAC whose range is normally zero to V_{ref} is offset by $-V_{ref}/2$. The output will now cover the range $-V_{ref}/2$ to $+V_{ref}/2$. Figure 8.7 shows an accurate way of producing the same effect using an $R/2R$ ladder DAC. Resistors R_1 and R_2 must be very accurately matched. Also shown is a plot of output voltage versus binary command.

For purposes of discussion, we will continue to address the basic unsigned binary data format in the remainder of this chapter.

8.4 ANALOG-TO-DIGITAL CONVERSION

The reverse of the DAC process is the generation of a digital word based on some analog signal, usually a voltage. Such a device is, of course, an **analog-to-digital converter**, or **ADC**. Because ADC does not flow from the tongue with ease, the name A-to-D is often used and sometimes written, simply, A/D. The digital word generated by an ADC is passed to an input port, which is then tied to the microcomputer bus. The port may be included on the ADC chip itself. To the programmer, an ADC and its input port appear as a memory or I/O location—or locations—which contains the binary representation of the analog signal.

A number of different techniques are used for analog-to-digital conversion. The most common ones use a DAC in feedback, as discussed next.

Counter-Based ADC

A block diagram of a typical **counter-based ADC**, a common and inexpensive scheme, is shown in Figure 8.8. When a new sample of the analog

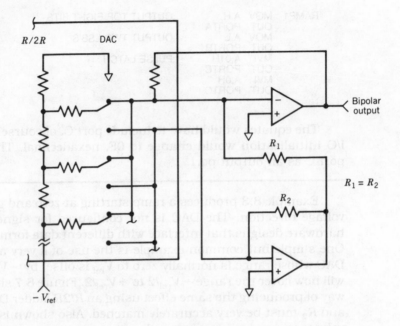

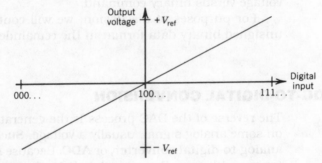

Figure 8.7
Bipolar *R/2R* DAC.

input is desired, the reset line is pulsed. This starts the counter, which counts the clock pulses up from zero. The DAC output thus moves upward in steps. During this time the analog comparator output remains a one. The clock pulses continue to propagate through the AND gate until the DAC output steps one LSB higher than the analog input. This causes the comparator output to drop to a zero, which prevents the clock from getting through the AND gate. At this point the binary number from the counter is the digital representation of the analog input voltage. This digital number is always rounded to the higher LSB since the counter does not stop until the analog voltage is exceeded.

The scaling of the binary output of the counter-based ADC is dependent on the DAC scaling. If we use an 8-bit MDAC with a reference V_r and

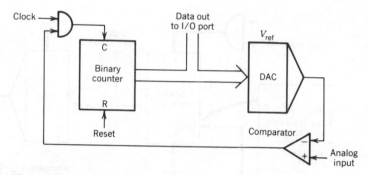

Figure 8.8
Counter-Based ADC.

an analog input of V_i, and achieve a digital output of d, the relation between the terms will be

$$V_r d/256 = V_i$$

The digital output is thus

$$d = 256 V_i / V_r$$

We obtain a digital number that is linearly related to the analog input voltage. Notice that the digital input is inversely related to the DAC reference. This ADC implementation can thus be used as a divider of two analog voltages, which yields a digital number as the quotient.

This type of conversion is slow since we must wait for the counter to go through all the lower-level numbers up to our final result. If the DAC settles in, say, 500 nanoseconds, we might use a one-megahertz clock. The one-megahertz clock allows one microsecond between clock steps, adequate time for the 500-nanosecond DAC to settle. One thousand of these one-microsecond periods are required for the counter to count through the full 10-bit—that is, 1024-step—range. Therefore, a full conversion with a 10-bit DAC would require one millisecond. The shortest conversion time is nearly zero; it occurs when the input is zero.

The counter-based ADC of Figure 8.8 can be modified to a tracking counter-based version as shown in Figure 8.9. The binary counter now counts up or down based on the state of the comparator. For a steady input signal the ADC will flicker, the LSB moving first above the signal and then below it.

The sample-hold input forces the counter to stay fixed when it is in the hold state. If this sample/hold input were under software control (using an output port, for example), the program might call for a sample at one specific time; it could later return to interrogate the ADC for the value being held. This form of ADC has a speed limitation which forces limits on the slew rate of the input signal. Slew rate is the rate at which the input signal changes, expressed in volts per second. If this slew rate exceeds the maximum rate at which the clock can step the DAC, errors will occur. An 8-bit version with a 10-volt reference and a one-megahertz

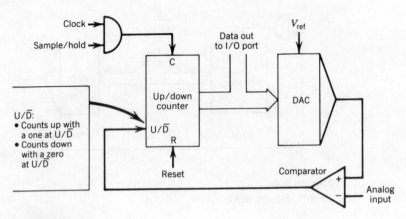

Figure 8.9
Tracking ADC.

clock would be limited to a change of 10 volts in 256 microseconds. This amounts to a voltage slew rate of 40,000 volts per second or 0.04 volt per microsecond.

The tracking ADC also has a speed limitation similar to that of the simple counter-based ADC. If a reset occurs or if the ADC has been in a hold state, the counter may need to pass through many states before the comparator is tripped again. As usual, this "reacquisition" time is limited by clock speed, which is in turn bounded by logic settling times.

Successive Approximation ADC

The **successive approximation ADC** is widely used for fast analog-to-digital conversion. As we will see, it also allows a very inexpensive ADC when controlled from software. The technique is one of successively approximating a value for a DAC, altering this value each time in such a way that it approaches the correct value. The process is very logical. We first set the MSB of a DAC with all other bits at zero. The DAC output will now be one-half the reference voltage. If the analog input signal is larger than the DAC output, we leave the MSB on. If not, we reset the MSB. The MSB will then have the proper state for the analog signal under question. The ADC process has now narrowed the search down to one-half the reference voltage range. A test with the next lower bit on will narrow the search further to the upper or lower half of this one-half reference range, that is, to one-quarter the reference range. The process continues until all the bits have been determined.

Converters that employ hardware to implement this successive approximation scheme, with conversion times as fast as the submicrosecond level, are now widely available. It is possible, however, to use a microcomputer program to implement this process. This allows us to build an ADC using only a DAC and a comparator. The process provides an insight into both the successive approximation ADC and the hardware-software trade-offs that are common to microcomputer design. Figure 8.10 shows an outline of the hardware necessary for this type of ADC.

The process starts by resetting all the bits of the DAC. The MSB is then set to a one. The comparator is read by the CPU. The MSB is then left set or is reset based on the comparator's state. This state is read by a normal input operation from the comparator port address. The next successive bit is set, the comparator is read, and the bit is left alone or is reset based on the comparator state. The process continues until the last bit has been established. A flowchart for this process is shown in Figure 8.11. Figure 8.12 shows the process four successive approximations deep. Following the different paths through this array amounts to tracing various plots of the digital approximation versus time.

A hardware-based successive approximation ADC can be quite fast, for it passes through a small number of states before ascertaining the digital result. Moreover, it will always take the same length of time to do any conversion. A 10-bit counter-based ADC moves through anywhere from zero to 1024 states to do a conversion; a successive approximation ADC can get the same 10 bits in a fixed, ten-state time period.

EXAMPLE 8.4 Software-Based ADC

If we add a comparator to Figure 8.6 of Example 8.3, we can implement a software-based ADC. The code can be kept simple by using only the top eight bits for control of the DAC. The I/O port must be initialized to have port A as output and port C as input. Port B is not used since we are

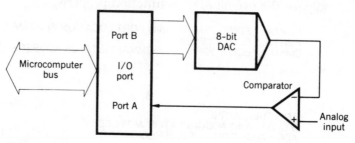

Figure 8.10
Hardware for Software-Based ADC.

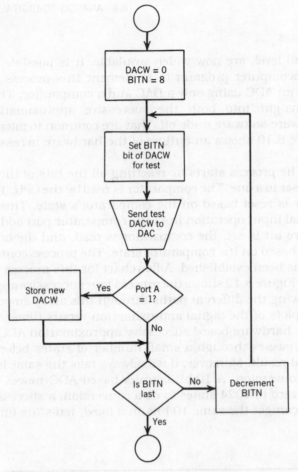

Figure 8.11
Flowchart for Software ADC. DACW is the running approximation to the analog input and the final output value of the routine. BITN is a pointer to the current bit in DACW. BITN is one for LSB.

building an 8-bit ADC. The filter capacitor shown on the DAC output in Figure 8.6 should be reduced in value because the DAC must settle rapidly for the overall ADC to function properly.

```
PORTA    EQU    21H        ;I/O PORT LOCATION IN I/O MAP
PORTC    EQU    23H
CMND     EQU    20H        ;COMMAND/STATUS ADDRESS
                 . . . . . .
                 . . . . . .
                 . . . . . .
;
;ADC SUBROUTINE
;B/C, D/E, AND ACCUMULATOR ALTERED
;ADC VALUE RETURNED IN REGISTER D
;
;CONFIGURE I/O PORTS
ADC      MVI    A,01H      ;PORT A OUTPUT, PORTS B & C INPUT
```

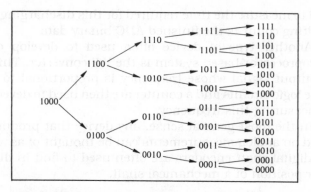

Figure 8.12
Successive Approximation. The decision is upward if
DAC output is not greater than input. The decision is
downward if DAC output is greater than input.

```
            OUT     CMND
        ;
        ;INITIALIZE
            MVI     B,08H       ;BIT POINTER, BITN IN FLOWCHART
            MVI     D,0         ;APPROXIMATION, DACW IN FLOWCHART
        ;
ADC1        MOV     C,B         ;SET THE BIT POINTED TO BY B
            MVI     A,0
            STC
ADC2        RAL
            DCR     C
            JNZ     ADC2        ;MORE
            ORA     D           ;SET THE BIT
        ;
            OUT     PORTA       ;GIVE IT A TRY
            MOV     E,A         ;TEMP
        ;
            IN      PORTC       ;CHECK PER FLOWCHART
            ANI     01H         ;LSB MASK
            JZ      ADC3        ;D OK AS IS
            MOV     D,E         ;NEW VALUE IS CORRECT
        ;
ADC3        DCR     B           ;NEXT BIT
            RZ
            JMP     ADC1        ;MORE
```

Other Techniques

A number of less direct ADC techniques have been developed for various
uses. For example, the "dual-slope integrator" type has very good noise
immunity and can be built using fairly inexpensive components; however, it tends to be slow. For this type of ADC, a capacitor is charged with
a current proportional to the analog input. This is done for a fixed length
of time. Next, the capacitor is discharged by fixed current. A counter is

used to measure the time required for this discharging to take place. The resulting count is the finished ADC binary data.

Another type of device often used to develop digital data for a microprocessor-based system is the V/F converter. This device produces an output signal whose frequency is proportional to its input voltage. Some logic circuits and a counter are then used to develop the digital data by measuring this frequency.

In the most general sense, any device that produces a digital value based on analog measurements can be thought of as an ADC. For example, digital shaft encoders are often used to find in digital form the angular position of a mechanical shaft.

Shannon's Sampling Theorem

In the late 1940s and early 1950s, C. E. Shannon and a group of others developed a very eloquent body of knowledge known as information theory. Although the subject of information theory is much too broad for this study, we will touch on one part of one of the major theorems.

We will first disregard another eloquent body of knowledge, quantum theory, and say that for all practical purposes, analog signals vary smoothly as time passes. Our microprocessor, however, will only accept discrete numbers related to the value of the analog signal at a discrete time. The microprocessor, along with its ADC, is said to sample the signal. The resulting sampling process is illustrated in Figure 8.13a. Figure 8.13b presents the reconstructed signal that results if the sampled data is returned as output to a DAC.

If the analog signal being sampled is changing quickly and the samples occur too slowly, there are serious distortions. An example of this undersampling is shown in Figure 8.14. The analog signal changes significantly between samples, and the resultant sampled data have little meaning. This process, where undersampling causes an input signal to be transformed to a radically different output signal, is called **aliasing**.

The rate at which an analog signal can change is determined by the highest significant frequency components in the signal. Shannon's sampling theorem provides that we must sample at a bare-bones minimum of twice the highest frequency component of interest. Very specific conditions must be met to achieve accurate operation at this minimum sampling rate. In the practical world of microcomputer design, the conditions can never be met; the result is that sampling should always be done at a significantly higher rate than twice the analog signal's highest frequency component.

If a high enough sampling rate is not provided, aliasing will occur. Alias outputs appear as components of the signal at a low-frequency rate—less than one-half the sample rate. Figure 8.14a shows a 1020-

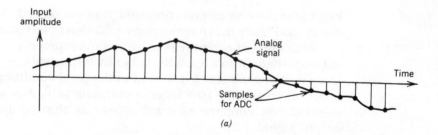

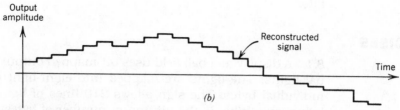

Figure 8.13
Signal Sampling and Reconstruction: (*a*) sampling, (*b*) reconstruction.

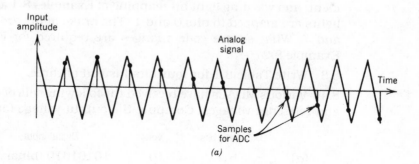

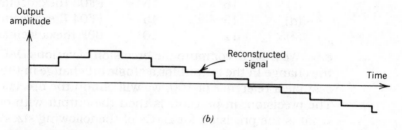

Figure 8.14
Improper Sampling: (*a*) low-frequency sampling, (*b*) extreme distortion at reconstruction of signal.

hertz signal sampled one thousand times a second. The reconstructed output in Figure 8.14b appears as a 20-hertz alias signal.

Shannon's theorem tells us that a microprocessor-based system using audio data from a 3-kilohertz-bandwidth telephone line must be sampled six thousand times a second under ideal conditions. In practice we might select, say, a 10-kilohertz sampling rate. Any stray signal above one-half this sampling rate will appear as aliasing and will distort the output signal.

To ensure that signals at frequencies greater than one-half the sampling rate do not corrupt the data, we can use a low-pass filter to remove these signals prior to sampling. This type of filter is called an **antialiasing** filter.

EXERCISES

8.1 A display at a ball field uses bit-mapped output to drive the individual lights. The lights are mapped into eight-light groups, which form individual bytes. The sign allows 210 lines of lights. Each line is 250 lights long. What is the minimum number of bytes required for this bit mapping? What is the largest square display possible using the 8085's I/O-mapped I/O?

8.2 A hardware change is made that changes all the light switch, filament, and warning light bit mapping of Examples 8.1 and 8.2. The headlights are mapped to bits 0 and 1. The brake lights are mapped to bits 6 and 7. What source code changes are required for Example 8.1? For Example 8.2?

8.3 Write Table 8.1 for four bits instead of three.

8.4 Various MDACs have received the following sets of digital commands and reference voltages. Compute the output voltage for each.

	DAC Size, bits	V_{ref}, volts	Digital Input
(a)	8	10	10101010 (binary)
(b)	10	5	1100000000 (binary)
(c)	16	15	FF03 (hexadecimal)
(d)	16	15	FF04 (hexadecimal)
(e)	12	10	00F (hexadecimal)

8.5 We wish to compute the precision of various DACs. By this we mean the change in the output for a single bit change in the digital input. If we assume a reference of 100, we will obtain the precision as a percentage. The precision, in percent, is then the output with only the LSB active. What is the precision for DACs of the following sizes?

(a) 8-bit
(b) 10-bit
(c) 12-bit

(d)   14-bit

(e)   16-bit

8.6   A 12-bit counter-based ADC is clocked at 100 kilohertz. What is its maximum conversion time? What is the maximum conversion time for a 14-bit ADC with the same clock? For a 16-bit ADC?

8.7   A counter-based ADC has an input voltage of 3 volts. The reference voltage is 10 volts. What will the digital output word be for the following ADC word sizes?

(a)   8-bit

(b)   10-bit

(c)   12-bit

(d)   14-bit

(e)   16-bit

8.8   Assuming the clock timing of the 8085, as presented in Table 6.2, how long does the software-based successive approximation ADC of Example 8.4 take to complete one conversion.

8.9   Digital compact disk (CD) sound recording uses 16-bit ADCs at the studio and 16-bit DACs in the playback machine. What is the ratio of the largest signal level out of such a device—commanded by FFFF, hexadecimal—to the smallest—commanded by 0001? If 15 kilohertz is the highest frequency to be reproduced, what is the absolute minimum sampling frequency that could ever be used based on Shannon's theorem? (Such machines use approximately 44-kilohertz sampling and do not use binary coding directly, as is implied here.)

8.10   A microprocessor-based, black-box flight recorder is required for airline use. The black box will record, on protected magnetic memory, various flight parameter data. The most dynamic system the recorder must monitor has its highest-frequency components at 10 hertz. How much time can lapse between samples in order to meet the Shannon sampling requirement?

CHAPTER NINE

INTERRUPTS

9.1 INTRODUCTION

For most applications, microprocessors perform a variety of different functions. Often the most critical of these functions happen only rarely. The simplest example of this are sudden, critical emergencies. The microprocessor program must be ready to service such critical conditions while still performing its more mundane tasks. Interrupt techniques allow rapid reordering of processor functions.

In a more general sense, interrupts allow synchronization of processor functions with the real world. As we have seen, the timing of microprocessor operation is rigidly controlled by internal timing states. In many applications the processor must follow the ebb and flow of the real world. Interrupt processing provides a direct way to perform these tasks.

After introducing the general concepts of interrupt processing, this chapter discusses two of the most common methods of control transfer to interrupt routines. Finally, we consider processing of multiple interrupts and the functions of certain other related exceptions to normal program processing.

9.2 BASICS

The transfer of control required to process an interrupt is straightforward. First, an external hardware action must occur to signal the CPU that an interrupt is requested. After this happens, the processor gracefully stops current processing. The interrupt processing software must now be executed in much the same way as a subroutine is called. Finally, this software signals, by a return instruction, that the interrupt processing is complete. The CPU returns to its former task. Figure 9.1 presents this process. We will examine each of these operations in detail.

Generally an interrupt is initiated by setting a logic state on one of the microprocessor pins. When this occurs, the interrupt is said to be **asserted** or **requested.** The hardware details vary from one microprocessor family to another. The Intel 8080 has a single pin that forces an interrupt operation when it is set to a one. The Motorola 68000 has three pins that cause an interrupt to occur if any one, or a combination of them, is forced to the ground level. We discuss some of the details of the Intel 8085 interrupt processing in the example at the end of this section.

An interrupt will generally be processed after the hardware request has been made. But there are important exceptions to this. They involve certain software, and sometimes hardware, schemes called interrupt masks. Interrupt masks and related interrupt prioritization will be reviewed in a later section.

Once the CPU recognizes an interrupt, it will finish the specific fetch/execute cycle that is being performed. The CPU must be able to return to its original task once the interrupt has been processed. The idea is for the interrupt software to be run with no impact on the interrupted processing except for a time delay. If the processor branched to the interrupt software without completing the current fetch/execute cycle, the flow of the interrupted program would be damaged.

At the end of the current fetch/execute cycle, the interrupt operation is quite similar to a subroutine call. As usual, the contents of the PC-register are pushed onto the stack. Various processor families may also save other processor data.

Having recognized an acceptable interrupt, finished the current fetch/execute cycle, and saved the contents of the PC (and perhaps other data), the processor next places the address of the start of the interrupt routine in the PC-register. The source of this address varies, as usual, from processor family to processor family.

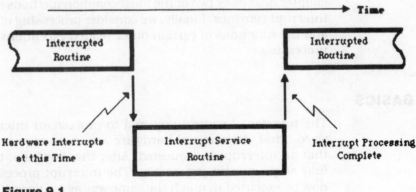

Figure 9.1
Interrupt Processing.

The general operation of determining the address for the interrupt routine is called **vectoring**. The address that is placed in the PC-register is called a **vector**. For now, we assume that this address can be determined.

With the PC-register set, the next instruction fetched will be the first of the interrupt service routine. The **interrupt service routine** is one specifically designed to respond to the particular hardware interrupt in progress. It is selected through the vectoring process just mentioned. Good programming practice dictates that various registers be saved so that the state of the interrupted routine can be reestablished at the end of interrupt processing. After this is done, the programmer can develop whatever software properly performs the operation dictated by the interrupt. As an example, if the interrupt hardware design asserted itself when an overpressure condition was sensed, the service routine might turn on a relief valve.

At the end of the interrupt service routine, the programmer must return the register data saved at its start. The last instruction in the interrupt service routine must be a return instruction—sometimes a specific interrupt return instruction. As might be expected, the microprocessor will pop the PC-register data from the stack and return to the interrupted routine by continuing the fetch/execute cycles at this reinstated address.

We can see in all this a very important difference between interrupt processing and the processing of a subroutine. When a subroutine is used, the programmer knows where, specifically, in the flow of the calling routine the call will be made; the programmer does not know where in the normal processing an interrupt will be requested. Nor does the programmer know, in designing the interrupt routine itself, what the status of the system might be prior to the interrupt request. The upshot of all this is that the programmer must be very careful in designing both the interrupting and the interrupted routines.

EXAMPLE 9.1   Aircraft VOR

An aircraft VOR (VHF omnidirectional range) instrument might use a microprocessor for control and computational purposes. The microprocessor would take data from a radio receiver. This information would then be transformed through whatever computational operations are required and prepared for the pilot's display. The display would show directional data relative to the fixed VOR transmitter. DME (distance-measuring equipment) is often included with these types of instruments. Here the microprocessor must develop displayed range information based on the signals received.

Because many different VOR frequencies and headings are possible, this instrument would be of little use without human input from the pilot. Interrupt processing provides a logical method for human interface. The microprocessor goes about its normal functions, calculating display data and, perhaps, performing a brief self-test on a regular basis; these critical operations are done as fast as possible, as though no outside interface were required. When the pilot requests a change through a keypad or other input device, interrupt processing is initiated. Depending on the pilot's input, the interrupt processing will modify parameters, output frequency data to the radio receiver, or change options for its main processing routine.

Let us assume the CPU interrupt happens during execution of the STA RESULT instruction of the following program fragment:

```
       .
       .
       .
ADD    M
STA    RESULT
INX    H
       .
       .
       .
```

Some total is found, stored in the address labeled RESULT, and the HL-pair is incremented. The interrupted STA instruction requires three read cycles: the operation code, 32, hexadecimal, is followed by two bytes giving the address RESULT. The CPU waits until this entire instruction is completed before processing the interrupt. As this point the PC points to the instruction INX H. This address is pushed onto the stack in response to the interrupt. The CPU then updates the PC with the address of the routine that services the interrupt. At the end of the interrupt service routine, the address of the INX H instruction is returned to the PC and the main program continues.

9.3 VECTOR TECHNIQUES

As we have mentioned, an interrupt vector defines the address of the start of an interrupt routine. Several methods of establishing this address can be used. A common way of classifying these interrupt vector techniques is based on the complexity of the interrupting device. If the interrupting device passes the vector data using the microprocessor bus structure, the process is said to be a **smart interrupt**. If the vector is fixed in the interrupt hardware design, we call the processes **hardware vectoring**.

Within each of the two major subsets of vector techniques are found two different addressing modes, direct and indirect. Direct addressing passes the location of the starting address of the interrupt routine: **indirect addressing** passes the address of the memory locations that contain the address of the interrupt routine. Figure 9.2 shows the various combinations of common interrupt vector techniques.

The simplest vectoring technique uses a fixed interrupt vector. Control is transferred to a fixed memory location when an interrupt is asserted. This fixed-vector technique is becoming less common for general-purpose microprocessors because of its obvious inflexibility.

Smart Interrupts

The smart interrupting device tells the CPU the interrupt vector data. This is done by a data transfer on the microprocessor bus, as shown in Figure 9.3. This vectoring technique requires an interrupting device that

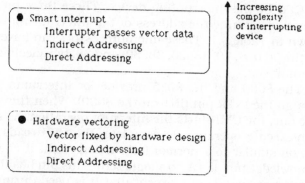

Figure 9.2
Vector Techniques.

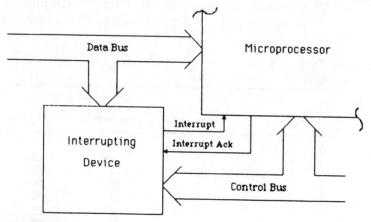

Figure 9.3
Smart Interrupt.

can drive the microprocessor's bus. It must do so with the proper vector data.

For direct vector addressing the interrupting device must, in the most general case, provide the full address of the interrupt routine. This requires the interrupting device to provide two bytes of data to the CPU for a typical, 8-bit system. The hardware implications of this operation lead one to consider other approaches. The common solution allows the interrupting device to transfer one byte of data. This byte is transferred with a normal data read operation. The CPU then uses the byte to develop an address for the interrupt routine.

Using this form of vectoring and assuming a simple 8-bit system, the interrupting device could specify as many as 256 different addresses. These address locations are generally grouped together in memory. Many 8-bit processors use substantially fewer than the full 256 possible locations. For example, the Intel 8080 and 8085 allow three bits to be sent to the CPU by the interrupting device. These three bits are multiplied by eight to determine the address of the interrupt routine. The process is shown in Table 9.1. These microprocessors can have interrupt routines starting at 0, 8, 10, 18, 20, 28, 30, and 38, hexadecimal, using this vector technique.

The 8080 and the 8085 provide for interrupts from smart devices through the INTR pin (INT on the 8080). When this pin is brought to a logic one, the CPU starts the interrupt operation. As soon as the current fetch/execute operation is complete, the CPU reads the data bus in a fashion similar to a normal instruction fetch. It changes the interrupt acknowledge pin, $\overline{\text{INTA}}$, to a logic zero. This pin has the same timing and function as the $\overline{\text{RD}}$ pin, except that it is used during this interrupt instruction read process. The interrupting device can provide any instruction; however, the restart instruction, RST, is intended to be used here. This instruction causes the PC contents to be pushed onto the stack. The PC is then changed to the interrupt routine address, as discussed earlier.

Table 9.1
8080/8085 Interrupt Vectors

Vector Bits			Vector Number	Vector Address	
				Decimal	Hexadecimal
0	0	0	0	0	0
0	0	1	1	8	8
0	1	0	2	16	10
0	1	1	3	24	18
1	0	0	4	32	20
1	0	1	5	40	28
1	1	0	6	48	30
1	1	1	7	56	38

Thus, RST 3 causes execution of the interrupt routine to start at location 18, hexadecimal.

Memory indirect addressing for interrupt vectors is done by a similar process. The interrupting device passes the necessary data to the CPU. These data are used to determine the memory locations that contain the interrupt routine starting address. For example, the Motorola 68000 family has a sequence of memory locations near the beginning of the memory map called a **vector table**. The parameter passed by a smart interrupting device is the number of the entry in the vector table.

A good question at this point is "How does the interrupting device know the location of the code for the interrupt routine?" Generally, the answer is that it is programmed. At initialization, the CPU sends the interrupting device the interrupt vector data. For example, if a serial programmed I/O device also provides an interrupt capability, the CPU would add information to the normal serial data transfer initialization. The CPU might request various start and stop bits, a word length, and a parity specification. After this setup, the CPU might then transfer an interrupt vector byte. The programmed I/O device would return this byte on the data bus whenever an interrupt is processed.

Hardware Vectoring

The details of how we apply the interrupt logic signal determine the vector for most microprocessors using hardware vectoring.

On the Intel 8085, one form of vectoring makes use of hardware vectoring. Any of four pins can be used as interrupt pins for this mode. Each of the four pins is associated with a specific memory location. Table 9.2 shows the pin names and these associated memory locations. If RST 6.5 is driven to a one, the processor starts interrupt processing at memory location 34, hexadecimal—assuming that the interrupt masking is set properly, as will be discussed later. Notice that the vector address is simply eight times the number associated with the interrupting pin. The routine for RST 6.5 is located between the routine for software vectors

Table 9.2

8085 Hardware Interrupt Vectors

Pin Name	Pin Number	Vector Address	
		Decimal	Hexadecimal
RST 4.5 (TRAP)	6	36	24
RST 5.5	9	44	2C
RST 6.5	8	52	34
RST 7.5	7	60	3C

RST 6 and RST 7. The CPU transfers to the indicated interrupt routine exactly as though an RST instruction had been executed.

The design of the interrupting device is simplified by using specific hardware pins as indicators of the interrupt service routine location. The device only needs to set the required pin to a specific logic level; the CPU will then know where to find the interrupt routine.

This approach can be extended to indirect addressing. The interrupting pins simply specify, by some formula, the location of the memory location containing the interrupt vector.

Because the vector data are fixed in hardware, the programmer cannot simply initialize the vector data in software. Thus, although this vectoring technique does not require as complex an interrupting device, it is less flexible.

EXAMPLE 9.2 Printer Control

A microprocessor is used to control a printer that is a peripheral to a large data processing system. The microprocessor accepts and stores ASCII character bytes in its buffer memory. Further, it uses the ASCII data to form the commands for the various stepper motors and hammers that actually do the printing. Normally, the microprocessor, an 8085, performs a main routine that does these printing actions based on the data in the buffer memory. When new data are ready from the outside world, there is an interrupt. The processor accepts the new data on a character-by-character interrupt basis, possibly slowing the printing action slightly.

The following code highlights the areas of the software that must be provided so that the interrupt can be serviced properly.

```
            ORG     0H
            DI                  ;NO INTERRUPTS UNTIL WE'RE READY
            JMP     MAIN
        .
        .
    RST6    EQU     0F7H        ;OP CODE FOR RST 6
    IOINTR  EQU     1FH         ;I/O INTERRUPT VECTOR REGISTER
    DATA    EQU     30H         ;VECTOR ADDRESS OF INTERRUPT
        .
        .
                                (Other equates)
        .
        .
        .
            ORG     DATA        ;ADDRESS OF INTERRUPT PROCESSING
            JMP     INPUT       ;DATA INPUT INTERRUPT SERVICE ROUTINE
        .
        .
            ORG     XXX         ;START OF MAIN ROUTINE
    MAIN    LXI     SP,STACK
            CALL    INIT        ;INITIALIZE
            EI                  ;BRING ON THE DATA
    MAIN1   .
        .
                                (Body of main program)
        .
            JMP     MAIN1       ;AROUND THE MAIN LOOP AGAIN
```

```
;SUBROUTINE INITIALIZES VARIOUS PORTS, ETC.
INIT    MVI    A,RST6  ;SET UP INTERRUPT SMART VECTOR FROM PORT
        OUT    IOINTR
         .
         .             (Other initialization)
         .
        RET
;
         .
         .             (Other subroutines)
         .
;
;INTERRUPT SERVICE ROUTINE
INPUT    .
         .             (Body of input routine)
         .
        EI
        RET            ;REENABLE INTERRUPTS
         .
                       (Other routines)
         .
```

These fragments of a much larger program start with a DI instruction that disables interrupt processing until the software has properly set up various parameters. This instruction is placed at location zero since the 8085 starts processing at this location upon power-up. As usual, the various parameters for the program are placed at the top of the source code for easy maintenance. The JMP instruction moves the PC to the main body of the program.

The next code executed, labeled MAIN, sets up a stack location. The program then calls the initialization subroutine, INIT. Here, among many other initialization operations, the interrupt vector data are passed to the I/O device. The label for this vector data is RST6. The actual value is based on the equates at the top of the listing and is F7, hexadecimal. Thus, the smart I/O device will return F7, hexadecimal, as the interrupt vector after an interrupt has been initiated. This is the operation code for restart number 6 (RST 6).

At the end of the INIT routine, control is passed back to the main program where interrupts are enabled (using an EI instruction) and the main printing loop is processed. When an interrupt occurs, the 8085 is vectored by the F7, hexadecimal, parameter to location 30, hexadecimal. The ORG INTR6 assembler directive forces the next instruction, JMP INPUT, to reside at location 30 based on the equates at the top of the listing. From here the interrupt service routine jumps to its main body at INPUT.

As we have discussed several times, all this indirection on top of indirection has a purpose. The finished code has English-like words for the various address and data parameters, rather than specific numbers. The equates at the top of the source code define the key parameters of the code in one organized grouping.

The code jumps to the interrupt service routine, rather than placing the routine directly at location 30, hexadecimal. This is done since location 34, hexadecimal, provides the vector address for the RST 6.5 hardware interrupt. Any reasonable service routine at location 30 would overwrite location 34 and disallow use of the RST 6.5 interrupt.

9.4 MULTIPLE INTERRUPTS

Many complex tasks require more than one interrupting device. A telephone-routing system must respond to calls repeatedly and process the telephone traffic properly. A robotics system can handle inputs from a variety of sources.

With proper design, repeated interrupts can occur with no difficulties. Interrupts act much like subroutines and can generally be nested extensively, assuming proper care in programming. Difficulties arise when the stack size is too small, parameter passing is not properly handled, registers are not maintained across the interrupt routines, or there are other such programming errors.

During system design the expected level of interrupt nesting should be considered. If multiple interrupts are processed, it is possible for a critical interrupt to be serviced long after it initially occurred. Interrupt masking and interrupt prioritization techniques often help avoid such problems.

Interrupt Mask

As its names implies, an **interrupt mask** screens interrupts. This is done by using either software or hardware.

To avoid the difficulties of nesting interrupts, many applications require that certain routines be performed without being disturbed. A software interrupt mask can be invoked at the start of such a routine. No additional masked interrupts will be recognized until the mask is removed at the end of the routine.

A software interrupt mask is an instruction that inhibits the recognition of further interrupts. In addition, such masks can often be established to inhibit only selected interrupts.

Hardware interrupt masks, using dedicated logic, simply inhibit the initiation of selected interrupts. Figure 9.4 shows a typical hardware interrupt mask implementation. Each of the mask lines disables a specific interrupt when the line is driven to a zero.

Many microprocessors have more than one form of interrupt. For example, a reset can be considered as a form of interrupt. This general category of unusual processing is often called **exception processing**. Some exceptions, such as a reset and often certain interrupts, cannot

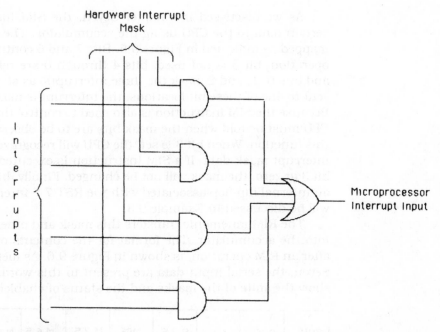

Figure 9.4
Hardware Interrupt Mask.

be masked, at least in software. Microprocessors are designed this way so that certain exceptions, such as a reset, can always be seen. These interrupts and exceptions are termed **nonmaskable.**

An interrupt mask is often invoked when normal processing requires that the CPU perform an operation without disturbance. For example, if a program has a critically timed routine, interrupts might be masked until the routine is completed. Let us assume a microprocessor is controlling a machine tool. If the CPU were to start the cutting tool downward and were then interrupted, the tool might do considerable damage before the CPU returned from interrupt processing. In such a situation, the programmer would invoke the interrupt mask during the routine that lowers the cutting tool.

The 8085 has five interrupts—INTR, RST7.5, RST6.5, RST5.5, and TRAP (RST4.5)—and a reset exception. Four of these are maskable—INTR, RST7.5, RST6.5, and RST5.5. The disable interrupt, DI, instruction disables, or masks, all four. Interrupts are disabled automatically when an interrupt is processed. A reset enables interrupts.

Many microprocessors allow the establishment of an interrupt mask that screens out only selected interrupts. For example, we have seen that the 8085 can be set to disable all maskable interrupts; however, in addition to this, it allows the selective masking of interrupts through the SIM (set interrupt mask) and RIM (read interrupt mask) instructions.

As we discussed in Chapter Seven, the SIM instruction transfers certain data to the CPU using the accumulator. The information is bit-mapped as indicated in Figure 9.5. Bits 7 and 6 control the serial output operation; bit 5 is not used, bits 4 through 0 are related to interrupts, and bits 0, 1, and 2 mask the three interrupts, as shown. When a one is sent to one of these bit locations, the interrupt is masked; it is disabled. Because the SIM instruction is also used to control the serial output, the CPU must be told when the mask bits are to be observed. Bit 3 performs this function. When bit 3 is set, the CPU will recognize bits 0, 1, and 2 as interrupt mask data. If a SIM instruction is executed with accumulator bit 3 at zero, the mask will not be changed. Finally, bit 4 is used to reset an internal flip-flop associated with the RST 7.5 interrupt. This flip-flop will be discussed in Example 9.3.

The RIM mnemonic transfers this mask and other information back into the accumulator. The format for the contents of the accumulator, after an RIM operation, is shown in Figure 9.6. As mentioned in Chapter Seven, the serial input data are present in this word. The last four bits show the state of the masks and the status of enablement of interrupts.

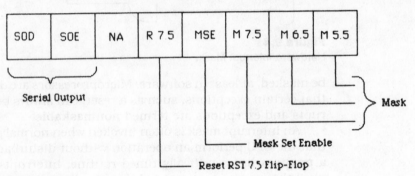

Figure 9.5
8085 SIM Bit Mapping.

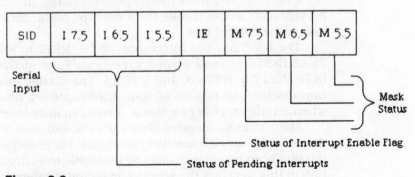

Figure 9.6
8085 RIM Bit Mapping.

Bits 4, 5, and 6 define the state of pending interrupts, as will be discussed in the next section.

The following code fragment first sets the mask with the RST 6.5 interrupt disabled and then enables interrupts. It later reads the mask to the accumulator and sends the mask byte out to the I/O location PRINT.

```
MVI    A,0AH    ;RST 6.5 MASKED OUT
SIM
EI
.
.
.
RIM             ;(mask to accumulator)
OUT PRINT       ;PRINT IT
```

The 8080-like INTR interrupt can only be disabled using the DI instruction. It cannot be selectively masked. The EI instruction enables only the interrupts that have not been masked by a previous SIM instruction.

Interrupt Priority Levels

The discussion of the previous section skirted on the edges of a discussion of interrupt priority levels. When the processor started to lower the cutting tool, it disabled interrupts. This action amounted to establishing the lowering operation at a higher priority level than any maskable interrupts. However, if during the tool-lowering routine the reset were initiated, the machine would be reset. In such an event, the reset would have been given a priority level higher than the tool-lowering routine.

Interrupt prioritization can take on several forms. What happens when there are two interrupts at the same time? What happens if an interrupt occurs during the processing of another interrupt? What happens if several interrupts occur while an interrupt is being processed? These issues can be addressed by proper hardware and software design.

As usual, the specifics of interrupt prioritization vary significantly from one microprocessor family to another. The 8085 is typical.

The basic interrupt prioritization scheme for the 8085 is shown in Table 9.3. Interrupt RST 4.5 is also known as the TRAP interrupt. Nonmaskable, it is the highest-priority normal interrupt. When two interrupts are simultaneous and one of them is the TRAP interrupt, TRAP will be executed. It is not even masked by the DI instruction. The only action having higher priority than TRAP is a hardware reset. TRAP will interrupt an interrupt routine being processed, including a routine from a previous TRAP.

Because of the high priority of TRAP, the 8085 TRAP input pin has special protection. It is both level- and edge-sensitive. It must go high and

Table 9.3
8085 Interrupt Priorities

Interrupt Name	Priority	Comments
RST 4.5 (TRAP)	1	Nonmaskable, hardware-vectored
RST 7.5	2	Maskable, hardware-vectored
RST 6.5	3	Maskable, hardware-vectored
RST 5.5	4	Maskable, hardware-vectored
INTR	5	Smart interrupt, similar to 8080 interrupt scheme

stay there until acknowledged. To be recognized again, it must go back low and return to a high state again. A steady one on the TRAP input will thus not cause perpetual interrupts.

Normally, the RIM instruction displays the IE-flag in its third bit. Because the TRAP interrupt occurs regardless of the status of this flag and because interrupts are disabled as soon as a TRAP is processed, an RIM operation at the start of a TRAP routine is designed to yield the previous status of the IE-flag rather than its current status. This feature is used when the machine status must be restored at the end of the TRAP service routine. The flag is sampled at the start of the TRAP routine; it is then saved; at the end of the routine, the IE-flag is reinstated.

The other three RST X.5 hardware interrupts have the priorities shown. If two interrupts occur at the same time, the higher-priority interrupt will win.

A normal step for most interrupt processing in the 8085 is to establish the processing for further interrupts. As mentioned, the start of interrupt processing automatically disables further maskable interrupts. The programmer can set up the interrupt mask in the interrupt service routine using SIM. The EI instruction must then be used to enable the nonmasked interrupts. The issue of interrupting an interrupt service routine can thus be resolved in the service routine software.

A key element of a good interrupt service routine is to save the complete status of the interrupted program, restoring it at the end of the routine. If the interrupt service routine changes the interrupt mask, the old mask status should be saved and restored at the end of the routine. Interrupts should be enabled at the end of the routine since, for INTR, RST7.5, RST6.5, and RST5.5, interrupts were obviously enabled at the time of the interrupt. A TRAP routine must use an initial RIM to determine the status of the interrupt mask.

If an interrupt occurs and is held while it is masked or disabled, the IX.5 bit returned by the RIM instruction will be set. These bits allow the program to determine whether any interrupts are pending. If the EI instruction is given with multiple interrupts pending, nonmasked interrupts are serviced in the order of their priorities.

We can now answer the questions asked earlier in this section assuming the use of an 8085. We first state that the TRAP, or RST 4.5, interrupt will always be immediately processed. Beyond this, what happens when two interrupts occur at the same time?

Given that they are not masked or disabled, the higher-priority interrupt is serviced.

What happens if an interrupt occurs during the processing of another interrupt?

The interrupt service routine determines which interrupts are to be recognized.

What happens if several interrupts occur while an interrupt is being processed?

Any masked or disabled interrupts that remain asserted when unmasked or enabled are processed based on the priority levels.

EXAMPLE 9.3 Building Monitor

A building monitor system uses prioritized interrupts to direct program flow. The main program reads a serial port tied to a modem. The modem receives news and other information. The microprocessor displays this information at various places in the building. The four interrupts used are

RST 5.5—A thermostat has changed state.

RST 6.5—A motion sensor has detected motion where none should be occurring.

RST 7.5—A door that should be locked has opened.

TRAP—A heat sensor has detected a fire.

The hardware used for the RST 7.5 interrupt produces a pulse rather than a steady logic level. The 8085's design allows the RST 7.5 interrupt to be held after such a pulse. When the RST 7.5 input changes to a one, an internal flip-flop changes state. The flip-flop holds the interrupt request, even if the input logic level drops back to a zero. This flip-flop is reset to the noninterrupt state when the interrupt is recognized by the CPU, when it is reset by a one at bit 4 of an SIM operation (see Figure 9.5), or when a hardware reset occurs.

Our building monitor program keeps interrupts disabled during interrupt processing except for the RST5.5 routine. For this low-priority interrupt, only further RST5.5 interrupts are masked. At the end of all the interrupt service routines, interrupts are reenabled.

The equates for this example contain vector data for each of the interrupt service routines, as follows.

```
                    ;
                    ;
                ORG     24H          ;FIRE ALARM VECTOR
                JMP     FIRE
                    ;
                ORG     2CH          ;THERMOSTAT CHANGE VECTOR
                JMP     THERMO
                    ;
                ORG     34H          ;MOTION SENSOR VECTOR
                JMP     MOTION
                    ;
                ORG     3CH          ;DOOR CHECK VECTOR
                JMP     DOOR
                    ;
                    ;
```

The main program initializes the interrupt mask and enables interrupts at start-up of the program.

```
                    ;
MAIN    MVI     A,18H        ;RESET RST 7.5 F/F, UNMASK INTERRUPTS
        SIM
        EI
```

Only the RST 5.5 interrupt service routine starts by setting the interrupt mask and enabling interrupts. At its conclusion, the routine must restore the mask properly. The routine does not destroy any register data.

```
THERMO PUSH PSW
        MVI     A,09H        ;MASK OUT FURTHER RST 5.5
        SIM
        EI
        
        MVI     A,08H        ;UNMASK RST 5.5
        POP     PSW
        RET
        ;
```

Let us assume that an arsonist breaks into the building by forcing a locked door. The arsonist quickly ignites a firebomb and exits back through the door. Figure 9.7 shows the path followed by the CPU through the various interrupt service routines.

We see that at the start the main program is running. When the

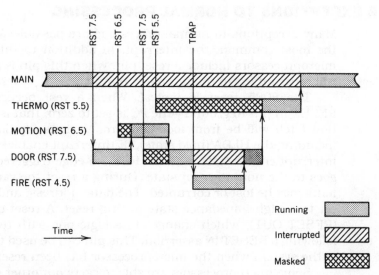

Figure 9.7
Interrupts for Example 9.3.

arsonist forces the door, RST 7.5 starts. It informs the building guard by means of a trouble panel. This takes some time since phone lines are used. Meanwhile, the RST 6.5 interrupt asserts because the motion of the arsonist has been sensed.

Once the DOOR interrupt service routine finishes, MOTION begins in response to the earlier RST 6.5. MOTION also calls the guard and takes some time. During this routine the arsonist leaves the building. This causes RST 7.5 to be pulsed. The internal RST 7.5 flip-flop sets. The new interrupt is not serviced because MOTION has disabled interrupts.

In addition, during the response to the RST 6.5, a thermostat changes state. The processor receives an RST 5.5 interrupt that would normally turn on a heater. Nothing happens, however, because interrupts are disabled.

At the end of MOTION, DOOR begins processing because interrupts have been enabled. While this routine is running, a TRAP occurs because of the fire. This interrupt service routine, FIRE, begins at once and calls both the fire department and the guard, who must be getting worried about this time. Once this routine is finished, the interrupted RST 7.5 completes its task.

Finally, the processor, having done all it can about the emergency, returns first to the task of turning on the heat, THERMO. This is the response to the pending RST 5.5 interrupt, which is only serviced when the other higher-priority tasks have been completed. After this routine the processor continues to display the news, something about a building fire.

9.5 OTHER EXCEPTIONS TO NORMAL PROCESSING

Many exceptions to normal processing are possible. We have discussed the most common, the interrupt. In addition to this exception, most microprocessors include a reset pin. When this pin is activated, the CPU will return itself to the normal turn-on state.

The 8085 reset is typical. When a rest occurs—by forcing the $\overline{\text{RESET IN}}$ pin to ground—the PC is set to zero, that is, the next instruction fetch will be from location zero. Various flip-flops are also reset, including the HLDA (hold state), IE (interrupt enable), which goes to the interrupt enable state, and the RST 7.5 edge-triggered interrupt, which goes to the noninterrupt state. During a reset the various register contents may be lost or corrupted. The data, address, and control buses are set to a high-impedance state during reset. A reset output is provided (RESET OUT), which changes to a logic one with the next clock cycle following a RESET IN assertion. This pin can be used to reset other parts of the system when the microprocessor has been reset.

Some microprocessors are able to carry out other exception processing. An example would be the illegal instruction vector provided on the Motorola 68000. If a fetched instruction is not part of the instruction set, the 68000 will vector out of normal processing. The programmer can provide code that resolves the difficulty. The 8085 does not support this particular feature.

Another common example of exception processing is a bus error routine. Here external hardware monitors each CPU addressing operation. If the CPU requests an address not in the system memory map or if some other data transfer error is detected, the CPU is forced into a special routine that can correct, or at least note, the error. The 8085 can be made to support this form of exception processing by connecting the external hardware to one of the interrupts, most likely the TRAP interrupt; the interrupt service routine can then dispose of the problem.

EXERCISES

9.1 The 8085 is normally given an RST instruction in response to an INTR interrupt. If the interrupt service routine is placed directly at the RST address, how long can we make the RST 1 routine without overflowing into the memory area for other interrupt vectors? The RST 2? The RST 7?

9.2 The start-up of the 8085 occurs at location zero in memory. How much code can be placed in this start-up space and still allow a TRAP interrupt to be serviced?

9.3 An 8085-based system has a 256-byte stack. Each interrupt service routine stores no more than the status word (PUSH PSW) on the stack.

Two subroutines are used. They are nested. How deeply can the interrupts be nested?

9.4 An 8085-based system uses all the interrupt vectors of the processor (RST X.X, INT, and TRAP). Using jumps to routines labeled INT1, INT2, INT3, and so on, write the assembly language code necessary to establish the vector table.

9.5 Modify the source code of Example 9.2 to use hardware interrupt RST 6.5.

9.6 Some processors have very simple interrupt processing, with only a single interrupt pin. When an interrupt is asserted, the processor simply saves the PC and transfers control to a fixed location. With proper software, multiple interrupt techniques can be used with these processors by feeding vector, mask, and priority data through normal I/O ports to hardware devices which provide the functions. Can such a technique be used with a processor like the 8085? What would be the advantage?

9.7 What is the net effect of an RST 0 on the 8085? How does it differ from a reset?

9.8 Show how the program of Example 9.3 would be modified so that RST 6.5 and RST 7.5 are serviced by the same routine, TROUBLE. TROUBLE must not allow itself to be interrupted by another RST 6.5 or RST 7.5.

9.9 Rats have caused repeated RST 6.5 interrupts of the program in Example 9.3. Because of this, the thermostat service routine has been delayed for long periods of time. Given that a real-time clock (simply counting hours, minutes, and seconds) is available at three of the I/O ports (35, 36, and 37, hexadecimal), how might MOTION avoid delaying a thermostat change by no more than a minute in the presence of repeated RST 6.5 interrupts.

9.10 The power supply for a robot, based on the 8085, has a power failure feature. If a power failure occurs, this line goes high. The microprocessor power will remain in force for 2 milliseconds after this event. There are 20 motors in the robot, each addressed at a byte in I/O-mapped I/O. Before the loss of microprocessor power, the processor must null the output to all these motors and save all its internal registers on the stack. The stack RAM is nonvolatile. What interrupt should be used? Does the processor have time to complete these tasks?

CHAPTER TEN

APPLICATION EXAMPLES

10.1 INTRODUCTION

This chapter demonstrates how a microprocessor system might be used in a variety of applications. The examples are treated in a simplified manner so that the techniques can be presented as directly as is possible. All the techniques are for **embedded** microprocessors, that is, computers programmed for one specific task.

As usual, this chapter uses the 8085 instruction set and hardware for all the examples. This does not imply that the 8085 is the best choice for these applications. Indeed, today the single-chip microcontrollers are the most popular for these kinds of applications.

The first three examples have to do with more and more complex implementations of sequence controllers. Example 10.3 is a complete digital clock using an interrupt for timing. Example 10.4 demonstrates a system using digital-to-analog conversion.

These examples are intended to be as realistic as possible. This intent often conflicts with the desire to place the example programs in the SDK-85 memory map. In real systems the object code might be located elsewhere. In addition, a real system must resolve the problems of start-up and initialization. All but one of the examples (and part of another) are based on the SDK-85 memory map. Example 10.2 uses a different memory map. Both Examples 10.1 and 10.2 address start-up.

10.2 SEQUENCING

Earlier we introduced the instructions provided by a microprocessor that allow transfer of data between the CPU and an I/O port. Such data might be the binary representation of numbers or letters; in addition, logical data might be transferred. **Logical data** define the state of some device, or of a command that brings a device to a required state. Logical data are generally bit-mapped. One of the examples in Chapter Eight manipulated logical data that defined the bit-mapped state of light switches and of filament current. The logical output there was a command for warning lights.

Sequencing of output commands is one of the simplest examples of the use of logical data. Typically, a sequencer activates a number of devices in a preset pattern with a preset time delay between each new device state. For example, a traffic light sequencer changes the state of each light in a set of traffic lights in a preset pattern. A specific time delay is required between each state.

A microprocessor is used as a sequence controller by directing the required output port lines to an on or an off state. This is done in the required sequence and with the required delays. Since the microprocessor can easily be crystal-controlled, the timing will remain very repeatable both over time and from one system to the next.

EXAMPLE 10.1 Traffic Light Sequencer

A simple traffic light sequencer would have no inputs. It would simply direct the various lights to shine in a predetermined sequence. A typical sequence in the United States might be red, left-turn arrow, green, yellow, red again, and so on. The road junction is shown in Figure 10.1. There are two roads labeled N/S and E/W. The lights are labeled RYGL for red, yellow, green, and left turn. Both N/S lights work in unison, as do the E/W lights.

The sequence that the controller must provide is shown in Figure 10.2. Notice that three different delay times are used during the complete cycle, and that the delay times are associated with specific lights. Delay 1 goes with the green lights; delay 2 is associated with the yellow; delay 3 is used only with the left-turn lights.

Table 10.1, called a **state table**, shows the sequence of light conditions required. We use this state table to define the bit-mapped output commands. That is, we assume a hardware design that causes the N/S red lights to go on when the MSB of the output byte is a one. When the next output bit is a one (bit 6 in the range zero to 7), the N/S yellow lights will be on. Thus, a single byte is adequate to define the state of the lights.

We build the sequencer by storing this state table in sequential memory locations; the program will be designed to step through the table one state at a time. At each step the state byte will be sent out to the lights. A delay will be initiated based on the specific bits present in the state byte. Thus, if the program arrives at a state in which the yellow lights are

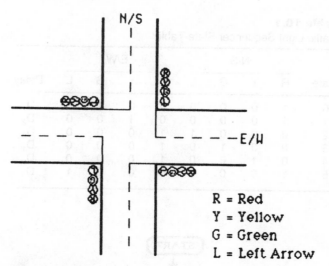

R = Red
Y = Yellow
G = Green
L = Left Arrow

Figure 10.1
Road Junction.

N/S				E/W				Delay
Red	Yellow	Green	Left	Red	Yellow	Green	Left	
On	Off	Off	Off	Off	Off	On	Off	D_1
On	Off	Off	Off	Off	On	Off	Off	D_2
Off	Off	Off	On	On	Off	Off	Off	D_3
Off	Off	On	Off	On	Off	Off	Off	D_1
Off	On	Off	Off	On	Off	Off	Off	D_2
On	Off	Off	Off	Off	Off	Off	On	D_3

D_1 = Green Light Delay
D_2 = Yellow Light Delay
D_3 = Left Turn Light Delay

Figure 10.2
Traffic Light Sequence.

on in either direction, the second delay time will be requested. At the end of the delay, the next sequential state will be called. This process will repeat until the program reaches the bottom of the state table. When this happens, the first state will be reselected and the process will begin again.

Figure 10.3 shows a flowchart for this traffic light sequencer. The assembly language program follows. Notice that the delay requests use

Table 10.1
Traffic Light Sequencer State Table

	N/S				E/W				
State	R	Y	G	L	R	Y	G	L	Delay
0	1	0	0	0	0	0	1	0	D_1
1	1	0	0	0	0	1	0	0	D_2
2	0	0	0	1	1	0	0	0	D_3
3	0	0	1	0	1	0	0	0	D_1
4	0	1	0	0	1	0	0	0	D_2
5	1	0	0	0	0	0	0	1	D_3

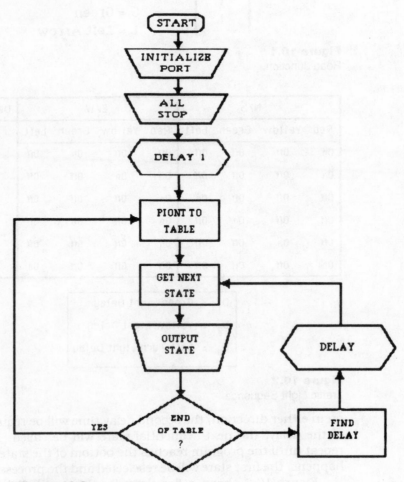

Figure 10.3
Flowchart for Example 10.1.

the same delay routine. They pass different parameters to specify the required delay times. The program runs starting at 2000, hexadecimal. We have established a 32-byte stack at the end of the code. The equates are placed near the top of the source code for clarity. This requires the JMP MAIN instruction so that the processor will not try to execute the state table as though it were a list of operation codes.

```
            ORG    2000H
            LXI    STACK
            JMP    MAIN
;
;STATE TABLE
;
                               N/S      E/W
                               R Y G L  R Y G L
STATE       DB     82H         ;1 0 0 0  0 0 1 0
            DB     84H         ;1 0 0 0  0 1 0 0
            DB     18H         ;0 0 0 1  1 0 0 0
            DB     28H         ;0 0 1 0  1 0 0 0
            DB     48H         ;0 1 0 0  1 0 0 0
            DB     81H         ;1 0 0 0  0 0 0 1
            DB     0H          ;DEFINES THE END OF STATE TABLE
;
RED         EQU    88H         ;1 0 0 0  1 0 0 0 ALL STOP
;
;LIGHT COLOR MASKS
MASK1       EQU    22H         ;0 0 1 0  0 0 1 0 GREEN MASK
MASK2       EQU    44H         ;0 1 0 0  0 1 0 0 YELLOW MASK
MASK3       EQU    11H         ;0 0 0 1  0 0 0 1 LEFT TURN MASK
;
;DELAY TIMES IN SECONDS
DELAY1 EQU  3CH                ;GREEN—60 IN HEX
DELAY2 EQU  04H                ;YELLOW
DELAY3 EQU  1EH                ;LEFT TURN—30 IN HEX
;
LIGHTS EQU  0                  ;OUTPUT PORT FOR LIGHTS
LCMND  EQU  2                  ;COMMAND PORT FOR LIGHTS OUTPUT PORT
;
MAIN        MVI    A,0FFH      ;INITIALIZE PORT
            OUT    LCMND
            MVI    A,RED       ;ALL STOP FOR ONE DELAY No. 1
            OUT    LIGHTS
            MVI    B,DELAY1
            CALL   DELAY
MAIN1       LXI    H,STATE     ;POINT TO STATE TABLE
MAIN2       MOV    A,M         ;NEXT STATE
            ANA    A           ;SETS FLAGS
            JZ     MAIN1       ;END OF TABLE
            OUT    LIGHTS
            MVI    B,DELAY1    ;FIND AND DO PROPER DELAY
            ANI    MASK1
            JNZ    MAIN3
            MVI    B,DELAY2
            MOV    A,M
            ANI    MASK2
            JNZ    MAIN3
            MVI    B,DELAY3
MAIN3       CALL   DELAY
            INX    H           ;NEXT STATE
            JMP    MAIN2
;
;DELAY ROUTINE—DELAY, IN SECONDS, ASSUMED IN B-REGISTER
```

```
            ;DESTROYS A-, C-, D-, AND E-REGISTER CONTENTS
            ;RETURNS ZERO IN B
DELAY   LXI     D,03E8H         ;1,000 TIMES THROUGH 1IMS DELAY
DLY1    DCX     D
        CALL    SDELAY          ;1MS DELAY ROUTINE
        MOV     A,D             ;TRICK TO TEST FOR ZERO IN DE
        ORA     E
        JNZ     DLY1
        DCR     B               ;ENOUGH 1-SEC DELAYS?
        RZ
        JMP     DELAY
;
;
        ;SHORT DELAY—1 MILLISECOND
        ;SLIGHTLY LESS TO ALLOW FOR OTHER DELAYS
        ;DESTROYS C-REGISTER CONTENTS
SDELAY  MVI     C,0D5H          ;213 TIMES GIVES ABOUT 980 MICROSEC
SDELAY1 DCR     C
        JNZ     SDELAY1         ;MORE
        RET
;
        DS      20H             ;STACK SPACE
STACK   END
```

The object code for this program is 83 bytes long. With the 32-byte stack, the total is 105 bytes.

For the traffic light sequencer application to run well in the real world, the program would require some modification. The stack requires RAM, but we would probably want masked ROM for the program. In our program they are addressed in the same range of memory. The most direct method of solving this problem is to provide RAM at some location. The program would load the stack pointer into this RAM—using the LXI instruction. Because the RAM is only being used as a stack for subroutine calls, we can eliminate the RAM entirely by writing the program without subroutines. This is straightforward if we eliminate the all-stop operation at the start of the program. The resulting code follows. It is more difficult to understand without the subroutines; however, it takes less storage space. This time we have started the code at the normal reset address for the 8085.

```
            ORG     0H          ;8085 START-UP
            JMP     MAIN
;
;STATE TABLE
;                               N/S             E/W
;                               R Y G L         R Y G L
STATE   DB      82H             ;1 0 0 0        0 0 1 0
        DB      84H             ;1 0 0 0        0 1 0 0
        DB      18H             ;0 0 0 1        1 0 0 0
        DB      28H             ;0 0 1 0        1 0 0 0
        DB      48H             ;0 1 0 0        1 0 0 0
        DB      81H             ;1 0 0 0        0 0 0 1
        DB      0H              ;DEFINES THE END OF STATE TABLE
;
;LIGHT COLOR MASKS
MASK1   EQU     22H             ;0 0 1 0        0 0 1 0 GREEN MASK
MASK2   EQU     44H             ;0 1 0 0        0 1 0 0 YELLOW MASK
MASK3   EQU     11H             ;0 0 0 1        0 0 0 1 LEFT TURN MASK
;
```

```
                    ;DELAY TIMES IN SECONDS
                    DELAY1    EQU    3CH        ;GREEN—60 IN HEX
                    DELAY2    EQU    04H        ;YELLOW
                    DELAY3    EQU    1EH        ;LEFT TURN—30 IN HEX
                    ;
                    ;
                    LIGHTS    EQU    0          ;OUTPUT PORT FOR LIGHTS
                    LCMND     EQU    2          ;COMMAND PORT FOR LIGHTS I/O PORT
                    ;
                    ;
                    MAIN      MVI    A,0FFH     ;INITIALIZE PORT
                              OUT    LCMND
                    MAIN1     LXI    H,STATE    ;POINT TO STATE TABLE
                    MAIN2     MOV    A,M        ;NEXT STATE
                              ANA    A          ;SETS FLAGS
                              JZ     MAIN1      ;END OF TABLE
                              OUT    LIGHTS
                              MVI    B,DELAY1   ;FIND AND DO PROPER DELAY
                              ANI    MASK1
                              JNZ    MAIN3
                              MVI    B,DELAY2
                              MOV    A,M
                              ANI    MASK2
                              JNZ    MAIN3
                              MVI    B,DELAY3
                    ;NOW THE LONG DELAY FOR B TIMES
                    MAIN3     LXI    D,03E8H    ;1,000 TIMES THROUGH 1MS DELAY
                    DLY1      DCX    D
                    ;NOW THE SHORT DELAY ONCE
                    SDELAY    MVI    C,0D5H     ;213 TIMES GIVES ABOUT 980 MICROSEC
                    SDELAY1   DCR    C
                              JNZ    SDELAY1    ;MORE
                    ;TEST AS PART OF 1-SEC DELAY
                              MOV    A,D        ;TRICK TO TEST FOR ZERO IN DE
                              ORA    E
                              JNZ    DLY1
                    ;FINISHED ANOTHER SECOND—MORE REQUIRED?
                              DCR    B          ;ENOUGH 1-SEC DELAYS?
                              JNZ    MAIN3
                    ;ONWARD TO NEXT STATE OF LIGHTS
                              INX    H          ;NEXT STATE
                              JMP    MAIN2
                    ;
                              END
```

This assembles to 64 bytes. No RAM is required. Figure 10.4 is a complete schematic for this application; the 115-volt lights are shown driven from solid-state relays (SSRs).

One might ask whether a microprocessor is really required for such a simple task. The answer is, perhaps, no. On the other hand, notice that the physical hardware is quite simple. Moreover, the operation of the lights can be changed completely with only a ROM change. With a RAM chip and an input port—for the 8085 family this is part of the RAM and the ROM devices—a very sophisticated light controller is possible, using only a handful of parts.

This last point is important. We have kept the examples as simple and direct as possible; however, the techniques can be extended to provide very flexible modern solutions to technical problems.

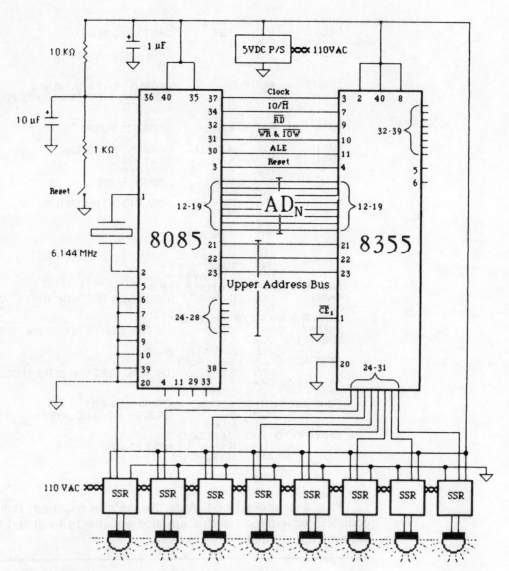

Figure 10.4
Schematic for Light Sequencer.

10.3 CONDITIONAL SEQUENCING

In some sequencing applications, a change of state may depend on an input condition, rather than the passage of a fixed delay. An example is a program that fills a tank during one of its sequential states. The microprocessor would hold the fill valve open until the tank-full input is true. No fixed delay would be needed. This process is termed **conditional**

sequencing. The microprocessor is made to loop until the required condition is met.

The traffic light sequencer in Example 10.1 can be made much more powerful with conditional sequencing. Pavement switches would be required to provide processor input regarding the movement of traffic. A first modification of the sequencer would be to change state only when new traffic is present. Another would be to skip the left-turn light if no left-turn traffic is present. A more exotic system would be one that changed the delays and sequence dynamically based on traffic patterns, time of day, moisture present, and so on. Aside from sensors and circuits to provide the input data, no new hardware would be required using the version that included RAM support.

Interrupt processing can be a form of conditional processing. The microprocessor filling a tank might turn on the fill valve; it might then go on about its business while waiting for a tank-full interrupt. The traffic light sequencer might have a separate sequence activated by an interrupt. Such an interrupt input might be activated by a special switch available to the police in emergencies.

EXAMPLE 10.2 Washing Machine Sequencer

A washing machine controller is a conditional sequencer using both external inputs and internal preset time delays. The principles of this example apply to many industrial sequencer configurations; its I/O requirements are shown in Table 10.2. The sequence of actions required of the washing machine are shown in Table 10.3. This is directly translated into the state table of Table 10.4. The table is so arranged that after a state with no time delay the next entry is the input action necessary for terminating this state and advancing to the next one.

The controller program simply steps through each state of Table 10.4 with the appropriate delays and with the required wait for conditional inputs. Since there are six controlled devices and two delay states, we have included the delay command bits with the 8-bit state word. The delay command bits are used, in turn, as input commands when no output is called. Thus, state 3 requests device 4—the pump—to go on for delay 2 time; state 4 turns the cold water on for the rinse and then performs a conditional wait for input 1—tub full.

The program that follows is located at the start of the 8085 memory. This is the location to which the 8085 will go at start-up or reset. No interrupts are allowed since we have written over the vector locations. If interrupts were used, the instruction at zero could be a jump to a program start point in higher memory.

The six output lines are assumed to be bit-mapped to port A, and the

Table 10.2

I/O Requirements for a Washing Machine Controller

Logical Outputs	Controlled Device
0	Hot-water control valve
1	Cold-water control valve
2	Water heater
3	Tub motor—wash/rinse speed
4	Pump motor (for emptying tub)
5	Tub motor—spin speed
Logical Inputs	Significance
1	Tub full
2	Water thermostat

Table 10.3

Simplified Washing Machine Sequence

State Number		Controlled Device						Action
		0	1	2	3	4	5	
Wash	0	ON	OFF	OFF	OFF	OFF	OFF	Fill tub with hot water.
	1	OFF	OFF	OFF	ON	OFF	OFF	Heat water until thermostat closes.
	2	OFF	OFF	ON	OFF	OFF	OFF	Rotate tub at wash/rinse speed for a fixed time D_1.
	3	OFF	OFF	OFF	OFF	ON	OFF	Empty tub for a fixed time D_2.
Rinse	4	OFF	ON	OFF	OFF	OFF	OFF	Fill tub with cold water until full.
	5	OFF	OFF	OFF	ON	OFF	OFF	Rotate tub at wash/rinse speed for fixed time D_1.
	6	OFF	OFF	OFF	OFF	ON	OFF	Empty tub for a fixed time D_2.
Spin	7	OFF	OFF	OFF	OFF	OFF	ON	Spin for fixed time D_1.
off		OFF	OFF	OFF	OFF	OFF	OFF	Stop.

two input lines are assumed to be bit-mapped to port B of a programmable I/O device. Notice that the program ends with a halt instruction. This halt causes the 8085 to stop until a reset occurs.

```
;WASHING MACHINE CONDITIONAL SEQUENCER
;
            ORG       0
            LXI       STACK
            JMP       MAIN
;STATE TABLE
;
STATE       DB        80H       ;1 0 0 0 0 0  0 0
            DB        02H       ;0 0 0 0 0 0  1 0
```

Table 10.4
Washing Machine Controller State Table

State Number	Controlled Device						Delay/Input		
	0	1	2	3	4	5	D_1/1	D_2/2	
0	1	0	0	0	0	0	0	0	
	0	0	0	0	0	0	1	0	Tub full
1	0	0	1	0	0	0	0	0	
	0	0	0	0	0	0	0	1	Thermostat
2	0	0	0	1	0	0	1	0	
3	0	0	0	0	1	0	0	1	
4	0	1	0	0	0	0	0	0	
	0	0	0	0	0	0	1	0	Tub full
5	0	0	0	1	0	0	1	0	
6	0	0	0	0	1	0	0	1	
7	0	0	0	0	0	1	1	0	
8	0	0	0	0	0	0	0	0	

```
            DB      20H     ;0 0 1 0 0 0   0 0
            DB      01H     ;0 0 0 0 0 0   0 1
            DB      12H     ;0 0 0 1 0 0   1 0
            DB      09H     ;0 0 0 0 1 0   0 1
            DB      40H     ;0 1 0 0 0 0   0 0
            DB      02H     ;0 0 0 0 0 0   1 0
            DB      12H     ;0 0 0 1 0 0   1 0
            DB      09H     ;0 0 0 0 1 0   0 1
            DB      06H     ;0 0 0 0 0 1   1 0
            DB      00H     ;0 0 0 0 0 0   0 0

DLYMSK      EQU     03H     ;"DELAY REQUIRED?" MASK
DLY2        EQU     02H     ;DELAY TWO REQUIRED MASK

INPUT       EQU     22H     ;INPUT PORT
OUTPUT      EQU     21H     ;OUTPUT PORT
IOCMND      EQU     20H     ;I/O PORT COMMAND ADDRESS
IOINIT      EQU     01H     ;INITIALIZATION BYTE

MAIN        MVI     A,IOINIT ;INITIALIZE OUTPUT PORT
            OUT     IOCMND
            LXI     H,STATE ;STATE TABLE POINTER

NEWSTATE    MOVE    A,M     ;OUTPUT STATE
            OUT     OUTPUT
            JZ      HALT    ;ZERO STATE IDENTIFIES END OF TABLE

            ANI     DLYMSK  ;ANY DELAY REQUIRED?
            JZ      COND    ;NO
            ANI     DLY2    ;IS IT DELAY TWO?
            JZ      D2      ;YES
            CALL    DELAY1  ;MUST BE DELAY ONE
            JMP     INCM
D2          CALL    DELAY2
            JMP     INCM

COND        INX     H       ;SINCE NO DELAY REQ'ED, DO INPUT OP
COND1       IN      INPUT
            SUB     M       ;TEST FOR CONDITION
```

```
                    JNZ      COND1      ;NOPE, NOT YET
        INCM        INX      H          ;NEXT
                    JMP      NEWSTATE
        HALT        HLT                 ;ALL CLEAN

        DELAY1      :::                 ;WASH/SPIN DELAY TIME
                    :::
                    RET

        DELAY2      :::                 ;EMPTY TUB DELAY TIME
                    :::
                    RET

                    DS       20H        ;STACK SPACE
        STACK       END
```

10.4 ADDITIONAL APPLICATIONS

We conclude this chapter with two applications, using the 8085 as usual. Because these programs are slightly more complex than the previous ones, the design will be modular and top-down. The first of these examples demonstrates the use of an on-board programmable timer to develop a real-time clock.

Many microprocessor applications require the performance of specific tasks at preset time intervals. The sequencers discussed earlier are good examples of this. When the number of tasks involved becomes large and the tasks themselves become complex, maintenance of very accurate timing can be quite a problem. An additional timer device will often head off such difficulties. Commonly, the timer hardware is configured so that a CPU interrupt occurs at a very accurately controlled interval, for example, at the 5-millisecond interval used below. The microprocessor interrupt service routine keeps track of the total number of interrupts. This total then provides the accurate measure of time; in one form or another, it represents real time.

Not only does such a timer allow development of cumulative real-time data, but it can also be used for other timer and delay applications. For example, real-time digital signal-processing programs often require that accurate time interval information be available; the sequencer applications just discussed are based on timing data. With an external timer the programmer has access to timing data without the need to burden the CPU with actually counting the time intervals.

The digital clock in Example 10.3 counts timer interrupts to form a regular, 24-hour clock. The program is designed to provide, by means of this clock, control functions at specific real times. It amounts to a microprocessor-based alarm clock; however, with the microprocessor, the clock can be expanded to a very large number of timed outputs. In addition, it can be programmed to include features such as conditional operation and the like. Microprocessor-based 24-hour clock timers have been used in many applications, for example, irrigation-control systems, requiring complex irrigation patterns around the clock. A conditional operation of such a system might include irrigation patterns based on current soil moisture or rainfall levels.

The timer hardware can, of course, be simply dedicated logic attached to a crystal oscillator and driving a microprocessor interrupt line. The programmable timer is more flexible. As one might guess by now, a programmable timer has both a timer output and a programming input.

As mentioned in Chapter Eight, the Intel 8155 includes a programmable timer. This timer is typical of the types available. It contains a 14-bit counter driven from an external clock pin. The user can program three different features. The first of these is the count length; this is the basic timing value for the counter and determines how many clock cycles must pass during a given timing operation.

The second feature determines the output waveform; two variations of two output types are possible. The output types are (1) a square wave whose period equals the count parameter and (2) a pulse that occurs when the count has been completed. The variations are (1) continuous output and (2) single-shot output. Thus, given a count parameter, we can program either a pulse or a square wave output occurring either continuously or as a single shot. Finally, start and stop commands provide our third control feature.

EXAMPLE 10.3 Digital Clock

This example develops a digital clock program for the 8085 using the 8155 programmable timer. We will use a top-down, modular design intended to produce a program that is easily maintained and expanded.

We must first determine what the program is to accomplish.

1. This will be a real-time clock.

2. It will display time of day on a 24-hour basis.

3. It will provide a bit-mapped output byte conditioned on a bit-mapped input byte and time of day.

4. Initialization will be at 12:00 noon, that is, we can assume the clock is started at noon.

5. Provision will be made for expansion.

6. Expansion might include additional I/O processing, fast/slow correction, and so forth.

Requirement 3 implies that we might be designing something like a programmable irrigation system. The eight outputs would be eight sprinkler system on/off valves; the eight inputs would be eight switches that turn each of the systems off, if desired.

Next, we must determine the hardware environment. The program will be designed to operate on an SDK-85 trainer board which has expansion RAM (A17) installed. In this configuration, RAM is available from 2000, hexadecimal, to about 20C0, hexadecimal, and from 2800 to 28FF, hexadecimal. A ROM routine at location 02B7, hexadecimal, is available to drive the board's numeric display. We will use bit-mapped I/O ported through an 8355 at I/O space addresses 0 (port A), 1 (port B), and 2 (data direction register).

The expansion RAM chip, an 8155, will also be used as the timer. Its command port is at I/O location 28, hexadecimal. We assume that the 8155 timer output has been patched to the RST6.5 interrupt of the 8085 (remove number 3 to number 5 ground jumper near A5, and patch number 5 to J5, pin 24). The SDK-85 vectors RST6.5 through ROM to location 20C8, hexadecimal. At this location we must of course provide a vector to our interrupt service routine.

One difference between this software and a normal application design is worth comment. In a real embedded microprocessor system, the program would normally be placed in ROM, with RAM located on a different chip. This program will place both program and data storage in RAM as is normal for the SDK-85.

The most critical programming steps can now be done. The overall flow of the program must be determined. Our top-level sequence is fairly simple.

1. Initialize all hardware and software parameters.
2. Allow expansion for real-time initialization and other user-based initialization.
3. Start timer.
4. Start main loop here.
5. Enable interrupts.
6. Allow for program changes based on later requirement changes.
7. Output current time of day.
8. Perform I/O routine.
9. Return to start of main loop, step 4.

For steps 2 and 6, no operations are to be performed in this version of the program; they are provided for expansion. At some time in the future, step 2 might be used to input a start time based on a keypad input. The user would then not have to wait until noon to start the clock.

Step 6 would allow a later version to have a fast/slow input to fine-tune the real-time clock.

We will use the timed-interrupt technique just discussed to establish timing for the program. The timer will be set to interrupt the CPU at very precise intervals. The software clock will simply count these interrupts. When an interrupt is not being serviced, the CPU will service I/O.

The top-level program can now be written fairly easily. It is a direct reflection of this sequence. As usual, we must tell the assembler where to start, or originate, the code. The CPU stack location must be defined. And, as usual, the program will be placed after the various label definition assembler directives—the equates.

```
                   ORG      2000H
                   LXI      SP,STACK
                   JMP      MAIN

;——EQUATES——
START      EQU      0C3H       ;TIMER AND PORT INITIALIZATION
CMND1      EQU      28H        ;TIMER COMMAND PORT

MAIN       CALL     INIT       ;INITIALIZATION—DISABLE INTERRUPTS
           CALL     USRINIT    ;ANY FUTURE USER INITIALIZATION
           MVI      A,START    ;TIMER START AND I/O PORT INITIALIZATION
           OUT      CMND1
MAINLP     EI
           CALL     CALIB      ;ANY FUTURE CALIBRATION ROUTINE
           CALL     TIMEOUT    ;DISPLAY TIME
           CALL     IO         ;I/O ROUTINE
           JMP      MAINLP     ;FOREVER

;——SUBROUTINES YET TO BE WRITTEN——
INIT       RET                 ;INITIALIZATION

USRINIT    RET                 ;ANY USER INITIALIZATION

CALIB      RET                 ;ANY USER CALIBRATION

TIMEOUT    RET                 ;DISPLAY TIME

IO         RET                 ;SERVICE I/O

;——INTERRUPT SERVICE ROUTINE YET TO BE WRITTEN——
ISR        RET                 ;TIMER INTERRUPT SERVICE

STACK      DS       20H        ;32-BYTE STACK
           END
```

The main program simply calls a series of functional modules. The timer start instructions are explicitly included at the beginning of the program, rather than in a subroutine, to make certain that the timer is, indeed, started.

Because the program timing will be based on interrupt counts, every interrupt after the start of the main loop must be seen. Therefore, the enablement of interrupts is redone at the start of each loop. This bit of caution is not really necessary as long as later updates of the subroutines never inadvertently add an interrupt disablement.

Each of the required subroutines is shown with a simple return statement at this point in the programming process. This is done for two reasons. The first is a matter of accounting. We can keep track of the software still to be written. The process is a little like writing a book: one first writes a table of contents and then fills in all the sections.

The second reason is more important. Software bugs are often difficult to locate; this is particularly true for a large program having many bugs. Providing all the required references allows the program to be debugged as it is written. If a computer-based assembler is being used, the program can be assembled at each stage. Any assembly errors can then be found and corrected before the next block of code is written. Moreover, the program can often be run as each stage is written. It will not perform all its proper actions, but most of the bugs can be detected. The current program can be assembled and run at this time. Such a process will allow us to find typing errors and the like. In operation, the program will simply lock in an endless loop at this point of development.

The debugging assistance provided by top-down modular programming has significant advantages. If we simply write, say, a 2000-line program and then proceed to debug it, the debugging will be a nightmare. The modular approach allows us to assemble and then test small blocks in the program's own context. We can do this as the blocks are written.

Assuming that we have test-assembled and run the code as it stands, we now proceed to fill in each of the missing routines.

On an equal level with the main routine is the interrupt service routine. As discussed in the last chapter, the CPU is vectored to a memory location for code to service the interrupt. We will name this routine and its location ISR, for interrupt service routine. The code itself will follow the main loop. We must later add the proper interrupt vector data to the assembly code.

The interrupt service routine follows the flowchart of Figure 10.5.

```
;INTERRUPT SERVICE ROUTINE
;'TIME' IS LOCATION OF COUNTS, SECS, MINS, AND HOURS
;SECS, MINS, AND HOURS IN BCD
;ASSUMES 5 MILLISECONDS PER INTERRUPT
;DESTROYS NO REGISTERS
;
ISR       PUSH      PSW       ;DON'T DESTROY REGISTERS
          PUSH      H
;
;COUNT UP TO ONE SECOND
          LXI       H,TIME
          INR       M
          MVI       A,0C8H    ;HAVE WE REACHED 200×.005 = 1 SEC?
```

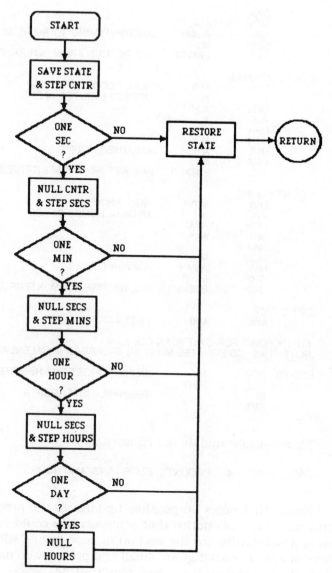

Figure 10.5
Interrupt Service Routine Flowchart.

```
            CMP     M
            JNZ     ENDISR    ;NO, RETURN FROM INTERRUPT
;
;COUNT SECONDS
            MVI     M,0       ;NULL COUNT
            INX     H         ;UPDATE SECONDS IN BCD
            MOV     A,M
            INR     A
```

```
              DAA
              MOV     M,A
              MVI     A,60H      ;ANOTHER MINUTE? NOTE: 60 (HEX) = 60 (BCD)
              CMP     M
              JNZ     ENDISR     ;NO, RETURN FROM INTERRUPT
;
;COUNT MINUTES
              MVI     M,0        ;NULL SECONDS
              INX     H          ;UPDATE MINUTES IN BCD
              MOV     A,M
              INR     A
              DAA
              MOV     M,A
              MVI     A,60H      ;ANOTHER HOUR?
              CMP     M
              JNZ     ENDISR     ;NO, RETURN FROM INTERRUPT
;
;COUNT HOURS
              MVI     M,0        ;NULL MINUTES
              INX     H          ;UPDATE HOURS IN BCD
              MOV     A,M
              INR     A
              DAA
              MOV     M,A
              MVI     A,24H      ;ANOTHER DAY?
              CMP     M
              JNZ     ENDISR     ;NO, RETURN FROM INTERRUPT
;
;DAY'S END
              MVI     M,0        ;NULL HOURS
;
;ENTRY POINT FOR CALENDAR CODE
;NOTE: 'TIME' DS EQUATES MUST BE ENLARGED IF CALENDAR IS ADDED
;
ENDIRS POP    H                  ;DON'T FORGET THE REGISTERS
       POP    PSW
       EI                        ;REENABLE INTERRUPTS
       RET
```

We must now update the equates with

```
TIME   DS   4   ;COUNTS, SECS, MINS, AND HOURS
```

Notice that notes on possible updates to the program are included with the code. Also notice that some savings could have been made by using a subroutine for the section of code from CMP M to Mov M,A in three places. The savings are small and probably do not warrant the loss of clarity incurred by the use of a subroutine.

The program now includes the main body and the interrupt service routine. After some testing we should next add the initialization and display routines, INIT and TIMEOUT. With these the program can be checked in detail as it stands since it displays time.

This process is continued. One routine after another is added and checked until the finished product is formed. This final program is listed as it would appear as the output of a software-based assembler. The assembler provides the address of the object code in the first column with the actual object code shown in the second column.

The code is written for the SDK-85 memory map. The SDK-85 vectors the RST 6.5 interrupt through its normal address to 20C8, hexadecimal.

```
                          ;
2000                          ORG  2000H
2000 31A128                   LXI  SP,STACK
2003 C31720                   JMP  MAIN

                          ;
                          ;**************************************************
                          ;——EQUATES——
00C3 =                    START    EQU  0C3H        ;TIMER INITIALIZATION
0020 =                    CMND1    EQU  28H         ;TIMER COMMAND PORT

02B8 =                    OUTPT    EQU  2B8H        ;MONITOR'S DISPLAY OUTPUT
                          ;                          ROUTINE

20C8 =                    RST65    EQU  20C8H       ;RST 6.5 VECTOR ADDRESS
                          ;                          IN SDK-85

2006                      TIME     DS   4           ;COUNTS, SECS, MINS, AND
                          ;                          HOURS
0012 =                    INITHR   EQU  12H         ;INITIAL TIME—
                          ;                          HOUR = 12 NOON

0010 =                    TMRCNTL  EQU  0B0H        ;TIMER COUNT LO/HI BYTES
0027 =                    TMRCNTH  EQU  0FAH
0024 =                    TMRCMNDL EQU  24H         ;TIMER COUNT LO/HI
                          ;                          COMMAND PORTS
0025 =                    TMRCMNDH EQU  25H

0000 =                    INP      EQU  0           ;BIT-MAPPED INPUT PORT
0002 =                    INPDDR   EQU  2           ;INP DATA DIRECTION
                          ;                          REGISTER
0000 =                    INPIN    EQU  0           ;SETS INP AS INPUT
0001 =                    OUTP     EQU  1           ;BIT-MAPPED OUTPUT PORT
0003 =                    OUTPDDR  EQU  3           ;OUTP DDR
00FF =                    OUTPOUT  EQU  0FFH        ;SETS OUTP AS OUTPUT

                          ;
                          ;ON/OFF TIMES MUST BE IN SEQUENCE FOLLOWED BY FF,
                          ;HEX
200A 02350315 ONOFF       DB   02H,35H,03H,15H
                          ;                          ON/OFF AT 2:35 / 3:15
200E 09121158             DB   09H,12H,11H,58H
                          ;                          ON/OFF AT 9:12 / 11:58
2012 22122214             DB   22H,12H,22H,14H
                          ;                          ON/OFF AT 22:12 / 22:14
2016 FF                   DB   0FFH            ;DELIMITS END OF ON/OFF'S

                          ;
0008 =                    IMASK    EQU  8           ;INTERRUPT MASK

                          ;
                          ;**************************************************
2017 CD2E20   MAIN        CALL INIT            ;INITIALIZATION—DISABLE
                          ;                          INTERRUPTS
201A CD5020               CALL USRINIT         ;ANY FUTURE USER
                          ;                          INITIALIZATION
201D 3EC3                 MVI  A,START         ;INITIALIZE I/O PORT AND
                          ;                          START TIMER
201F D320                 OUT  CMND1
2021 FB       MAINLP      EI
2022 CD5120               CALL CALIB           ;ANY FUTURE CALIBRATION
                          ;                          ROUTINE
2025 CD5220               CALL TIMEOUT         ;DISPLAY TIME
```

```
2028 CD0028              CALL  IO            ;I/O ROUTINE
202B C32120              JMP   MAINLP        ;FOREVER
      ;
      ;
      ;*****************************************************
      ;INITIALIZATION ROUTINE
02E 210620    INIT       LXI   H,TIME        ;TIME IS INITHR:00:00
031 3600                 MVI   M,0
033 23                   INX   H
034 3600                 MVI   M,0
036 23                   INX   H
037 3600                 MVI   M,0
039 23                   INX   H
03A 3612                 MVI   M,INITHR      ;INITIAL HOURS
03C 3E10                 MVI   A,TMRCNTL     ;INTERRUPT TIME LOW BYTE
03E D324                 OUT   TMRCMNDL
040 3E27                 MVI   ,TMRCNTH      ;INTERRUPT TIME HIGH BYTE
042 D325                 OUT   TMRCMNDH
044 3E00                 MVI   A,INPIN       ;SET UP INPUT PORT
046 D302                 OUT   INPDDR
048 3EFF                 MVI   A,OUTPUT      ;SET UP OUTPUT PORT
04A D303                 OUT   OUTPDDR
04C 3E08                 MVI   A,IMASK       ;SET INTERRUPT MASK
04E 30                   SIM
04F C9                   RET
      ;
      ;
      ;*****************************************************
      ;FOLLOWING PROVIDED FOR FUTURE UPGRADES
050 C9        USRINIT    RET                 ;ANY USER INITIALIZATION
      ;
      ;
      ;*****************************************************
      ;FOLLOWING PROVIDED FOR FUTURE UPGRADES
051 C9        CALIB      RET                 ;ANY USER CALIBRATION
      ;
      ;*****************************************************
      ;DISPLAY CURRENT TIME—DESTROYS ALL REGISTERS
      ;CALLS MONITOR OUTPT ROUTINE
052 210620    TIMEOUT    LXI   H,TIME        ;OUTPUT SECONDS
055 23                   INX   H
056 3E01                 MVI   A,1           ;PUT IN DATA FIELD
058 0600                 MVI   B,0           ;NO DOT
05A CDB802               CALL  OUTPT         ;MONITOR'S DISPLAY
      ;                                       ROUTINE
05D 23                   INX   H             ;POINT TO MIN/HOURS
05E 3E00                 MVI   A,0           ;PUT IN ADDRESS FIELD
060 0600                 MVI   B,0           ;NO DOT
062 CDB802               CALL  OUTPT
2065 C9                  RET
      ;
      ;*****************************************************
      ;*****************************************************
2800                     ORG   2800H         ;NEXT RAM CHIP
      ;
      ;*****************************************************
      ;SERVICE I/O - DESTROYS A, B, D/E AND H/L
2800 110620   IO         LXI   D,TIME        ;POINT TO TIME
2803 13                  INX   D             ;AT HOURS
2804 13                  INX   D
2805 13                  INX   D
2806 210A20              LXI   H,ONOFF       ;ONOFF = ON/OFF TIME SEQ
      ;                                       HR,MIN,ETC
      ;
```

```
2809 7E      IO1        MOV  A,M       ;NEXT ON HOURS
280A FEFF               CPI  OFFH      ;CHECK FOR LAST
280C CA4628             JZ   TURNOFF   ;NO MORE
280F 23                 INX  H         ;POINT TO MINUTES
             ;
2810 EB                 XCHG
2811 46                 MOV  B,M       ;CURRENT HOURS
2812 2B                 DCX  H         ;POINT TO MINUTES
2813 EB                 XCHG
             ;
2814 B8                 CMP  B         ;HAVE WE REACHED ON
                                        TIME?
2815 DA2328             JC   IO2       ;PAST ON TIME—CHECK
             ;                          OFF TIME
2818 C24628             JNZ  TURNOFF   ;HAVEN'T REACHED NEXT
             ;                          ON TIME
             ;
281B 46                 MOV  B,M       ;REACHED ON HRS, CHECK
             ;                          ON MINUTES
281C EB                 XCHG
281D 7E                 MOV  A,M       ;CURRENT MINUTES
281E EB                 XCHG
281F B8                 CMP  B         ;HAVE WE REACHED ON
             ;                          TIME?
2820 DA4628             JC   TURNOFF   ;NO
             ;
2823 23      IO2        INX  H         ;POINT TO NEXT OFF
             ;                          HOURS
2824 13                 INX  D         ;POINT TO CURRENT HOURS
             ;
2825 7E                 MOV  A,M       ;NEXT OFF HOURS
2826 23                 INX  H         ;POINT TO MINUTES
             ;
2827 EB                 XCHG
2828 46                 MOV  B,M       ;CURRENT HOURS
2829 2B                 DCX  H         ;POINT TO MINUTES
282A EB                 XCHG
             ;
282B B8                 CMP  B         ;HAVE WE REACHED OFF
                                        TIME
282C DA3A28             JC   IO3       ;PAST OFF TIME—
             ;                          CONTINUE
282F C23F28             JNZ  TURNON    ;WE'RE ON
             ;
2832 46                 MOV  B,M       ;REACHED OFF HRs,
             ;                          CHECK OFF MINs
2833 EB                 XCHG
2834 7E                 MOV  A,M       ;CURRENT MINUTES
2835 EB                 XCHG
2836 B8                 CMP  B         ;REACHED OFF TIME?
2837 DA3F28             JC   TURNON    ;NO
             ;
283A 23      IO3        INX  H
283B 13                 INX  D
             ;
283C C30928             JMP  IO1
             ;
             ;
283F DB00    TURNON     IN   INP       ;TURN ON BASED ON INPUT
2841 D301               OUT  OUTP
2843 C34A28             JMP  ENDIO
             ;
             ;
2846 3E00    TURNOFF    MVI  A,0       ;TURN OFF
2848 D301               OUT  OUTP
             ;
284A C9      ENDIO      RET
```

```
;
;**************************************************
;——INTERRUPT SERVICE ROUTINE——
;'TIME' IS LOCATION OF CNT, SEC, MIN, AND HR
;SEC, MIN, AND HR IN BCD
;ASSUMES 5-MILLISECONDS PER INTERRUPT
;DESTROYS NO REGISTERS
;
284B F5        ISR      PUSH PSW      ;DON'T DESTROY REGISTERS
284C E5                 PUSH H
;
;COUNT UP TO ONE SECOND
284D 210620             LXI  H,TIME
2850 34                 INR  M
                        MVI  A,0C8H    ;HAVE WE REACHED
                                       200*0.005 = 1 SEC?
2851 BE                 CMP  M
2852 C27E28             JNZ  ENDISR    ;NO, RETURN FROM
                                       INTERRUPT
;
;COUNT SECONDS
2855 3600               MVI  M,0       ;NULL COUNT
2857 23                 INX  H         ;UPDATE SECONDS IN BCD
2858 73                 MOV  A,M
2859 3C                 INR  A
285A 27                 DAA
285B 77                 MOV  M,A
285C 3E60               MVI  A,60H     ;ANOTHER MINUTE? NOTE:
                                       60, HEX = 60, BCD
285E BE                 CMP  M
285F C27E28             JNZ  ENDISR    ;NO, RETURN FROM
                                       INTERRUPT
;
;COUNT MINUTES
2862 3600               MVI  M,0       ;NULL SECONDS
2864 23                 INX  H         ;UPDATE MINUTES IN BCD
2865 7E                 MOV  A,M
2866 3C                 INR  A
2867 27                 DAA
2868 77                 MOV  M,A
2869 3E60               MVI  A,60H     ;ANOTHER HOUR?
286B BE                 CMP  M
286C C27E28             JNZ  ENDISR    ;NO, RETURN FROM
                                       INTERRUPT
;
;COUNT HOURS
286F 3600               MVI  M,0       ;NULL MINUTES
2871 23                 INX  H         ;UPDATE HOURS IN BCD
2872 7E                 MOV  A,M
2873 3C                 INR  A
2874 27                 DAA
2875 77                 MOV  M,A
2876 3E24               MVI  A,24H     ;ANOTHER DAY?
2878 BE                 CMP  M
2879 C27E28             JNZ  ENDISR    ;NO, RETURN FROM
                                       INTERRUPT
;
;DAY'S END
287C 3600               MVI  M,0       ;NULL HOURS
;
;ENTRY POINT FOR CALENDAR CODE
;NOTE: 'TIME' DS EQUATES MUST BE ENLARGED IF
;CALENDAR IS ADDED
;
287E E1        ENDISR   POP  H         ;DON'T FORGET THE
                                       REGISTERS
;
```

```
287F F1              POP  PSW
2880 FB              EI              ;REENABLE INTERRUPTS
2881 C9              RET
      ;
      ;***************************************************
2882                 DS   20H        ;32-BYTE STACK
28A2       STACK     DS   1
      ;
      ;***************************************************
20C8                 ORG  RST65      ;SET JUMP VECTOR FOR
      ;                               INTERRUPT 6.5
20C8 C34B28          JMP  ISR
      ;
20CB                 END
```

The timer command bytes are based on a (6.144/2) megahertz clock used to develop a 5-millisecond interrupt period. This requires a count to 15,360 between interrupts. In binary numbers this is 11101010110000. The 8155 produces continuous pulses at the programmed interval if the first two bits of the high-order command byte are ones. The remainder of the two command bytes define the count interval. The two command bytes taken together must be 1111101010110000. The high-order command byte is thus 11111010 (FA, hexadecimal). The low-order byte is 10110000 (B0, hexadecimal).

The final example demonstrates the use of a programming technique called a **look-up table.**

In many applications complex mathematical operations are required, such as trigonometric or logarithmic calculations. There are several ways to perform such calculations. Large computers, including most minicomputers, provide special hardware as part of the ALU so that such functions can be included in the assembly language instruction set. On the other hand, certain of the most powerful microprocessors allow a special external chip, called a **math coprocessor.** The Intel 8087 and 80287 and the Motorola 68881 are examples of very powerful coprocessors designed for their respective microprocessor families. For more basic devices, such as the 8085, it is possible to arrange an interface with coprocessor devices; however, it is much more common to take one of two other approaches.

For highly accurate, multiprecision work, we can calculate complex mathematical functions directly by series techniques. The function is reduced to a long sequence of additions, subtractions, multiplications, and divisions. For the 8085, as well as many 8-bit microprocessors, the multiplications and divisions must be further reduced to multiple additions and subtractions. This process can produce very accurate results; however, it is quite slow and requires a great deal of complex code.

The other common way of generating complex functions is usually applied when speed and code efficiency are very important. The function is simply tabulated in memory. The result is the digital equivalent of math tables. If the sine of an angle is required, the CPU is directed to look in the memory location corresponding to this angle. This amounts to memory-mapped data. Of course, this look-up table technique can be used for numerical function data that are not blessed with a mathematical definition. For example, tax rate tables define output tax data based on input income numbers.

At first this seems such a simple solution to the problem of complex mathematical operations. We might conclude that series solutions or coprocessors are not really needed. A look at some examples will demonstrate that, although the look-up technique is quite powerful, it does have limitations.

Consider a sine look-up table. If we require only a single byte of precision for both the argument and the result, we need to be able to find the one-byte sine for any of 256 angles. This is so since the argument is allowed to be simply one byte; there are 256 possible arguments represented using this one byte. In truth, we can store the table in 64 bytes of memory. The sines for the angles between 90 and 360 degrees can be computed given the sines for the angles less than 90 degrees.

If we require more accuracy in the output value of the sine look-up table, we must store multiprecision data. Our 64-byte table becomes a 64 times 2-byte, or 128-byte, table for 16-bit precision. High-quality coprocessors often use 80-bit precision. This would require a 640-byte table, still not too bad.

The picture becomes grim if high precision is required for the argument. If the angle is specified by a 16-bit number, the table must contain sine data for over 64,000 angles. Even with the trick of storing only the first 90 degrees worth of our sines, the table is huge. If 80-bit accuracy is required along with tangent, inverse trigonometric, and logarithm calculations, the look-up approach is hopelessly inadequate.

One technique that is sometimes used to extend the value of a look-up table is interpolation. Here intermediate values between table entries are approximated by a process of estimation. Generally, the function is assumed to be linear between the two table entries on either side of an input argument. With this assumption, a reasonably good estimate can be made.

Many nontechnical applications require relatively few table entries, each of which must be precise. An example of this is the tax rate table mentioned earlier. In such applications look-up tables are used quite commonly.

EXAMPLE 10.4   Waveform Generation

This example illustrates the use of a look-up table as the basis for a sine wave generator. Figures 10.6 and 10.7 show that the process is one of

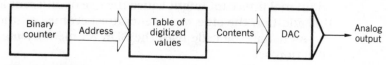

Figure 10.6
Waveform Generation.

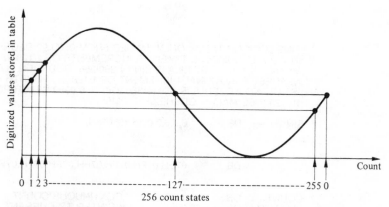

Figure 10.7
Sine Wave Look-up Table.

linearly counting through the memory-mapped sine table. The table value is then used as output to a DAC. If the DAC is configured as a multiplying DAC, or MDAC, the reference for the DAC can be used to control the sine wave magnitude. The rate at which the counter is incremented determines the frequency of the output waveform.

The code to be shown uses a very simple, endless loop as the main body of the program. An interrupting timer is assumed to provide the proper timing. The interrupt service routine requires that only the first 90 degrees of the sine table be provided. With an assumed 8-bit precision requirement, the table is 64 bytes long. Although the initialization routine and associated equates are not given, the first and last elements of the look-up table are.

The table contains signed values. The MSB is the sign bit with a one indicating negative. The remaining seven bits code numbers in the sequence 0, 1/128, 2/128, 3/128, and so on. The formula for computing these values is shown in the comments of the software.

A more extensive version of this program might include processing in the main body. Such processing might call routines that interrogate input ports. Such input might include new timer programming values, which would provide for variable frequency operation. Another input port might have magnitude commands that the program would provide as output to a DAC; the DAC would then drive the reference of the primary MDAC. An additional interrupt might cause the use of different look-up tables. With this addition the sine wave generator becomes a function generator.

As usual, the code uses the SDK-85 memory map and the 8085 instruction set.

```
;
;
            ORG     2000H
            LXI     SP,STACK
            JMP     MAIN
;
;SINE LOOK-UP TABLE. ONLY VALUES FROM 0 TO 90 DEGREES ARE
;INCLUDED. NUMBERS TAKEN AS INCREMENTS OF 1/128, IE "K"
;MEANS "K/128." FORMULA IS SIN (N*360/256) ROUNDED TO
;NEAREST FRACTIONAL INCREMENT OF 1/128. IE, FOURTH ENTRY
;(STARTING AT ZERO) IS SIN (4*360/256) = 0.0980 WHICH ROUNDS TO
;13/128 (DECIMAL) = OD (HEXADECIMAL).

SIN         DB      0,3,6,9,0DH,10H,13H, . . .
                    . . . .
                    . . . .
                    . . . .
            DB      07EH,07FH,07FH,07FH,07FH,07FH,07FH,07FH
;
COUNT       DS      1                 ;CONTINUOUS COUNT
SPOINTR     DS      2                 ;POINTER TO CURRENT SINE TABLE VALUE
;
RST65       EQU     20C8H             ;RST 6.5 VECTOR ADDRESS IN SDK-85
;
;
;———ADD OTHER EQUATES AS REQUIRED———
IMASK       EQU     . . .
DAC         EQU     . . .

MAIN        DI                        ;NO INTERRUPTS WHILE WE GET SET
            CALL    INIT
            EI
MAIN1       JMP     MAIN1             ;FOREVER

INIT        SIM     IMASK
            MVI     A,0               ;START AT ZERO
            STA     COUNT
            LXI     H,SIN             ;START AT START OF TABLE
            SHLD    SPOINTR
            . . .                     ;OTHER INITIALIZATION AS REQUIRED
            RET
;
ISR         PUSH    PSW
            PUSH    H
            PUSH    D
;
            LXI     H,COUNT    ;STEP FIRST, THEN OUTPUT
            INR     M          ;SO COUNT AND OUTPUT MATCH AT RET

            LXI     H,SPOINTR  ;NOW STEP THROUGH TABLE
            LDA     COUNT      ;DETERMINE DIRECTION OF STEP
            ANI     40H        ;BASED ON BIT 6
            JZ      ISR1
            DCX     H          ;90 TO 180 OR 270 TO 360
```

```
          JMP      ISR2
ISR1      INX      H             ;0 TO 90 OR 180 TO 270
ISR2      SHLD     H
;
          MOV      D,M           ;GET VALUE AND DETERMINE SIGN
          LDA      COUNT         ;SIGN BASED ON MSB OF COUNT BYTE
          ANI      80H
          ORA      D             ;NOW WE HAVE CALCULATION
;
          OUT      DAC           ;DAC, COUNT, AND SPOINTR MATCH
;
          POP      D
          POP      H
          POP      PSW
          RET
;
          DS       20H           ;32-BYTE STACK
STACK     DS       1
;
          ORG      RST65         ;SET JUMP VECTOR FOR INTERRUPT 6.5
          JMP      ISR
;
          END
```

Some code could have been saved if the full, 256-byte table had been used. This version adds, perhaps, 25 bytes of operation codes but saves almost 200 entries in the table.

EXERCISES

10.1 Modify the source code of Example 10.1 to provide a 90-second green light with a 45-second left-turn light.

10.2 Check the timing of the delay routines of Example 10.1 to verify that they produce the proper time delay.

10.3 Update the source code of Example 10.1 to allow for a left turn only if there is a left-turn request. Such a request for N/S traffic will be indicated by a one in bit position zero at input port 10, hexadecimal, in the I/O space. Bit position 4 of this byte is a one any time left-turn traffic is waiting for the E/W direction. The command port for this I/O port is located at 11, hexadecimal, and is programmed in a fashion similar to the original port shown.

10.4 Write properly timed-delay routines for Example 10.2. DELAY1 must be about 6 minutes long, DELAY2 about 4 minutes long.

10.5 Change the time display at start-up of Example 10.3 to 9:00 A.M.

10.6 In Example 10.3 the third turn-on time was supposed to be 20:12. In addition, two new on/off operations are required; on/off at 14:30/15:00 and on/off at 22:30/23:10. Correct the source code.

10.7 How many bytes are required for a look-up table of 16-bit data referenced by a 12-bit word for addressing the data?

10.8 For Exercise 10.7, describe how the 16-bit table data word might be addressed.

10.9 Rewrite the source code of Example 10.4 using a full 256-byte look-up table.

10.10 The SDK-85 moves the RST 6.5 vector address to 20C8, hexadecimal. The code for Example 10.4 is to be moved to a system that uses normal 8085 vector addressing. Modify the source code to reflect the change. Do not forget to provide for a start-up vector. This should jump the processor to the location 2000, hexadecimal, for the program.

GLOSSARY

Access Time The delay time of a memory device; the time between its being selected and its producing an output.

Accumulator A register used to store the results of arithmetic and logical operations; generally, one of the sources of data for such operations. Some processors have more than one accumulator available.

ACIA (Asynchronous Communications Interface Adapter) A programmable I/O device designed to implement various asynchronous serial communication protocols.

Address The number assigned, through hardware design, to a specific memory or I/O location.

Address Bus A collection of logic signal lines which are used by the CPU to transmit an address command. Each address line conveys a specific binary digit. The 8085 and similar devices use 16 address lines for 64K memory locations. Some small or special-purpose processors use a smaller address bus; 20-, 24-, and 32-bit address bus schemes are popular, along with segmented memory.

Address Decode Dedicated logic which translates CPU address bus data into specific commands for the addressed location.

Addressable Memory Memory whose storage locations can each be activated by use of the address bus; RAM and ROM, as opposed to such nonaddressable memory as mass storage devices.

Addressing Modes Various methods of specifying an address in software, for example, direct addressing, register indirect addressing, and so forth. This is an important feature of a processor's instruction set.

ALU (Arithmetic Logic Unit) The portion of a microcomputer system that performs arithmetic and logic operations on binary data; generally, part of the CPU. In many microprocessor devices, including the 8085, the accumulator is the source for one of the binary words used by the ALU; it is also the destination of the results of ALU operations for such devices.

Architecture The arrangement of subsystems and functional components within a microprocessor. A system's architecture defines such matters as its memory space, I/O mapping, and number of and kinds of internal registers.

ASCII (American Standard Code for Information Interchange) A standardized binary code using seven bits to represent letters and numbers. Both uppercase and lowercase letters can be represented. A number of special control words are included, as are punctuation marks and other common characters.

Assembler A computer program which converts typed assembly language source code into object code usable by a processor. An intermediate hex code or relocatable code step is often involved in the conversion process.

Assembler Directives Assembly language mnemonics which control the assembly operation rather than generate specific machine instructions.

Assembly Language A method of representing CPU operations in a more readable format. An assembly language program is a sequence of assembly language statements. Each statement generally translates into a specific machine instruction—op code. Assembly control instructions—assembler directives—are the principal exceptions to this.

Asynchronous Not synchronized. A given operation starts without regard to external commands. Some processors use asynchronous bus data transfers in which bus operation timing is not tied tightly to a fixed clock. Asynchronous serial communication occurs without the use of an external clock; data transfer start and stop are specified by embedded command data using a predetermined protocol.

Auxiliary Carry Flag A flag used for BCD arithmetic. The 8085 auxiliary carry flag is set if there has been a carryout of the low-order nibble.

Bank A sequential block of memory locations treated as a group.

Batch Processing Processing which is not performed immediately. Batch processing is done on data collected previously; its speed and execution timing does not have to match the external world. Batch processing also refers to computer processing done without the need for human interface; an example would be a number of programs left to run, sequentially, overnight.

Baud Rate A method of specifying information flow rate; using the shortest data element, the number of elements per second. For binary serial data transfer the baud rate is the number of bits per second (bps) based on the shortest bit period. The usable data transfer rate in bps is generally somewhat less than the baud rate because delay states, parity and error checking data, and command data (such as start and stop bits) are almost always included in the serial data stream.

BCD (Binary-Coded Decimal) Coding of decimal digits into nibbles of a binary word. An 8-bit binary word can be used to represent two decimal numbers in BCD.

BC-Pair The 8085 B- and C-registers taken together as a 16-bit word.

Bidirectional A bus or driver used to carry data in either direction.

Binary Data and other signals represented using only two electrical states. The fundamental binary data representation system uses binary numbers, whereby each bit is assigned a weighting equal to a power of two. Thus, 1101 represents the total of one eight, one four, no twos, and one one (8 + 4 + 1

= 13). A binary word can also represent data in other formats, such as ASCII, BDC, and machine op codes.

Bit   Binary digit. A single binary element.

Bit-Mapped   Binary data with each specific bit assigned a unique meaning independently of the other bits; often used for I/O, in which each bit has an assigned function.

Bit Slice   A microprocessor technology in which processor functions are partitioned in hardware into one-bit sections; the overall machine is made by connecting several chips together to form a complete **CPU**. A bit-slice system has a central processing chip type that performs all CPU operations on only one bit. Eight such chips would be connected in parallel to make an 8-bit machine. Bit-slice systems are often used for very high-speed designs based on bipolar or on other fast, but not extremely dense, technologies.

Bottom-Up Programming   Software development in which small individual tasks are first programmed. These tasks are later combined into larger and larger program elements.

Branch   The process of passing computer control to a new section of program instructions. A branch may be conditional, with the change in control occurring only when certain conditions are met, or unconditional, always occurring. A branch is the same as a jump. A subroutine call is different, implying a return to the calling software at the end of the subroutine; a branch implies no automatic return.

Break point   A software debugging tool. Program execution is made to stop at a predetermined point—the break point; the contents of the various registers and the state of the machine can then be examined to determine whether there are any programming errors.

Bug   Once a whimsical reference to bugs that eat through the insulation of wires, causing errors to occur. Today, bugs are simply software errors.

Bus   A collection of logic lines used to transfer data. A microcomputer system has three primary buses: a data bus, which carries machine instructions and data; an address bus, which specifies the memory or I/O location in use; and a control bus, which carries various signals that control the use of the other buses.

Bus Contention   A situation in which more than one device is attempting to drive a bus simultaneously.

Bus Driver   A device designed to drive signals onto a bus. Bus drivers are commonly three-state devices.

Bus Glue   Dedicated logic used to interface various components to a microprocessor bus. Bus glue includes such components as address decoders and memory access timing devices.

Byte   Usually an 8-bit binary word. Byte is sometimes used to mean a binary word of any size.

Cache Memory   An element of some microprocessor architectures, where program instructions (and sometimes other data) that are likely to be used in the near future are held in very fast-access memory, sometimes on the microprocessor IC itself. The CPU attempts to use this cache if possible. The result is often a significant increase in speed, depending on the routine being executed.

Call   A software operation which initiates a subroutine.

Carry Flag A flag used for arithmetic operations. The 8085 carry flag is set if there has been a carryout of the byte in question.

Clear To establish the binary zero state.

Clock A steady, high-frequency digital signal used as the basis for timing logic operations. Sometimes a multiphase clock is used. The CPU increments through its detailed operations with each transition of the clock.

Code Computer program data in any form.

Comments Information added to a program that is not used in generation of object code. Comments are very important to the human understanding of any program.

Compile The process of reducing a high-level language program to specific machine instructions that can be stored as a completed program. A compiler takes the program (generally in ASCII for microcomputers) and develops the machine instructions that will perform the desired process. Compilers often use intermediate code steps. An assembly language program is often developed by a compiler and is then assembled to the machine code. Another approach is to reduce the high-level program to a standardized instruction set (pseudocode for a pseudomachine), which is then translated into specific instructions for the computer in use.

Conditional Assembly A special feature of many assemblers that allows the programmer to specify the use of certain blocks of source code. It is implemented by assembler directives.

Condition Code Register Flag register.

Control Bus The bus used in a microcomputer system to control the operation of devices connected to the other buses.

Counter/Timer A peripheral device designed to allow counting of external events or the generation of timing data based on an external clock. Counter/timers are normally programmable for a variety of functions.

CPU (Central Processing Unit) The primary control element of a microcomputer. The CPU generally includes instruction decode logic, timing and control circuits, various registers, and the ALU. For most small systems the microprocessor itself is the CPU.

Cross Assembler An assembler program run on one computer type, which uses the assembly language of and generates object code for another computer type. If a 68000-based computer is used to assemble 8085 assembly language into 8085 operation codes, the program used is a cross assembler.

Data Bus The bus used in a microcomputer system to transfer data and program instructions.

Debug To remove the bugs; to find and correct errors in software. Debugging can be the most difficult and time-consuming part of programming.

Decimal Adjust An operation used to complete a BCD arithmetic operation. The BCD number is first treated as a normal binary number for an arithmetic operation; the decimal adjust step then makes certain corrections that yield the correct BCD result based on the binary result.

Decrement To reduce in value. Most microprocessors include various decrement instructions in their instruction sets.

DE-Pair The 8085 D- and E-registers taken together as a 16-bit word.

Development System A special-purpose computer system designed for microprocessor system development. A development system will include a computer with one or more assemblers and, perhaps, compilers, a method of saving and cataloging program files, debugging programs, possibly debugging hardware features, and, generally, an emulation capability.

Diagnostic   A computer program designed to diagnose any hardware difficulties. A common diagnostic program technique is to write data to RAM; when reading the data back, the diagnostic program can determine whether any RAM errors have occurred. Diagnostic programs are often included as part of normal system start-up.

Digital   Based on integer digits; possessing a limited number of specific states. A digital system is almost always a two-state, or binary, system.

Direct Addressing   An addressing mode. The address is included with the instruction.

Displacement   Movement from one address location to another. In relative addressing, the final address is found by moving a given number of locations from some specified address, such as the PC contents; the number of locations is said to be a displacement.

DMA (Direct Memory Access)   A method of loading data into memory directly without incurring the delay of passing the data through the CPU. During a DMA operation the CPU address bus drivers are brought to a high-impedance state; an external DMA controller then directs addressing and data transfer to memory.

DOS (Disk Operating System)   An operating system using disk drives for mass storage.

Dynamic Memory   A RAM which can hold its data for only a short time. Dynamic RAM must be updated (refreshed) on a regular basis. This can normally be done using a simple memory read operation.

EAROM (Electronically Alterable Read-Only Memory)   PROM that can be erased when special electrical input conditions occur.

Editor   A device used to aid the programmer in writing source code. An editor allows code to be entered, filed, and updated.

Embedded Microprocessor System   A use of microprocessor technology whereby the computer is programmed for a specific, dedicated application. The program is usually held in ROM. Examples include numerically controlled machine tools and various sequencers, such as traffic light controllers. A general-purpose personal computer is an example of a nonembedded system; the computer can be reprogrammed for many applications.

Emulator   A specialized hardware system designed to operate exactly like a given microprocessor with respect to both hardware and software functions. An emulator allows extensive debugging to be performed, such as tracing internal processor states and inserting break points. An emulator also allows easy downloading of object code using its internal RAM.

EPROM (Erasable, Programmable Read-Only Memory)   PROM that can be erased, often using ultraviolet light.

Exception Processing   Program execution brought about by special conditions, such as an interrupt or reset. Some processors provide extensive exception processing schemes that allow the programmer to direct the system through bus errors, illegal program instructions, or power failures, among other difficulties.

Execute Cycle   The second half of the fetch/execute operation of a computer.

During the execute cycle the operation required by a program instruction is performed. The time required for this cycle varies significantly from instruction to instruction for most common microprocessor systems.

Execution Time The time, generally given in T-states, required to execute a specific machine instruction.

Extended Addressing Some microprocessors allow various forms of addressing, performed rapidly over a limited range of memory. For such systems addressing over the entire memory in use is often called extended addressing.

Fetch Cycle The first part of the fetch/execute cycle. During the fetch cycle the next sequential program instruction is brought from memory. This cycle requires at least one memory read cycle and may require several, depending on the number of words included in the instruction.

FIFO (First In, First Out) A type of stack in which the oldest data are always the next to be sent out.

Flag Information, generally expressed as a single bit, indicating the state of some element of processing; for example, most machines have a zero flag that is set whenever a zero results from specific operations. Flags are generally collected into a flag byte for use by the programmer.

Flag Byte Flags bit-mapped into a byte and held in the CPU flag register.

Flowchart A structured method of representing program flow. Flowcharts are an aid to documentation of program operation.

Handshaking A technique by which various forms of digial communication are regulated. The handshaking protocol defines how each element determines the readiness of the other element(s) for data transfer. It also defines how a given element displays transfer completion and transfer success.

Hardware The physical devices used to make up a computer system. Hardware includes ICs, printer circuit boards, wiring, power supplies, and the like.

Hex Code Machine program instructions stored as hexadecimal numbers, generally in ASCII.

Hexadecimal Notation The number system with a base of 16. Numbers are counted from zero to fifteen as 0, 1, 2, 3, 4, 5, 6, 7, 8, 9, A, B, C, D, E, and F. Hexadecimal numbers are used extensively because a byte can be represented compactly and conveniently by two hexadecimal digits.

High-Impedance State The state of a three-state bus driver in which it does not affect bus voltages. This allows some other device to control the bus.

High-Level Language Any of a number of programming languages whereby a specific statement may be translated into a great number of machine instructions. Most statements define a process rather than specific machine operations. Thus, a high-level language can commonly be used with a number of different machines having significantly different instruction sets. High-level language programs must be either compiled or interpreted.

HL-Pair The 8085 H- and L-registers taken together as a 16-bit word.

IC (Integrated Circuit) A small (a few tenths of an inch on a side), thin piece of semiconductor material containing many individual circuit elements, up to hundreds of thousands. Designing the IC to perform as a subsystem doing many individual tasks on the same bit of silicon allows great improvements in computer size, speed, cost, and ruggedness.

Immediate Addressing An addressing mode in which the address data are immediately available in the fetched instruction itself.

Increment To increase in value. Most microprocessors provide various increment instructions in their instruction sets.

Indexed Addressing An addressing mode in which the instruction provides an address, and an index register provides a displacement, or offset, from this address to determine the final address for the instruction.

Index Register The register used to hold the index for indexed addressing.

Indirect Addressing An addressing mode with which the address is found in a register or a memory location.

Instruction A specific command directing the next CPU operation. An instruction is fetched into the CPU as one or more bytes.

Instruction Set The complete set of machine instructions that a specific computer can perform.

Interpreter A program which reads a high-level language instruction and performs the required task immediately. An interpreter allows a high-level program to be run immediately with no compiling required. However, a long program runs significantly more slowly using an interpreter rather than a compiled version of the program.

Interrupt A powerful computer system technique whereby an external device can be used to stop current program execution so that the computer can attend to a critical function. During an interrupt the state of the interrupted program is saved so that, at the end of the interrupt service, it can be continued.

Interrupt Mask A means of disabling interrupts (or selected interrupts) in hardware or software.

Interrupt Prioritization Techniques which are used to make sure that interrupts occur only in the priority and sequence desired. Interrupt prioritization allows the design of a system in which a critical interrupt is attended to immediately; in addition, interruption of a critical interrupt can be prevented.

Interrupt Service Routine The program executed when an interrupt occurs. Some systems require several interrupt service routines to account for various possible interrupts.

I/O Input and output. Devices and techniques which regulate the flow of data into and out of a computer.

I/O-Mapped I/O I/O-addressed using special instructions and a special address space reserved for I/O.

I/O Port An I/O device designed to connect directly to the microprocessor buses.

Jump The process of passing computer control to a new section of program instructions. A jump may be conditional, with the change in control occurring only when certain conditions are met, or unconditional, always occurring. A jump is the same as a branch. A subroutine call is different, implying a return to the calling software at the end of the subroutine; a jump implies no automatic return.

K When used in the computer field, 1024; a corruption of kilo, meaning 1000. The number 1024 is the power of two nearest 1000.

Label An assembly language technique whereby a number, address, or other datum is given a unique, convenient name for use throughout the program.

Library In software engineering, a collection of routines, any of which can be selected for use in new programs. High-level languages often provide extensive libraries, which can be brought into a program as desired.

LIFO (Last In, First Out) A type of stack whereby the newest datum in the stack is the next to be brought out. The next datum to be read would be the next oldest, and so forth. Most microprocessors use a LIFO for their main stack.

Linker A program used to link specified program modules into a complete program. The linker concatenates the modules and adjusts various addresses and other references.

Loop A programming technique whereby a block of code is repeated until some condition occurs.

LSB (Least Significant Bit) The binary digit which represents two to the power zero. The LSB is the rightmost bit when a word is written in a normal format.

LSI (Large-Scale Integration) IC technology whereby the chips contain large functional blocks, such as adders or counters. A rule of thumb is that an LSI device has over a hundred gates but fewer than a thousand.

M When used in the computer field, 1,048,576; a corruption of mega, meaning 1,000,000. The number 1,048,576 is the power of two nearest 1,000,000.

Machine Language Object code; specific binary instructions which direct the CPU through a program.

Macro A feature of some assemblers (macro assemblers) whereby a block of source code can be included in a program using a single label. Whenever the assembler encounters a request for a specific macro, using its label, the macro's source code is automatically included in the program. Extensive libraries of macros are often used.

Mask A binary word used with logic instructions to select one or more bits from a binary data word.

Memory Where data and program instructions are stored, an important part of any microcomputer system.

Memory-Mapped I/O I/O-addressed as though it were ordinary memory.

Microcomputer A complete microprocessor-based computer, including the CPU, memory, and I/O.

Microcontroller Generally, a single-chip computer having limited memory and, often, special-purpose I/O devices. A microcontroller is designed specifically for embedded applications.

Microprocessor An IC containing the complete CPU for a computer system.

Microprogram In general, any stored program used to decode and implement user instructions. Microprogramming is commonly a method whereby fetched instructions initiate internal control programs, which in turn perform the desired action—in effect, a computer within a computer. A user cannot normally tell whether a CPU is microprogrammed or uses dedicated logic for implementation of the instruction set. Microprogramming allows the CPU designer to use a relatively simple internal architecture to execute a rich instruction set.

Microprogrammable Pertaining to a microprogrammed system that allows the user to change the microcode (microprogram).

Mnemonics Memory aids. Short words—two to four letters—used to represent machine instructions in assembly language.

Modem Modulator/demodulator. A device used to interface a computer serial I/O port to a communication system, such as telephone lines.

Modular Programming Development of large programs from a number of smaller program modules. Each module is designed to perform a specific task.

MSB (Most Significant Bit)   The binary digit which represents the highest power zero. The MSB is the leftmost bit when a word is written in a normal format.

MSI (Medium-Scale Integration)   IC technology in which the chips contain small functional blocks, such as flip-flops or decoders. An MSI device has approximately ten to a hundred gates.

Multiplex   Any of a number of methods using a single communication channel to transmit multiple signals. For example, the 8085 microprocessor time-multiplexes one-half of the address bus as a data bus. At one time the bus carries address information; at another it carries data bus information. The timing is controlled by signals on the control bus.

Nesting   The execution of one or more routines while an initial routine is suspended. Subroutines and interrupt service routines are often nested separately or together, and they can be nested again and again. When this happens, the routines are said to be nested deeper and deeper. A routine that can be nested upon itself is said to be reentrant.

Nibble   A four bit binary word.

Nonaddressable Memory   Memory whose storage locations cannot be activated directly by use of the address bus. Nonaddressable memory generally uses mass storage devices, as opposed to addressable memory, such as RAM or ROM.

Nonmaskable Interrupt   An interrupt which cannot be masked in software.

Nonvolatile Memory   Memory which does not change when power is removed.

NOP (No Operation)   An assembly language instruction which only increments the program counter; also called No-Op. It is used for various purposes, such as providing a short delay or leaving unused memory space in object code.

Object Code   A program directly readable by a computer; a sequence of machine instructions.

Octal Notation   The number system with a base of eight.

One's Complement   The one's complement of a binary word is the result of a bit-by-bit complement of the word; all ones are changed to zeros and all zeros are changed to ones.

Operating System   The program which controls the operation of a general-purpose computer. The operating system initializes the system, regulates I/O from the keyboard and to the display, controls the flow of data to and from mass storage, directs any sharing between multiusers, directs any sharing between multitasks, and directs other operations, such as diagnostics. If a disk system is included with the computer, the operating system is generally termed a disk-operating system (DOS).

Operation Code (Op Code)   A binary machine instruction.

Page   A bank of memory usually having a number of the most significant address bits in common. For example, a system with 16-bit addressing might use as a page a bank of memory with a constant high-order byte. The zero page is the page where these high-order bits are all zero. In our example the zero page would start with 0000, hexadecimal, and end with 00FF.

Parallel Communication   Binary communication in which the data are sent one word at a time over multiple, parallel lines.

Parameter Passing   Exchange of data between routines.

Parity   A method of detecting single-bit errors in data transmission. A bit is added to a binary word so that the total number of one bits, including the parity bit, is either even or odd. The even/odd decision is a system design choice.

Parity Flag   A flag which indicates parity status. The 8085 parity flag is set to a one when it detects even parity within the byte in question.

PC (Program Counter)   A CPU register which points to the next program instruction that is to be executed.

Peripheral   In general, a device connected to an I/O port.

Pipelining   A technique which breaks down complex operations into smaller, sequential suboperations, each of which is then performed on sequential data. For example, a pipelined processor might be completing an ALU operation while decoding the next instruction, fetching the next, and checking the cache for the one after that. Pipelined processors are significantly more complex than their nonpipelined cousins; they are generally significantly faster.

Point To   To provide an address. A register or memory location containing an address is said to point to that address.

Polling   Sampling various devices for status data. Polling is often used for interrupt processing; the CPU polls I/O devices when an interrupt occurs to determine the interrupting device.

Pop   A microprocessor instruction used to remove data from a LIFO stack. An alternate term is "pull."

Port   An I/O port; a device designed to communicate between external hardware and the microprocessor buses.

Prefetch   A pipeline technique used to improve the speed of some processors. The next instruction is fetched during execution of the current instruction.

Program   A computer performs instruction commands in sequence. A program is the set of such instructions necessary to complete a specific task.

Programmable I/O   I/O devices whose operation can be changed under software control.

PROM (Programmable Read-Only Memory)   A ROM whose stored data can be entered by the user by means of special electrical techniques.

Protocol   The predetermined details for digital communication. A specific protocol might be "Asynchronous serial duplex at 9600 baud with one start bit, two stop bits, and even parity."

Pseudoinstruction   An assembler directive.

PSW (Program Status Word)   The 8085 assembly language reference for the accumulator and flag register taken together. It is used with the PUSH and POP instructions.

Pull   A microprocessor instruction used to remove data from a LIFO stack. An alternate term is "pop."

Push   A microprocessor instruction used to put data into a LIFO stack.

Pushdown Stack   A LIFO stack.

RAM (Random Access Memory)   Addressable memory whose contents can be both read and modified using normal bus operations.

Real-Time Processing   Computer processing which uses input data as they become available and generates output data as they are needed. The alternate is batch processing, whereby input data are gathered for later, and perhaps slower, processing. A real-time processor must be fast enough to keep up with the demands of the outside world.

Reentrant   A subroutine or interrupt service routine which can be nested upon itself.

Refresh   Cycling dynamic RAM so that the contents are not lost. Dynamic RAM requires a refresh at regular intervals.

Register   A temporary storage location generally contained within the CPU. A register can be addressed easily and quickly.

Relative Addressing   An addressing mode in which the address is located with reference to some internal pointer. A common form of relative addressing uses the program counter as the reference. The address is determined to be a given number of locations away from the PC; the number of locations away might be included with the instruction. Relative addressing is used for writing relocatable code and is generally a fast addressing mode. The 8085 does not directly support relative addressing.

Relocatable Code   A routine which can reside and be run from anywhere in memory. The term is used in two senses: (1) relocatable object code and (2) intermediate code from a compiler, which will later be assigned a specific address in a linker. At that time address data will be filled into the final object code.

Reset   (1) To initialize a system or subsystem; (2) to fix a bit to the zero state.

Return   The process of returning computer control to the original program at the end of a subroutine or certain exception processing routines, such as interrupts.

ROM (Read-Only Memory)   Addressable memory whose data cannot be modified by normal write operation. ROM is nonvolatile; it does not change when power is removed.

Routine   All or part of a program.

RS-232   A standardized serial data transfer interface.

Segmented Memory   Memory which is used in large blocks, or banks. For example, a large memory may be segmented into 64K-byte banks.

Serial Communication   Binary communication whereby the data are sent one bit at a time over a single line.

Set   To fix a bit to the one state.

Sign Flag   A flag which indicates sign status. The 8085 sign flag is set if the MSB of the byte in question is a one.

Slice   A microprocessor technology whereby processor functions are partitioned in hardware into one or more bit sections, and the overall machine is made by connecting several chips together to form a complete CPU. For example, a one-bit-slice system would have a central processing chip type that performed all CPU operations on only one bit. Eight such chips would be connected in parallel to make an 8-bit machine. Slice systems are often used for very high-speed designs based on bipolar or other fast, but not extremely dense, technologies.

Software   Computer programs.

Software Interrupt   A trap. An instruction which causes control to be transferred to a specific location in a fashion similar to the transfer of control that occurs for a normal, hardware, interrupt.

Source Code   Computer code in the language originally written. Source code may be the program in assembly language or in a higher-level language, such as FORTRAN, BASIC, or C. Source code is assembled or compiled into object code. An interpreter can be said to operate on source code, generating and running object code immediately.

SSI (Small-Scale Integration) IC technology in which the chips contain a few basic gates that may be connected to provide a simple function.

SP (Stack Pointer) A LIFO stack is normally established as a sequence of memory locations. The SP is a register that holds the address of the top of the LIFO stack in a microprocessor.

Stack Temporary storage locations which can be used by the programmer to write and read data based on their sequence rather than on specific addressing. The most common type of stack found in microcomputers is the LIFO stack; the newest data in the stack are to be read next.

Start Bit A bit added to a serial data transmission to indicate that transmission of a word is beginning.

Static RAM Memory which will maintain its contents without the refresh required for dynamic RAM.

Status Register A register which contains various status flags; a flag register.

Stop Bit(s) Bits added to a serial data transmission to indicate that transmission of a word has been completed.

Structured Program Loosely, a program written in a carefully crafted and ordered fashion, generally a modular program. More specifically, a program written to follow specific, strict programming rules. These rules are designed to yield programs that run with little debugging and are easy to debug when errors do occur.

Subroutine A program designed to perform a specific task as part of a larger task. The program performing the larger task passes computer control to the subroutine whenever its specific task must be carried out; when the subroutine is finished, control is returned to the original program.

Synchronous Serial communication whose transmission is controlled by external timing, not embedded in the serial data train.

Syntax Rules which establish the specific structure of statements in a language.

Three-State Driver A bus driver designed to produce a high-impedance output state in addition to the two normal binary states. The high-impedance state allows some other device to drive the bus.

Top-Down Programming Software development in which the overall program operation is decided first. Smaller and smaller program modules are later added.

Trap An instruction which causes control to be transferred to a specific location in a fashion similar to the transfer of control carried out for a normal, hardware interrupt.

T-State Time state; a specific time interval associated with a particular computer. The various machine instructions require different numbers of T-states for completion.

Two's Complement Numbers A number system which allows signed arithmetic to be performed using ordinary binary arithmetic operations.

UART (Universal Asynchronous Receiver/Transmitter) A programmable I/O device designed to implement various asynchronous serial communication protocols.

Vector Datum brought to the CPU which defines the location for further program execution. Vectors are generally used to define the location for interrupt and other exception processing.

Vector Table A sequence of memory locations containing program vectors. The CPU will go to a specific element in this table to locate the desired vector.

Vectored Interrupt An interrupt scheme which directs the CPU to an interrupt service routine through a vector. The vector may come from the interrupting device or from a vector table.

VHSIC (Very High-Speed Integrated Circuit) A military VLSI program for which device speed, along with dense integration, is a primary goal.

VLSI (Very Large-Scale Integration) IC technology in which the chips contain complete digital subsystems (such as a CPU) or other very large functional blocks (such as hundreds of thousands of memory locations). A device containing over a thousand gates is often said to be a VLSI device.

Volatile Memory Memory whose contents are lost when power is removed.

Wait States If memory or an I/O port is not able to respond to a command within the time allowed for a normal read/write cycle, the device can signal that a delay is required. The microprocessor then inserts a delay until the device is ready. Such additional delay intervals are called wait states.

Word (Binary) A group of bits taken together. A word may be of any length, although for some microprocesor systems the term is reserved for 16-bit groups.

Zero Flag A flag which indicates a zero condition. The 8085 zero flag is set if the byte in question contains only zeros.

APPENDIX ONE
REVIEW

This text uses some basic concepts from the study of binary number systems and logical arithmetic. The discussion in this appendix is intended to provide summary material concerning these concepts. The material is basic and, of course, does not attempt to present the full richness of Boolean mathematics or the mathematics of number systems. It can be used as a refresher or as an introduction. Several problems related to number systems and logical operations are included at the end for further study.

Binary Numbers

Computers use a two-state number system called the binary system, which is best explained by first considering a typical number in the common decimal system. The decimal system uses ten symbols, zero through 9. The value of a symbol is weighted by its position in relation to the other symbols making up the number. Thus,

$$49536 = 4 \times 10000 + 9 \times 1000 + 5 \times 100 + 3 \times 10 + 6 \times 1$$

10^4	10^3	10^2	10^1	10^0	weighting
4	9	5	3	6	example

Each of the five digits in this example is one of the ten symbols zero through 9. The weighting of each digit is a power of ten. Hence, these decimal numbers are said to be based on the number ten, base ten.

Binary numbers are constructed in the same way, except that they have a base of two. Consequently, there are only two symbols, 0 and 1, and digit weightings are powers of two. Thus,

$$10111 = \quad 1 \times 16 \; + \; 0 \times 8 \; + \; 1 \times 4 \; + \; 1 \times 2 \; + \; 1 \times 1$$

2^4	2^3	2^2	2^1	2^0	weighting
1	0	1	1	1	example

This is equivalent to 23 in the decimal system.

To convert a number from decimal to binary, first determine whether it is even or odd. If it is odd the right bit is a "1" and 1 should be subtracted from the number. If it is even, the right bit is "0" and no subtraction is required. Divide the result by two. Repeat the preceding sequence until the decimal number is reduced to zero. An example follows:

Convert 37 to Binary

Number odd 1
Subtract 1 yields 36
Divide by 2 yields 18
Number even 01
Divide by 2 yields 9
Number odd 101
Subtract 1 yields 8
Divide by 2 yields 4
Number even 0101
Divide by 2 yields 2
Number even 00101
Divide by 2 yields 1
Number odd 100101
Subtract 1 yields 0 and we're finished.
Thus, 37 in base ten equals 100101 in binary.

Another method of converting decimal numbers to binary numbers uses Table A1.1.

Table A1.1 is designed for numbers up to 16 bits in length. The process is to find the bit locations (zero to 15) that contain ones. The others contain zeros. The table entry that is just smaller than the number to be converted is located. This bit position is a one. The table value is subtracted from the number, and the process is repeated until the remainder is zero.

For example, 3871 has a one at bit position 11. The remainder is $3871 - 2048 = 1823$. Therefore, bit position 10 is also a one, leaving a remainder of $1823 - 1024 = 799$. Bit position 9 is also a one, leaving 799 $- 512 = 287$. Again, a one is at the next position, number 8; $287 - 256 = 31$. Bits 7 through 5 are zero; bits 4 through zero are ones. The binary number is 0000111100001111.

To convert a binary number to a decimal number, identify each bit from the right with the binary sequence (1, 2, 4, 8, 16, 32, . . .) from the table. Sum the product of each binary digit (0 or 1) and its associated

Table A1.1
Powers of Two

Bit Position	Weighting
15	32,768
14	16,384
13	8,192
12	4,096
11	2,048
10	1,024
9	512
8	256
7	128
6	64
5	32
4	16
3	8
2	4
1	2
0	1

weighting. Thus, 100101 in binary converts to decimal as follows:

$$1 \times 32 + 0 \times 16 + 0 \times 8 + 1 \times 4 + 0 \times 2 + 1 + 1 = 37$$

Hexadecimal Numbers

When we examine the operation of a microprocessor system, binary patterns are always being considered. This can be very tedious for the programmer. Moreover, binary numbers can be difficult to transmit between computer devices using common formats. The most useful code for the microcomputer is the ASCII code, as discussed in the text. It is not designed for transmission of binary data. For these reasons alternative methods are often used to convey binary information.

The method used is to group a number of bits together and then represent this group with an equivalent coded number or character. The method most commonly used is hexadecimal (base 16) coding, which is based on a four-bit group. There are sixteen combinations of four binary digits; hence sixteen symbols, or characters, are required. These sixteen symbols are the ten numeric digits, zero through 9, plus the six alphabetic characters, A through F. The binary codes and corresponding hexadecimal symbols are shown in Table A1.2.

Some examples of binary patterns and their equivalent hexadecimal representations are

$$\underset{6}{\underline{0110}}\,\underset{D}{\underline{1101}} = 6D \text{ (hexadecimal)}$$

Table A1.2
Binary to Hexadecimal

Binary	Hexadecimal
0000	0
0001	1
0010	2
0011	3
0100	4
0101	5
0110	6
0111	7
1000	8
1001	9
1010	A
1011	B
1100	C
1101	D
1110	E
1111	F

$$\underbrace{1111}_{F}\underbrace{0010}_{2} = \text{F2 (hexadecimal)}$$

$$\underbrace{1011}_{B}\underbrace{0100}_{4}\underbrace{1000}_{8}\underbrace{1110}_{E} = \text{B48E (hexadecimal)}$$

As seen in these examples, the conversion from hexadecimal to binary is by direct substitution of a four-bit binary pattern for each hexadecimal digit.

Conversions between normal decimal numbers and hexadecimal ones can often require very large numbers. To convert from hexadecimal to decimal, we first note the decimal value of the hexadecimal digits given in Table A1.3.

Next we must know the multiplier for each hexadecimal bit position, as given in Table A1.4. They are the powers of 16.

Table A1.4 covers numbers as large as a 32-bit binary number. The process, as usual, is to multiply the bit position weighting by the value in the position for each hexadecimal digit. The answer is the sum. Thus, hexadecimal D4A5 is

$$13 \times 4,096 + 4 \times 256 + 10 \times 16 + 5 \times 1 = 54,437$$

The reverse process, changing from decimal to hexadecimal, is more painful. First, divide by 16. The fractional part of the quotient, multiplied by 16, is the position zero value. Divide by 16 again. The fractional part, multiplied by 16, gives the value for position one. The process is continued until the complete number is found. For example, to change 68,941,

Table AI.3

Hexadecimal to Decimal Conversion

Hexadecimal	Decimal
0	0
1	1
2	2
3	3
4	4
5	5
6	6
7	7
8	8
9	9
A	10
B	11
C	12
D	13
E	14
F	15

Table A1.4

Hexadecimal Bit Positions

Position	Decimal Multiplier
0	1
1	16
2	256
3	4,096
4	65,536
5	1,048,576
6	16,777,276
7	268,435,456

decimal, to hexadecimal, we divide by 16:

$68,941/16 = 4,308 \ 13/16$

The position zero digit is D (hexadecimal for 13). Now, divide by 16:

$4308/16 = 269 \ 4/16$

Digit one is 4. Again,

$269/16 = 16 \ 13/16$

The position two value is D. Now

$16/16 = 1 \ 0/16$

Value number three is zero:

$1/16 = 0 \ 1/16$

The position four value is 1. Thus, the whole number is 10D4D, hexadecimal.

BCD Numbers

When a microprocessor is used in a system that must constantly interface with a human operator—a calculator or a digital voltmeter, for example—it is often more convenient to operate in the decimal number system, in spite of the inefficiency. In these situations binary-coded decimal coding is normally used. In the BCD system a group of four bits is used to represent one decimal digit. Thus, only the combinations 0000 to 1001, that is, zero to 9, are used.

Some examples of binary patterns and their equivalent decimal representations are

$$\underbrace{0110}_{6}\underbrace{1001}_{9} = 69 \text{ (decimal)}$$

$$\underbrace{0111}_{7}\underbrace{0101}_{5} = 75 \text{ (decimal)}$$

Digital Logic

Digital computers derive much of their power from their ability to make logical decisions and to alter their course of actions based on these decisions.

The logical functions used in this text are AND, OR, NOT, and XOR (exclusive OR). Each of these functions is available on a bit-by-bit basis in the instruction set of the Intel 8085 microprocessor and virtually all other microprocessors. Furthermore, the hardware itself, both the microprocessor and all the peripheral logic chips used to make up a microcomputer, are composed primarily of logic gates that are electronic circuits, which implement these four basic logic functions. It is therefore of fundamental importance for the reader to be familiar with these functions.

Consider the statement, "The noon whistle will blow if it is twelve o'clock and the plant is functioning properly." The word "and" in this sentence can be thought of as a logical operator that implies a certain condition will be true—the noon whistle will blow—if and only if two other conditions are true—it is twelve o'clock **AND** the plant is operating properly. This is precisely the function of the AND operator in digital logic. The condition "true" is often represented by the symbol 1, and the condition "false" is represented by the symbol 0. If we now assign symbols to the conditions in the statement just given, we can apply a shorthand notation in the form of an equation similar to an algebraic expression:

Let X = true, or 1, if the whistle blows.

A = true, or 1, if the time is twelve o'clock.

B = true, or 1, if the plant is functioning normally.

Then the logical expression

$$X = A \times B$$

expresses the same thing as the sentence used in this example but in a more compact form. Note that the AND operation is expressed in the same way as multiplication is expressed in ordinary algebra.

The result of any logical operation can be defined by an exhaustive table of all combinations of the input variables and the resulting output. Such a table is called a **truth table.** The truth table for the AND operation is shown in Figure A1.1, along with the symbol for the logic gate that implements this function.

Now consider another English language statement: "A driver is breaking the law if he is exceeding the speed limit or driving on the wrong side of the road." The use of the word "or" does not exclude the possibility that the driver is speeding and on the wrong side of the road. Thus, it is referred to as an "inclusive or"; it is true with either condition true and with both conditions true; being true "includes" the situation in which both conditions are true. This use of the English word "or" corresponds to the logical function (OR), which is usually symbolized by a plus sign. It should not be confused with the addition operation of ordinary algebra. With variables properly defined, the statement could be written

$$X = A + B$$

In this operation X is true if A is true, B is true, or both are true. A truth table for the OR function, along with the symbol for the logical OR gate, is shown in Figure A1.2.

Another logical function is negation, or the NOT function. It simply reverses the sense of its input; that is, if the input is true, the output is false and vice versa. The truth table and symbol for a NOT gate or inverter are shown in Figure A1.3. The circle, or bubble, on the output of the gate symbol signifies inversion. A triangle without a bubble symbolizes a buffer. A buffer is sometimes used to drive heavy loads or to restore logic levels. The negation, or complement, of a logical variable is usually ex-

Truth Table

Input		Output
0	0	0
0	1	0
1	0	0
1	1	1

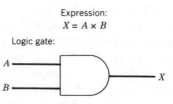

Expression:
$$X = A \times B$$

Logic gate:

Figure A 1.1
AND Operation.

Truth Table

Input		Output
0	0	0
0	1	1
1	0	1
0	0	1

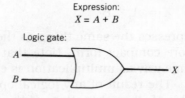

Expression:
$X = A + B$

Logic gate:

Figure A 1.2
OR Operation.

Truth Table

Input	Output
1	0
0	1

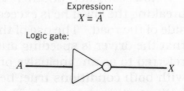

Expression:
$X = \overline{A}$

Logic gate:

Figure A 1.3
NOT Operation.

pressed as the original variable symbol with a bar over it, as shown by the logic expression of Figure A1.3.

We now have the basic tools with which to derive other functions. At the beginning of this section, we mentioned another logic function, the exclusive OR or XOR function. This function can be expressed as follows. "If X is the output of an XOR gate and A and B are the inputs, then X is true if either A or B is true but not both." We can put together a collection of AND, OR, and NOT functions to implement this XOR function as follows.

1. Use an AND to generate the function $A \times B$.
2. Use an OR to generate the function $A + B$.
3. Use a NOT function to get the complement of the function in item 1.
4. Combine the outputs of the NOT and the OR with another AND.

What about the "but" in our XOR English language description? We have replaced the "but not" construct with "AND NOT." This results in the correct logical function, and it will have to do until someone invents a BUT gate. The truth table for the logical function XOR, along with the circuit we just designed to implement it and the symbol for the XOR gate, are all shown in Figure A1.4. This figure also shows the logical expression for the output of the XOR gate. Notice the bar over the composite variable $A \times B$. This is read as NOT (A AND B). Also note that the symbol for the XOR operation in logical expressions is a plus sign with a circle around it.

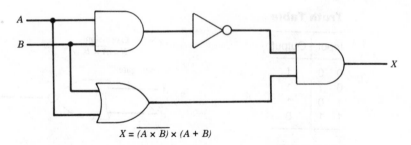

$$X = \overline{(A \times B)} \times (A + B)$$

Truth Table

Input	Output
0 0	0
0 1	1
1 0	1
1 1	0

Expression:
$X = A \times B$

Logic gate:

Figure A 1.4
XOR Operation.

Additional gate types are often used because they are easy to manu-facture in a particular device technology. These are NAND (NOT AND) gates and NOR (NOT OR) gates. The symbols for these gates and their truth tables are shown in Figure A1.5. In each case, the bubble on the output signifies inversion. It is interesting to note that the minimum set of logic functions required to synthesize all logical expressions is two: either NOT and AND or NOT and OR. Any combinational logic function can be synthesized by using only NAND gates or by using only NOR gates.

In a microprocessor, logical operations can be performed on bytes on a bit-by-bit basis. For example, the 8085 instruction ANA B causes the contents of register B to be "ANDed" with the contents of the accumula-tor; the result is stored in the accumulator.

EXAMPLE A1.1

The B-register contains 11010011, and the accumulator contains 01010101. What byte will be left in the accumulator after the ANA B instruction is executed?

Referring to the truth table for the AND function, we AND each bit of the contents of the B-register with the corresponding bit of the accumu-lator to yield the result 01010001.

Similarly, the CMA performs a NOT operation on each of the bits in the accumulator, and the ORA and XRA perform bit-by-bit OR and XOR

Truth Table

Input		Output
0	0	1
0	1	1
1	0	1
1	1	0

Expression:
$X = \overline{A \times B}$

Logic gate:

(a) NAND

Truth Table

Input		Output
0	0	1
0	1	0
1	0	0
1	1	0

Expression:
$X = \overline{A + B}$

Logic gate:

(b) NOR

Figure A 1.5
Inverse Logic Operation.

operations, respectively, on the contents of the accumulator and the contents of the register or memory location specified as the argument of the function. Some of the uses of these functions, such as bit masking, are demonstrated in the text.

EXERCISES

A1.1 Convert the following decimal numbers into their equivalent binary numbers:

35   67   224

A1.2 Convert the following binary numbers into their equivalent decimal numbers:

10111   1010101   11011011

A1.3 Convert the following decimal numbers into their equivalent hexadecimal numbers:

27   96   3334

A1.4 Convert the following hexadecimal numbers into their equivalent decimal numbers:

   C3   2F   2C9E

A1.5 Convert the following decimal numbers into their equivalent BCD numbers and give their binary form and hexadecimal form:

   132   764   5308

A1.6 Write a logic expression to implement the following operation: "The alarm is to sound if the motion sensor detects motion in the warehouse, or if both of the two smoke detectors are triggered and the night watchman has not disabled the alarm."

A1.7 Draw the logic diagram (using standard logic gate symbols) to implement the logical expression

$$X = (A + B) + (C \times D)$$

A1.8 Perform the bit-by-bit logical AND operation on the following bytes:

   11010101   10110011

A1.9 Perform the bit-by-bit logical OR operation on the following bytes:

   11101001   10101100

A1.10 Perform the bit-by-bit logical XOR operation on the following bytes:

   10110001   01011011

APPENDIX TWO
THE INTEL 8085
INSTRUCTION SET

The information in the tables in this appendix are reproduced by courtesy of Intel Corporation. The following symbols and abbreviations are used.

A, B, C, D, E, H, L   represent one of the internal processor registers.

M   represents the memory address currently held in register pair HL.

byte   represents an 8-bit (2 hexadecimal character) data quantity.

dble   represents a 16-bit (2 byte) data quantity.

addr   represents a 16-bit (2 byte) memory address.

port   represents an 8-bit I/O port address.

Register pairs are denoted as follows:

PSW   represents register pair AF.

B   represents register pair BC.

D   represents register pair DE.

H   represents register pair HL.

SP   represents the 16-bit stack pointer.

PC   represents the 16-bit program counter.

The processor flag bits are

CY   carry flag

Z   zero flag

S   sign flag

P   parity flag

AC   auxiliary carry

Data Transfer Group

This group of instructions transfers data to and from registers and memory. No condition flags are affected by any instructions in this group.

Move			Move (*cont.*)			Move Immediate		
MOV—	A, A	7F	MOV—	E, A	5F	MVI—	A, byte	3E
	A, B	78		E, B	58		B, byte	06
	A, C	79		E, C	59		C, byte	0E
	A, D	7A		E, D	5A		D, byte	16
	A, E	7B		E, E	5B		E, byte	1E
	A, H	7C		E, H	5C		H, byte	26
	A, L	7D		E, L	5D		L, byte	2E
	A, M	7E		E, M	5E		M, byte	36

						Load Immediate		
MOV—	B, A	47	MOV—	H, A	67	(Register Pair)		
	B, B	40		H, B	60	LXI—	B, dble	01
	B, C	41		H, C	61		D, dble	11
	B, D	42		H, D	62		H, dble	21
	B, E	43		H, E	63		SP, dble	31
	B, H	44		H, H	64			
	B, L	45		H, L	65	Load/Store A direct		
	B, M	46		H, M	66	LDA addr		3A
						STA addr		32

						Load/Store A indirect		
MOV—	C, A	4F	MOV—	L, A	6F	LDAX B		0A
	C, B	48		L, B	68	LDAX D		1A
	C, C	49		L, C	69	STAX B		02
	C, D	4A		L, D	6A	STAX D		12
	C, E	4B		L, E	6B			
	C, H	4C		L, H	6C			
	C, L	4D		L, L	6D			
	C, M	4E		L, M	6E			

						Load/Store HL direct		
MOV—	D, A	57	MOV—	M, A	77	LHLD addr		2A
	D, B	50		M, B	70	SHLD addr		22
	D, C	51		M, C	71			
	D, D	52		M, D	72			
	D, E	53		M, E	73			
	D, H	54		M, H	74	Exchange HL/DE		
	D, L	55		M, L	75	XCHG		EB
	D, M	56						

Data Manipulation Group—Arithmetic

This group of instructions performs arithmetic operations on data in registers and memory.

Add[1]

ADD—
A	87
B	80
C	81
D	82
E	83
H	84
L	85
M	86

ADC—
A	8F
B	88
C	89
D	8A
E	88
H	8C
L	8D
M	8E

Subtract[1]

SUB—
A	97
B	90
C	91
D	92
E	93
H	94
L	95
M	96

SBB—
A	9F
B	98
C	99
D	9A
E	9B
H	9C
L	9D
M	9E

Add/Subtract Immediate[1]

ADI	byte	C6
ACI	byte	CE
SUI	byte	D6
SBI	byte	DE

Double Add[2]

DAD—
B	09
D	19
H	29
SP	39

Increment/Decrement[3]

INR—
A	3C
B	04
C	0C
D	14
E	1C
H	24
L	2C
M	34

DCR—
A	3D
B	05
C	0D
D	15
E	1D
H	25
L	2D
M	35

Increment/Decrement Register Pair[4]

INX—
B	03
D	13
H	23
SP	33

DCX—
B	0B
D	1B
H	2B
SP	3B

Decimal Adjust A[1]

DAA	27

Complement/Set CY[2]

CMC	3F
STC	37

Complement A[4]

CMA	2F

[1] All flags (CY, Z, S, P, AC) are affected.
[2] Only the carry flag is affected.
[3] All flags, except the carry flag, are affected.
[4] No flags are affected.

Data Manipulation Group—Logical

This group of instructions performs logical operations on data in registers and memory.

AND[1]			OR[1]			Exclusive-OR[1]		
ANA—	A	A7	ORA—	A	B7	XRA—	A	AF
	B	A0		B	B0		B	A8
	C	A1		C	B1		C	A9
	D	A2		D	B2		D	AA
	E	A3		E	B3		E	AB
	H	A4		H	B4		H	AC
	L	A5		L	B5		L	AD
	M	A6		M	B6		M	AE
ANI	byte	E6	ORI	byte	F6	XRI	byte	EE

Compare[1]

CMP—	A	BF
	B	B8
	C	B9
	D	BA
	E	BB
	H	BC
	L	BD
	M	BE
CPI	byte	FE

Rotate[2]

RLC	07	$\boxed{CY} \leftarrow \boxed{7 \leftarrow 0} \leftarrow$
RRC	0F	$\rightarrow \boxed{7 \rightarrow 0} \rightarrow \boxed{CY}$
RAL	17	$\boxed{CY} \leftarrow \boxed{7 \leftarrow 0} \leftarrow$
RAR	1F	$\rightarrow \boxed{7 \rightarrow 0} \rightarrow \boxed{CY}$

[1] All flags are affected.
[2] Only the carry flag is affected.

Transfer of Control Group

This group of instructions alters normal sequential program flow. The following condition codes are used:

NZ not zero (Z = 0)	PO parity odd (P = 0)
Z zero (Z = 1)	PE parity even (P = 1)
NC no carry (CY = 0)	P plus (S = 0)
C carry (CY = 1)	M minus (S = 1)

Jump			Call			Return	
JMP addr	C3		CALL addr	CD		RET	C9
JNZ addr	C2		CNZ addr	C4		RNZ	CO
JZ addr	CA		CZ addr	CC		RZ	C8
JNC addr	D2		CNC addr	D4		RNC	DO
JC addr	DA		CC addr	DC		RC	D8
JPO addr	E2		CPO addr	E4		RPO	EO
JPE addr	EA		CPE addr	EC		RPE	E8
JP addr	F2		CP addr	F4		RP	FO
JM addr	FA		CM addr	FC		RM	F8

Jump Indirect

PCHL   E9

Input/Output Group

This group of instructions performs I/O operations between the A-register and a specified port.

IN	port	DB
OUT	port	D3

Machine Control Group

This group of instructions manipulates the contents of the stack and alters/controls the state of the processor.

Stack Operations (Register Pairs)

PUSH—	B	C5	POP—	B	C1
	D	D5		D	D1
	H	E5		H	E1
	PSW	F5		PSW	F1

XTHL	E3	(L) ↔ ((SP))
		(H) ↔ ((SP) + 1)
SPHL	F9	(SP) ← (HL)

Interrupt Control

EI	FB	(enable interrupts)
DI	F3	(disable interrupts)
RIM	20	(read interrupt mask)
SIM	30	(set interrupt mask)

Restart Control

RST—	0	C7
	1	CF
	2	D7
	3	DF
	4	E7
	5	EF
	6	F7
	7	FF

Processor Control Operations

NOP	00	(no operation)
HLT	76	(halt)

APPENDIX THREE
THE INTEL SDK-85
COMMANDS AND
OPERATION

The Intel SDK-85 uses the 8085 CPU and provides RAM, ROM, I/O, and user interface through a keypad and a display. The following is a discussion of the use of this single-board computer.

Commands to the monitor of the system (shown in Figure 4.5) are selected by pressing keys on the push-button keypad. The response of the monitor is displayed on the numeric display. This response is either an echo of the particular key pressed or an output from the monitor. In addition, a character (prompt) may be displayed, indicating that further inputs are required from the user. All the displayed digits are in hexadecimal code and are split into two areas (fields); the leftmost four digits are the address field, and the rightmost two digits are the data, or contents, field. A memory address, for example, is specified by four hexadecimal digits (16 bits) and the corresponding contents by two digits (8 bits).

The typical monitor commands available with the single-board system are listed next. The SDK-85 keypad has 24 keys. Sixteen keys are marked with hexadecimal digits. Ten of these do double duty in identifying various registers—A-, B-, C-, D-, E-, F-flags, H, L, SP high, SP low, PC high, PC low, and I-interrupt mask. The remaining eight keys perform the following monitor commands:

Reset (RESET)
Substitute memory (SUBST MEM)
Go (GO)
Examine register (EXAM REG)
Single step (SINGLE STEP)
Vectored interrupt (VECT INTR)
Next (NEXT ,)
Execute (EXEC .)

The SDK-85 prompt is a dash at the left edge of the display. The monitor also shows a special prompt when it expects more data. This prompt is a period at the right edge of the field where the data are being placed.

The "reset" command enables the user to force the monitor to restart from the beginning. The system is normally reset automatically on power-up. Most single-board systems display some kind of message on reset to indicate that they are ready. The SDK-85 single-board system always displays "– 8085" on power-up or manual reset.

The "substitute memory" command allows the user to examine the contents of successive memory locations and, if required, to modify their contents. This command is therefore particularly useful for entering a user's program into RAM. The user first writes a program in assembly language form, converts this into hexadecimal form, and then uses the substitute memory command to load the program into RAM. The substitute memory command also allows the user to modify specific RAM locations should any errors be found in the program during execution.

After the user presses the SUBST MEM key, the address prompt appears. Any address from 0000 to FFFF can then be entered, followed by the NEXT key. The data from the memory location appear in the data display along with the data entry prompt. The data display can be changed at this point by entering hexadecimal numbers. The NEXT key enters this new value and displays the next memory location. The process continues until the user presses the EXEC key. This key operates like the NEXT key, except that the monitor returns to "waiting for a new command."

If the user attempts to use this substitute memory command to write to ROM, an error indication will appear.

After a program has been written, coded, and loaded into memory, it can be executed using the "go" command. To execute a program that is already stored in RAM, the user first presses the GO key. The current program counter will be displayed. The user should then enter the four-digit address at which the program starts. The EXEC key causes the user program to run. Once a user program is running (a lone "E" is displayed), the monitor regains control of the system only if the reset key is pressed or certain instructions are executed in the user's program—RST 0, causing a reset; RST 1, causing a warm start (a restart without any memory erasure); JMP 0, causing a reset.

Many students are confused by the apparent difference between the machine's operation under the monitor and the operation of a user program. The monitor is nothing more than a fixed program that services the keypad and display. It also allows transfer of data to and from memory, the display, and the keypad. When the go command is performed, the monitor program simply makes a change (transfer of control command) that causes the next instruction fetched to be located where the user has specified. This is done by changing the PC to the value specified. To return control to the monitor, the user resets PC to the first address of the monitor program (location 0).

The "examine register" command allows the user to display and, if required, modify the contents of each of the microprocessor registers. This facility is particularly useful in concert with the "single step" command since it enables the user to monitor the status of the microprocessor during program execution. This often helps in locating program errors.

The EXAM REG key works much the same as the SUBST MEM key. The monitor asks for a register, and the NEXT key causes the contents of the register to be displayed; it then causes the value in the data display field to be moved to the register and the next register to be displayed. The process continues until finally the EXEC key stores the display value and returns the monitor to the command mode. The sequence of register display is A-B-C-D-E-F-I-H-L-SPH-SPL-PCH-PCL. After PCL the NEXT key yields the same operation as the EXEC key.

When a program has been loaded into RAM, it is usually executed using the go command just outlined. If the program contains errors, however, the microprocessor will not perform the required tasks. It is then necessary to find the erroneous instructions so that they may be corrected. This can often be time-consuming without additional aids; however, the monitor provides such aids, called software aids.

The single-step command is such a software aid since it enables the user to examine the state of the complete system as each program instruction is executed. Thus, any program instructions that do not produce the required effect are readily identified. To step through a program that is already stored in memory, the user first presses the SINGLE STEP key. The operation is similar to the go command; the PC value will be seen along with the instruction (in the data field) at the PC address. The PC can be modified. The NEXT key causes the instruction at the PC to be executed; the next PC address and instruction will be displayed. This can be continued. The EXEC key stores the PC as before, but the program step is not performed. The user can then examine the registers.

Since control is with the monitor, the user may, if required, examine the contents of the various processor registers and memory locations to verify the results of the previous instruction. The user can then return to the single-step mode by pressing the SINGLE STEP key as before. Through this process, the user can obtain an in-depth understanding of the operation of the program at hand.

The VECT INTR key forces an interrupt to be performed. This is the RST 7.5 interrupt that is vectored through the normal location on to 20CE, hexadecimal. Interrupt processing is discussed in Chapter Nine.

APPENDIX FOUR
DEVELOPMENT AIDS

Introduction

A **development aid** is a device used to assist in the development of microprocessor-based systems. Although many microprocessor applications require only a minimal amount of hardware and software, others can be very complex, with a multitude of hardware interface requirements and thousands of lines of code. The development aids required for these projects thus span a range from simple, single-board systems, such as the Intel SDK-85, referred to throughout this text, to multiuser systems with a large computer as a host supporting multiple workstations. These workstations are often quite powerful and complex systems in their own right. Because so many hardware and software tools are used in the development of a microprocessor-based product, the term **target system** has come into use to refer to the actual product under development and to differentiate between this product and the tools used to arrive at it. This appendix is intended to provide a brief overview of the features and capabilities provided by various development aids.

Single-Board Systems

Single-board systems can serve as development aids for small projects. Microprocessor manufacturers often provide single-board microcomputers at a low cost for each of their product lines. A simple single-board system will usually have a monitor in ROM that provides functions, such as resetting the processor, substituting memory contents, single-stepping through a program, and other basic functions. The functions provided by the Intel SDK-85 are typical of such systems and were described in Appendix Three.

With the advent of 16- and 32-bit microprocessors, single-board microcomputers have become somewhat more powerful. These systems often require a CRT terminal, the common television-like cathode-ray tube display, and contain special-purpose development aid software stored in ROM. Still, they are suitable only for relatively small development projects and for educational purposes. Major microprocessor-based development programs require the more powerful hardware and software features found in complete development systems described in the next section.

Development Systems

A **microprocessor development system (MDS)** is an integrated system of hardware and software designed to aid in the development of microprocessor-based products. The usual MDS includes a computer with mass storage capability, a CRT display, a printer, and various other special hardware features. A general-purpose MDS will normally support many different microprocessor types using the same basic host computer hardware and software. Only items that are unique to a particular microprocessor must be purchased in upgrading the system for another application. Assemblers and other special-purpose software, as well as certain hardware items, fall into this category; thus, to upgrade an 8080 development system for use with the 8085, one might need to buy a new assembler, certain other special software (for example, a compiler, as discussed later in this section), and any hardware directly related to the target device.

A variety of software tools are provided with these systems, including editors (for creating and correcting source code), assemblers, compilers (for high-level languages, such as C, BASIC, or Pascal), linkers, debuggers, and library management programs. These software tools are described, along with the hardware features of common development systems, in the following sections.

A large-scale microprocessor development project might be defined as one that requires more than, say, 1000 lines of source code. Some projects require hundreds of thousands of lines of source code. Such projects often require the collaboration of many hardware and software designers. The phases of development in a project of this type are concept definition, major design decisions (such as choice of processor type and programming languages), detailed hardware design, software design, programming, hardware and software debugging, design verification, and software maintenance. This final element, software maintenance, includes locating and correcting deficiencies that manage to slip through the debugging process, as well as responding to changing requirements or special applications that require modifications to the original source code.

Software Tools

In most modern projects with embedded microcomputers, the coding and debugging of the software is the most time-consuming and expensive part of the project. It thus becomes imperative to provide the programmers with the best available tools to enhance productivity and reduce errors. To this end, manufacturers of development systems provide a variety of powerful software tools to run on the systems that they manufacture.

The primary interface between the programmer and the MDS is the operating system. This is a software package that provides facilities for data storage, file manipulation, and execution of programs, such as assemblers. Some operating systems provide a variety of useful functions, such as archiving and software configuration management. These facilities help to keep a record of the various versions of a program as it is developed and enable the user to determine, quickly and easily, what specific things are changed from one version to the next. Many of the modern development systems use UXIX, an operating system developed by AT&T, or some variation of UNIX. This very powerful operating system has many advanced features and enhancements. Manufacturers of development systems often provide an alternative menu-driven operating system, called a *shell* in UNIX terminology, which operates in conjunction with UNIX. Programmers can have the best of both worlds. Less experienced users are able to perform most of the necessary tasks with the user-friendly, menu-driven shell while learning UNIX. As they gain more experience, they are able to take full advantage of the many powerful features of UNIX.

An editor is a program designed specifically for creating and modifying text data, such as source code for programs. There are two main types of editors, line-oriented and screen-oriented. A line-oriented editor assigns a line number to each line of the text and allows the user to issue commands to move from one line to another and add, delete, or modify text in each line. A screen-oriented editor displays one screenful of text at a time on the CRT terminal and allows the user to "point" to the region of interest in some manner, thus maintaining a continuous visual interaction between the user and the program. Pointing to the text may be by means of a cursor, such as an underline displayed on the screen. The cursor can be moved around the screen via special keys on the keyboard or by a device called a mouse. A light pen, with which the operator touches the screen, is an even faster method of pointing. Text can be inserted or deleted at the cursor position, or it can be highlighted in blocks and moved from one place to another. Various editors available provide a variety of additional features too numerous to mention here. The manuscript of the current text was created using a screen-oriented editor, a word processor. Modern MDS editors are often language-oriented; that is, they have built-in capabilities for detecting syntax errors and for helping the programmer put the code into the proper format for the assembler or compiler to be used.

Once the source code has been created and corrected using the editor, it must be assembled or compiled. Since the assembler or compiler used in the MDS is generally executed on a processor other than the target processor, these tools are generally called cross assemblers and cross compilers. Manufacturers make every attempt to write cross assemblers and cross compilers that generate compact and fast object code.

Assemblers available for development use do considerably more than translate instruction mnemonics into binary codes. For instance, it is not necessary to specify absolute addresses for data or program steps. Instead, symbolic names, or labels, are used for data items, and labels also specify locations within the program. Labels free the programmer from the tedious and error-prone process of keeping track of memory locations and make the program more readable. In addition, avoiding specific addresses in the code yields a program that can be relocated to anywhere in memory.

Another useful feature of these assemblers is the use of *macros.* If a list of instructions is required many times in a program, a macro may be defined to specify this group of instructions. Then, each time these instructions are needed, only the macro name is written. The assembler inserts the block of code directly into the program. Of course, the same saving in programming effort can be had through the use of subroutines, except for one problem. A subroutine requires some overhead in processor time. Time is lost saving register contents on the stack and actually performing the subroutine call and return, with the attendant need to save and retrieve the contents of the program counter. In embedded microprocessor applications, execution time is often critical; as a rule macros make the program execute faster than subroutines. But as usual, there is no free lunch; macros take more memory.

Compilers used in development are often multipass compilers, with the last stage being an optimizer that performs operations on the object code to enhance the speed, or make efficient use of memory, or both. Sometimes there is a trade-off between speed and compactness of code. Some modern compilers allow the user to choose between optimizers for speed and those for compactness.

Programs are often broken down into smaller units called modules. Each module is designed to perform a specific task and is written and tested as a unit. Once the module has been debugged, it is assembled or compiled, and the resulting object code is placed into a library of such modules. Software tools included in the MDS are able to link these modules into larger units, called run-time modules. In many embedded computer applications, the software is written in a combination of high-level language, such as Pascal or C, and assembly language. Modules that must execute very fast might be written in assembly language, whereas the rest of the program is written in a structured, high-level language for programming efficiency and ease of maintenance. The run-time modules generated by the assembler and the compiler must be compatible and capable of being linked together. Instead of compiling to object code, most compilers in these systems compile to assembly language modules, which use the same assembler as that of modules written directly in assembly language.

In-Circuit Emulators

Once the software is written and the prototype hardware has been constructed, the hardware and software must be integrated and debugged. This could be a very difficult task were it not for in-circuit emulators (ICEs). Because the target processor is a single chip of silicon, it is not possible to observe the conditions within the microprocessor itself. An ICE is a peripheral device of the MDS that replaces the microprocessor in the target system. Since it is under control of the MDS, while it is operating it can be used to monitor the behavior of the system under development.

The ICE behaves exactly as the target processor when it is plugged into the socket normally occupied by the processor. It allows the user access to the memory and the CPU for debugging purposes. It reads the correct sequence of program instructions either from the target memory or from an internal RAM, and it generates the correct bus signals during their execution. The MDS is able to keep a record, in an area of its own memory, of the sequence of actions that take place in the target system during operation. This record is known as a *real-time trace,* and it can be examined later by the MDS system software to locate possible errors. The real-time trace can include any or all the bus signals and other microprocessor logic lines, as well as register contents. Normally, the user can set break points based on certain conditions occurring, such as accessing a particular memory location or I/O port, and save data both before and after the event occurs.

Summary

For applications that require only a small amount of software, fewer than 1K bytes, it is feasible to use a single-board system for their development. For larger applications, however, it is advantageous to use an MDS.

For a single-board system, it is necessary to write all software in assembly language and perform a translation process by hand. For an MDS, it is possible to use a high-level language, in addition to assembly language, reducing considerably program development time.

An MDS also contains an editor program that facilitates the modification of a source program and possibly an ICE to help develop the application hardware and software.

INDEX

MICROPROCESSOR INDEX

8085, 7, 28–32, 51, 52, 62, 75, 159
8155/6, 47–49, 169–173
8212, 139–142
8251, 155–159
8755, 41–44, 145–151

SUBJECT INDEX

Access time, 233
Accumulator, *see* Register, Accumulator
ACI, 95, 261
ACIA (asynchronous communications
    interface adaptor), 233
ADC, 96, 261
Add, 65, 89–91, 261
Address, 9, 50, 51, 233
  Decode, 26, 27, 51, 233
Addressing:
  Direct, 67, 71, 190, 237
  Extended, 238
  Immediate, 67, 69, 70, 90, 238
  Indexed, 75, 239
  Indirect, 67, 73, 90, 92, 188, 191, 239
  Modes, 66, 67, 75, 233
  Register, 67, 68, 90, 92
  Relative, 243
ADI, 7, 8, 90, 261
ALU (arithmetic logic unit), 19, 20, 29, 233
ANA, 102, 262
Analog-to-digital converter (ADC),
    173–182
  Counter based, 173–175
  Integrator type, 179

Software based, 177–179
Successive approximation, 176, 177
V/F converter, 180
AND, 19, 30, 101
  Gate, 252, 253
ANI, 101, 262
Architecture, 2, 17, 32, 234
Arithmetic:
  Logical, 100–107
  Multiprecision, 94–97
ASCII, 12, 87, 234
ASR-33, 53
Assembler, 76, 234
  Cross, 236, 272
  Directives, 63, 234
Assembly, conditional, 236
Assembly language, 62–64, 76, 77, 234
Asynchronous, 153, 234

Babbage, Charles, 1
Bank, 234
Batch processing, 234
Baud rate, 152, 234
BCD (binary coded decimal), 87, 97–100,
    234, 252
Bidirectional, 23, 234
Binary, 9, 84, 234, 247–249
  Signed, 84–86
Bit, 11, 235
Bit-mapped, 88, 235. *See also* I/O, Bit-
  mapped
Bit slice, 14, 235
Branch, 9, 235
  Conditional, 9, 66
  Unconditional, 9, 66

275

Break point, 235
Bug, 235
Bus, 10, 21, 22, 235
   Address, 22–24, 233
   Contention, 235
   Control, 22–24, 236
   Data, 22–24, 236
   Driver, 235
   Glue, 51, 235
Byte, 11, 235

Cache memory, 235
Calculator, 2, 7
Call, 115, 235, 262
CC, 116, 263
Clear, 236
Clock, 236
CM, 116, 263
CMA, 105, 261
CMC, 106, 261
CMOS (complementary MOS), 13
CMP, 105, 262
CNC, 116, 263
CNZ, 116, 263
Code, 236
Comments, 64, 236
Compare, 105
Compile, 236, 272
Computer, digital, 1–3, 6–13
Coprocessor, math, 19, 227
Counter/timer, 216, 236
CP, 116, 263
CPE, 116, 263
CPI, 105, 262
CPO, 116, 263
CPU, *see* Microprocessor
Cycle time, 14
CZ, 116, 263

DAA, 98, 261
DAD, 94, 261
Data, 83–87
Data, logical, 206
DCR, 92, 261
DCX, 92, 261
Debug, 236
Decimal adjust, 97–100, 236
Decrement, 92, 236
Development system, 78, 236, 270
DI, 120, 263
Diagnostic, 237
Digital-to-analog converter (DAC),
   167–173
Disk, magnetic, 57, 58
Displacement, 237

DMA, 23, 237
Documentation, 122–124
DOS (disk operating system), 237

EAPROM (electrically alterable PROM), 41,
   237
ECL (emitter-coupled logic), 13
Editor, 237, 271
EEPROM (electrically erasable PROM), 41
EI, 120, 263
Embedded system, 205, 237
Emulator, 237, 273
ENIAC, 2
EPROM (erasable PROM), 39–44, 237
   Erasure, 39
   UV (ultraviolet), 39–41
Exception processing, 194, 202, 237
Execution time, 238

Feature size, 5, 6
Fetch/execute cycle, 7–10, 20, 31, 237, 238
Flag, 30, 238, 259
   Auxiliary carry, 30, 234
   Borrow, 18, 30
   Carry, 18, 19, 30, 95, 236
   Parity, 30, 242
   Sign, 18, 30, 243
   Zero, 18, 30, 245
Flowcharts, 125, 238
Framing error, 154
FSK (frequency shift keying), 54

Gallium arsenide (GaAs), 15

Handshake, 142–145, 238
Harvard machine, 8
Hexadecimal, 12, 238, 249–251
Hex code, 238
High-impedance state, 22, 238
HLT, 120, 263
HSCMOS (high speed CMOS), 13

I/O (input/output), 10, 26, 120, 133–182,
   239
   Bit-mapped, 163–167
   I/O-mapped, 26, 135–139, 239
   Memory-mapped, 26, 240
   Port, 26, 134, 139–142, 239
   Programmable, 145–147, 242
   Serial, 151–160
IC (integrated circuit), 2–6, 13, 238
IIL (integrated-injection logic), 13
IN, 120, 263
Increment, 91, 239
INR, 92, 261

Instruction, 7, 239
  Decode, 7, 31
  Set, 9, 239
Interpreter, 239
Interrupt, 20, 21, 32, 185-202, 216, 239
  Mask, 194-197, 239
  Multiple, 194-201
  Nonmaskable, 195, 241
  Priority, 197-199, 239
  Service routine, 187, 239
  Smart, 188-191
  Software, 243
  Vectored, 245
INX, 92, 261

JC, 112, 263
JM, 112, 263
JMP, 66, 110, 262
JNC, 112, 263
JNZ, 112, 263
JP, 112, 263
JPE, 112, 263
JPO, 112, 263
Jump, 109-113, 239
  Conditional, 111
  Unconditional, 109
JZ, 112, 263

K (Kilo-), 24, 239
Kansas City standard, 54

Label, 64, 109, 110, 239
LDA, 71, 260
LDAX, 74, 260
LHLD, 72, 260
Library, 239
Linker, 240
Logic, digital, 252-256
Long word, 11
Look-up table, 227
Loop, 9, 240
LSB (least significant bit), 4, 240
LSI (large scale integration), 2, 240
LSTTL (low-power STTL), 13
LXI, 69, 70, 260

M (Mega-), 240
Machine cycle, 10
Machine language, 240
Macro, 240, 272
Macroassembler, 63
Mark I, 2
Marking, 153
Mask, 240
Mass storage/memory, 24, 52-59

Memory, 10, 17, 23, 24, 35-59, 240
  Addressable, 23, 233
  Floppy disk, 57-59
  Magnetic core, 2
  Magnetic tape, 54-57
  Map, 24, 25
  Nonaddressable, 23, 241
  Nonvolatile, 24, 241
  Paper tape, 53-56
  Read/write, 44-49
  Segmented, 243
  Volatile, 24, 245
Microcomputer, 240
Microcontroller, 240
Microprocessor, 2, 3, 10, 17-21, 236, 240
Microprogram, 240
Mnemonics, 63, 240
Modem, 152, 240
Modular design, 124
Modular programming, 240
Monitor, 76, 265
MOS (metal oxide semiconductor), 13
MOV, 65, 68, 73, 76, 77, 260
MSB (most significant bit), 241
MSI (medium scale integration), 4, 241
Multiplex, 241
  Time, 23
Multiplying DAC (MDAC), 169
MVI, 69, 73, 77, 111, 260

Nesting, 118, 241
Nibble, 11, 241
NMOS (n-channel MOS), 13
NOP, 66, 120, 241, 263
NOT, 30, 254

Object code, 63, 241
Octal, 241
One's complement, 241
Op code (operation code), 241
Operand, 64
Operating system, 241
OR, 19, 102
  Gate, 254
ORA, 102, 262
ORI, 102, 262
OUT, 66, 120, 263
Overrun error, 154

Page, 241
Parallel communication, 139-151, 241
Parameter passing, 117, 241
Parity, 12, 241
PC, see Register, PC
PCHL, 121, 263

Peripheral, 242
Personal computer, 3, 24, 53, 54
Pipelining, 242
PMOS (*p*-channel MOS), 13
Polling, 242
POP, 118, 119, 263
Prefetch, 242
Processor, *see* Microprocessor
Program, 7, 242
Programming:
  Bottom-up, 235
  Top-down, 125, 244
PROM (programmable ROM), 38–44, 242
Prompt, 265
Protocol, 242
Pseudoinstruction, 242
PUSH, 118, 119, 263

R/2R Ladder, 169, 173
RAL, 104, 262
RAM (random access memory), 24, 44–49,
  242
  Dynamic, 44–47, 237
  Static, 44, 244
RAR, 104, 262
RC, 116, 263
Real-time processing, 242
Reentrant, 243
Refresh, 46, 243
Register, 17, 18, 29–31, 61, 62, 243, 259
  Accumulator (A), 18, 29, 62, 233
  B and BC, 31, 62, 234
  Condition code, 18, 236
  D and DE, 31, 62, 236
  Flag, 18, 29, 62, 238, 244
  H and HL, 31, 62, 238
  IM, 62. *See also* Interrupt Mask
  Index, 19, 239
  Instruction, 19, 29
  Invisible, 19, 30
  PC (Program counter), 10, 18, 31, 62, 242
  PSW (Program status word), 242
  SP (Stack pointer), 19, 29, 62, 244
  Status, 18, 244
  TMP (Temporary), 29
  Visible, 62
Relocatable code, 243
Reset, 21, 31, 243
RET, 115, 262
Return, 243
RIM, 195–197, 263
RLC, 104, 262
RM, 116, 263
RNC, 116, 263

RNZ, 116, 263
ROM (read only memory), 24, 35–44, 243
  Diode-matrix, 36, 37
  Mask programmable, 24, 37, 38
Rotate/shift, 104
Routine, 243
RP, 116, 263
RPE, 116, 263
RPO, 116, 263
RRC, 104, 262
RS-232, 151, 152, 156, 243
RST, 121, 190–194, 262
RZ, 116, 263

SBB, 96, 261
SBI, 95, 261
SCC (Serial communications controller),
  154
SDK-85, 78–80, 265–267
Sequencing, 205–215
  Conditional, 212–215
Serial communication, 151–160, 243
  Full-duplex, 151
  Half-duplex, 152
  Simplex, 152
Set, 243
Shannon's sampling theorem, 180–182
SHLD, 72, 260
SIM, 160, 195–197, 263
Slice, 243
Software, 243
Source code, 63, 243
SP, *see* Register, Stack pointer
SPHL, 120, 263
SSI (small scale integration), 4, 244
STA, 71, 77, 260
Stack, 19, 31, 118, 119, 244
  FIFO (first in, first out), 238
  LIFO (last in, first out), 19, 240
  Pop, 19, 242
  Push, 19, 242
Start bit, 153, 244
Status register, *see* Register, Flag
STAX, 74, 260
STC, 106, 261
Stop bit, 153, 244
Structured program, 244
STTL (Schottky-clamped TTL), 13
SUB, 91, 261
Subroutine, 66, 113–118, 244
  Nested, 118
Subtract, 91
SUI, 91, 261
Synchronous, 153, 244

Syntax, 244

Tape:
    Magnetic, 54–56
    Paper, 53
Three-state logic, 22, 244
Timing and control, 19–21, 27
Transistor, 2–5
TRAP, 197, 244
T-state, 114, 244
TTL (transistor-transistor logic), 13
Two's complement, 244

UART (universal asynchronous receiver/
    transmitter), 154, 244
UNIVAC I, 2
UNIX, 271
USART (universal synchronous/
    asynchronous receiver/transmitter),
    154

Vacuum tube, 2
Vector, 188–194, 244
    Hardware, 191, 192
    Table, 191, 245
VHSIC (very high speed IC), 4, 245
VLSI (very large scale integration), 4,
    245
Von Neumann, John, 1
Von Neumann machine, 2, 8

Wafer, 3
Wait states, 245
Word, 11, 245

XCHG, 69, 260
XOR (exclusive OR), 19, 30, 102
    Gate, 255
XRA, 103, 262
XRI, 103, 262
XTHL, 119, 263